ICE CREAM
and Related Products

other recent AVI books on food processing

ICE CREAM
and Related Products

by J. H. FRANDSEN, M. S.

Emeritus Head, Department of Dairy Industry
University of Massachusetts

and W. S. ARBUCKLE, Ph.D.

Professor Dairy Manufacturing
University of Maryland

WESTPORT, CONNECTICUT

THE AVI PUBLISHING COMPANY, INC.

1961

Printed in the United States of America
BY MACK PRINTING COMPANY, EASTON, PENNSYLVANIA

Preface

In the last ten years, there have been tremendous advances made by the ice cream industry. These advances have resulted from improvements in technology, development of new and improved ingredients, new equipment and improved methods of processing, packaging and merchandising. The industry has become fully mechanized and has encountered various degrees of continuous processing and automation in many of the manufacturing processes.

Technological developments have made available improved dairy products, new sweetener blends, different stabilizer and emulsifier materials, and new flavoring products for use in the manufacture of ice cream.

New processing standards and a Federal Frozen Dessert Definitions and Standards of identity have been established.

The manufacturing of ice milk and mellorine type products have become important in some areas.

The purpose, therefore, of this book is to present modern information on the technology of ice cream manufacture to be used by the student, the dairy and food technologists, and the ice cream manufacturer.

The contents includes information accumulated by the authors in their many years experience in teaching and research in ice cream making and their association with those engaged in the manufacture of ice cream. Data are presented on all major phases of ice cream technology and include reference material, lists of formulas, product composition, standards, mix calculations, ingredients, and product quality information.

The authors wish to thank the following who reviewed and criticized portions of the book:

Professor A. C. Dahlberg, Dairy Industry Dept., Cornell University, Ithaca, N. Y.

Mrs. Barbara Evers, National Dairy Council, Chicago, Ill.

Professor H. B. Henderson, Head, Dairy Dept., University of Georgia, Athens, Georgia

Mr. Joseph Merory, President of Merory Food Flavors, Lake Hiawatha, New Jersey

Dr. Frank E. Potter, Dairy and Animal Science Dept., University of Massachusetts, Amherst, Massachusetts

Mr. Robert Rosenbaum, Treasurer, David Michael & Co., Inc. Philadelphia, Pa.

We especially appreciate the painstaking work of Dr. Frank E. Potter, Dairy and Animal Science Dept. University of Massachusetts, Amherst, Massachusetts who made many helpful suggestions and reviewed the entire manuscript.

Special thanks are also due the following for information, suggestions, and illustrative material:

American Dairy Association, Chicago, Ill.
Mr. Carroll Biddison, H. Kohnstamn & Co., Inc., New York, N. Y.
Mr. Marion Boyer, Eberts Ice Cream Co., Hagerstown, Md.
Creamery Package Manufacturing Co., Chicago, Ill.
Dr. C. W. England, President, C. W. England Laboratories, Washington, D. C.
Mr. Paul W. Hammond, Vice President, Devale Dairies, Inc., Baltimore, Md.
Mr. Maurice Hyman, American Food Laboratories, Brooklyn, N. Y.
Mr. Lyman Jordan, Sealtest Foods, Southern Division, Washington, D. C.
Manton Gaulin Manufacturing Co., Inc., Everette, Mass.
Mr. J. W. Nisonger, Mojonnier Bros., Chicago, Ill.
Mr. N. John Wilson, Cherry-Burrell Corp., Cedar Rapids, Iowa
Mr. C. R. Zarfoss, Western Maryland Railway Co., Baltimore, Md.

A selective reference section is presented which expands the major subject areas.

The authors are grateful to fellow teachers, research personnel, leaders in the dairy industry and commercial workers in the ice cream field, too numerous to mention individually, on whose work they have freely drawn.

To these men and women who have contributed to the modern knowledge of ice cream technology this book is dedicated.

J. H. FRANDSEN

W. S. ARBUCKLE

April 1, 1961

Contents

equivalent, ratio of fat to m.s.n.f., relation of Baumé to concentration, blended syrups, sugar substitutes, sources of egg solids. Food additives.

List of Illustrations

List of Tables

CHAPTER 1

History of the Ice Cream Industry

Ice cream is a delicious, wholesome, nutritious frozen dairy food and is often called "The Great American Dessert." It is made of pure sweet cream, milk, skim milk, condensed milk or other concentrated dairy products, or a combination of these, plus added sugar and flavoring, with or without stabilizer or color, and with the incorporation of air during the freezing process.

Although the product is typically American, we cannot claim its origin. Early history of ice cream making is very scanty; however, the product is definitely known to have been introduced from Europe. The ice cream industry as we know it today has been mainly developed in the United States.

Water ices were made in Southern Europe as long ago as the 15th century. It is believed that frozen ices may have been the result of what might be called a fortunate accident. The practice in early times of cooling drinks in ice and snow containing saltpeter is a matter of record. It seems possible that in over-cooling some punches, the "ice" was discovered. At any rate, various records of frozen ices have been found in European history of the 16th century. Ices are still far more popular in continental Europe than is ice cream. The first printed record of "cream ice" appeared in "The Experienced English Housekeeper" in 1769, more than 190 years ago. Since that time ice cream making has continued to grow in popularity in England though not nearly as rapidly as in the United States.

The introduction of ice cream into the United States has been credited to Mrs. Alexander Hamilton. Reference has been found in records kept by George Washington regarding the "purchase of a machine for making ice cream." Records also indicate that ice cream was advertised by New York retailers as early as 1777 but the bulk of ice cream making remained a household task until 1851 when Jacob Fussell, a Baltimore milk dealer, started the first business of wholesale ice cream manufacture. Ice cream at that time was definitely considered a luxury and early prices were as high as $1.25 per quart. In fact, until about 1920 ice cream was associated with candies and other sweetmeats as a luxury item and was retailed mainly through confectionery stores. However today, ice cream with a high fat-and-sugar content, and even "fancy ice cream," is no longer considered in the luxury class.

The development of the ice cream industry can be most quickly told by listing the approximate dates of some important methods of processing and merchandising.

1700   Ice cream probably came to America with the English colonist. A letter written in 1700 by a guest of Governor Bladen of Maryland described having been served ice cream.

1774   First public recorded mention of ice cream in America was made by Philip Lenzi, a caterer, announcing in a New York newspaper that he was prepared to supply various confections including ice cream.

1777 to 1800   Early advertisement of ice cream by Philip Lenzi, New York *Gazette Mercury*, May 19, 1777, and November 24, 1777; by J. Corree in 1779 and 1781 in the *Gazette;* by Joseph Crowe in the New York *Post Bay,* June 8, 1786; by A. Pryor on May 18, 1789. Mr. Hall was selling ice cream in New York in 1785 and Mr. Bosio, in Germantown, Pennsylvania, established a retail business in 1800.

1789   Mrs. Alexander Hamilton, wife of the Secretary of the Treasury, served ice cream at a dinner attended by George Washington.

1811   Ice cream was served in the White House by Mrs. Dolly Madison, wife of the fourth President (Fig. 1).

1848   Patents granted on a revolving household type of hand freezer with dasher (Fig. 2).

1851   The father of the wholesale ice cream industry of America, Jacob Fussell, a Baltimore, Maryland, milk dealer, began to manufacture ice cream in Baltimore. He established plants in Washington, D. C., in 1856; and in New York in 1864 (Fig. 3).

1856   Patent granted Gail Borden in August 1856 for the process of condensing milk. The first condensed milk factory was established in Wolcottville, Connecticut.

1858   Ice cream plant was opened in St. Louis by Perry Brazelton, who learned the business from Jacob Fussell.

1864   The Horton Ice Cream Company was started in New York.

1879   Ice cream soda was introduced at Centennial Exposition, Philadelphia.

1892   The Pennsylvania State College established the first course in ice cream making. Iowa State College offered instruction in 1901.

1895   Pasteurizing machines were introduced.

1892 to 1906   Investigation and development of the dry milk industry in America. One of the first dry milk plants was established by Merrell Soule Company at Arcade, New York, in May 1906. The first spray process plant was built in Ferndale, California, in 1911.

1899   The homogenizer was invented in France and was in use within two years. The United States patent was dated April 11, 1904.

FIG. 1. "A SURPRISE"

From a painting based on records that Dolly Madison served ice cream to her White House guests.

Courtesy of Ice Cream Trade Journal

FIG. 2. THE ICE AND SALT FREEZER

Quite commonly used in ice cream plants in the early part of
the twentieth century.

1900   The Association of Ice Cream Manufacturers was formed and later the name was changed to International Association of Ice Cream Manufacturers.

1902   The horizontal circulating brine freezer was invented.

1904   The ice cream cone appeared at the World's Fair, St. Louis.

1905   The "Ice Cream Trade Journal" was made the official organ of the Association.

1910   First State Experiment Station Bulletins concerning ice cream were published including, "Principles and Practices of Ice Cream Making," Vermont State Bull. 155 by R. W. Washburn, 1910; "Classification of Ice Cream and Related Frozen Products—Score Cards for Judging Ice Cream," Iowa State Bull. 123, M. Mortensen, 1911; "Bacteria in Ice Cream," Iowa State Bull. 134, B. W. Hammer, 1912.

1911   The homogenizing process was applied to condensed or evaporated milk.

1913   Direct expansion freezer was introduced. The continuous freezing process was patented.

1915   Textbooks on ice cream were published in the United States, "The Manufacture of Ice Creams and Ices," J. H. Frandsen and E. A. Markham, 1915; "The Ice Cream Laboratory Guide," by W. W. Fisk and H. B. Ellenberger, 1917; "The Book of Ice Cream," W. W. Fisk, 1919.

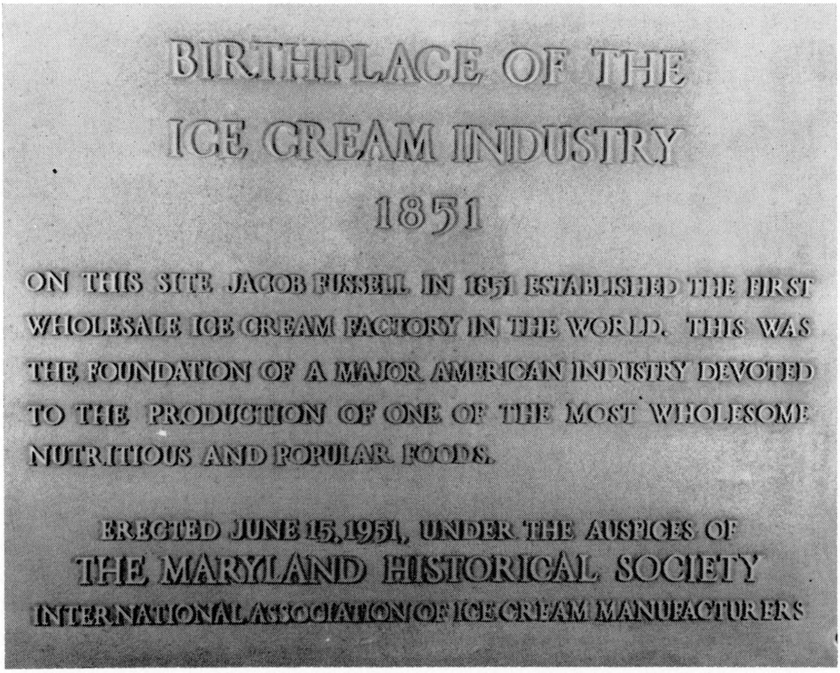

BIRTHPLACE OF THE
ICE CREAM INDUSTRY
1851

ON THIS SITE JACOB FUSSELL IN 1851 ESTABLISHED THE FIRST
WHOLESALE ICE CREAM FACTORY IN THE WORLD. THIS WAS
THE FOUNDATION OF A MAJOR AMERICAN INDUSTRY DEVOTED
TO THE PRODUCTION OF ONE OF THE MOST WHOLESOME
NUTRITIOUS AND POPULAR FOODS.

ERECTED JUNE 15, 1951, UNDER THE AUSPICES OF
THE MARYLAND HISTORICAL SOCIETY
INTERNATIONAL ASSOCIATION OF ICE CREAM MANUFACTURERS

Courtesy of C. R. Zarfoss, Western Maryland Railway Co.

FIG. 3. BIRTHPLACE OF THE ICE CREAM INDUSTRY

Plaque erected on site of the first wholesale ice cream factory, Hillen and Exeter Streets, Baltimore, Maryland.

1920 Ice cream was generally recognized as a protective and essential food.

1921 The Eskimo Pie was patented by C. Nelson, Waukon, Iowa. This was the first of the coated ice cream and novelty sticks.

1922 Development of direct expansion refrigeration adapted to freezers.

1925 Dry ice (solid CO_2) was used to facilitate delivery of ice cream.

1926 The counter freezer for soft ice cream appeared.

1928 The Vogt continuous freezer was developed by Henry Vogt of Louisville, Kentucky.

1929 to 1935 Development and acceptance of continuous freezers. The Vogt instant freezer was first introduced by Cherry Burrell and installed commercially in 1929. The Creamery Package continuous freezer was introduced in 1935.

1940 to 1945 Development of low temperature storage units for the home.

TABLE 1

PRODUCTION AND PRODUCTION PER CAPITA BY YEARS, OF ICE CREAM AND RELATED PRODUCTS. UNITED STATES, 1859–1959

Year	All Products Reported Total[1] 1,000 Gallons	All Products Reported Per Capita, Quarts	Ice Cream 1,000 Gallons	Ice Cream Per Capita, Quarts	Ice Milk 1,000 Gallons	Ice Milk Per Capita, Quarts	Sherbet 1,000 Gallons	Sherbet Per Capita, Quarts	Water Ices 1,000 Gallons	Water Ices Per Capita, Quarts	Other Frozen Dairy Products[2] 1,000 Gallons	Other Frozen Dairy Products Per Capita, Quarts	Mellorine-Type Products 1,000 Gallons	Mellorine-Type Products Per Capita, Quarts
1859	4	...	4	...										
1869	24	0.004	24	0.004										
1874	59	0.004	59	0.004										
1879	144	0.01	144	0.01										
1884	350	0.02	350	0.02										
1889	851	0.06	851	0.06										
1894	2,067	0.12	2,067	0.12										
1899	5,021	0.27	5,021	0.27										
1904	12,199	0.59	12,199	0.59										
1909	29,637	1.31	29,637	1.31										
1914	72,000	2.91	72,000	2.91										
1916	93,564	3.67	93,564	3.67										
1917	106,419	4.12	106,419	4.12										
1918	142,912	5.54	142,912	5.54										
1919	152,982	5.86	152,982	5.86										
1920	171,248	6.43	171,248	6.43										
1921	175,366	6.46	175,366	6.46										
1922	191,091	6.95	191,091	6.95										
1923	214,277	7.66	214,277	7.66										
1924	213,325	7.48	213,325	7.48										
1925	240,018	8.29	240,018	8.29										
1926	238,333	8.12	238,333	8.12										
1927	251,385	8.45	251,385	8.45										
1928	253,967	8.43	253,967	8.43										
1929	277,237	9.11	277,237	9.11										
1930	255,439	8.30	255,439	8.30										
1931	226,437	7.30	226,437	7.30										
1932	170,158	5.45	167,950	5.38			2,208[3]	0.07						
1933	163,749	5.22	161,792	5.16			1,957	0.06						
1934	194,776	6.16	191,560	6.06			3,216	0.10						

Year														
1935	222,720	7.00	219,134	6.89			3,586	0.11						
1936	263,857	8.24	258,585	8.08			5,272	0.16						
1937	297,049	9.22	291,057	9.04			5,992	0.18						
1938	292,412	9.01	286,366	8.82			6,046	0.19						
1939	319,565	9.77	305,772	9.35			13,793	0.42						
1940	339,544	10.29	318,088	9.64	10,457[3]	0.32	8,089	0.24			2,910[3]	0.09		
1941	414,919	12.47	390,282	11.73	12,444	0.37	8,060	0.24			4,133	0.13		
1942	491,481	14.68	464,172	13.86	13,974	0.42	8,772	0.26			4,563	0.14		
1943	474,268	14.13	411,646	12.27	10,021	0.30	47,218	1.41			5,383	0.15		
1944	507,407	15.27	444,886	13.39	8,350	0.25	49,481	1.49			4,690	0.14		
1945	560,516	16.92	477,162	14.41	11,722	0.35	65,117	1.97			6,455	0.19		
1946	746,710	21.33	713,769	20.39	15,296	0.44	12,019	0.34			5,626	0.16		
1947	662,584	18.48	631,023	17.60	15,572	0.44	10,447	0.29			5,542	0.15		
1948	613,043	16.79	576,484	15.78	19,362	0.53	12,211	0.34			4,986	0.14		
1949	626,645	16.86	558,054	15.02	29,526	0.79	13,616	0.37	18,695[3]	0.50	6,754	0.18		
1950	634,764	16.79	554,351	14.66	36,870	0.98	17,018	0.45	18,299	0.48	8,230	0.22		
1951	665,750	17.36	568,849	14.83	45,804	1.20	20,469	0.53	21,683	0.57	8,945	0.23		
1952	718,719	18.46	592,705	15.22	53,702	1.38	25,637	0.66	26,315	0.68	9,172	0.24	11,188[3]	0.28
1953	761,138	19.23	605,051	15.29	64,710	1.63	31,079	0.79	26,851	0.68	9,240	0.23	24,207	0.61
1954	773,731	19.20	596,821	14.81	80,019	1.98	34,170	0.85	26,555	0.66	4,787	0.12	31,379	0.78
1955	819,934	19.96	628,525	15.30	90,185	2.20	37,365	0.91	28,158	0.69	3,440	0.08	32,261	0.78
1956	844,473	20.20	641,333	15.34	103,052	2.47	35,721	0.85	27,464	0.66	3,430	0.08	33,473	0.80
1957	864,087	20.30	650,583	15.29	111,165	2.61	36,712	0.86	28,149	0.66	3,317	0.08	34,161	0.80
1958	881,627	20.36	656,652	15.16	116,135	2.68	37,014	0.86	28,388	0.66	3,867	0.09	39,571	0.91
1959[4]	943,542	21.40	700,615	15.89	123,970	2.81	39,740	0.90	31,900	0.72	3,867[5]	0.09	43,450	0.99

[1] Data from 1859 to 1919 indicate only the estimated trend of production. Source of production volume, the Bureau of Agricultural Economics, U. S. Department of Agriculture.

[2] Reported by Bureau of Agricultural Economics, U. S. Department of Agriculture, years 1940 to 1949, as frozen custards and frosted or frozen malted milk.

[3] Not previously reported.

[4] Estimated.

[5] Estimated for the year 1959, not available for other frozen dairy products. The 1958 volume is included for the year 1959.

Note: Per capita figures for ice milk and Mellorine-type products are computed for the United States as a whole.

1946 Carry home packages marketed through chain grocery stores gained popularity. Soft ice cream and drive-in stores appeared.

1950 Appearance of vegetable fat products in the ice cream industry.

1942 to 1953 Food and Drug hearings on Federal standards for ice cream.

1951 Ice cream centennial held in Baltimore, Maryland, June 15.

1953 High temperature short-time pasteurization of ice cream mix (175°F. for 25 seconds) approved by U. S. Public Health Service, February 13, 1953.

1960 Definitions and Standards for Frozen Desserts approved by the Food and Drug Administration of the U. S. Department of Health, Education, and Welfare (see Chapter 24).

The United States has gained undisputed leadership among all other countries in the production of ice cream. Available records seem to indicate that the ice cream industry grew very slowly until after 1900. Since 1920 when the value of ice cream as a protective and essential food was generally recognized, the growth has been unusually rapid. Table 1 illustrates this point.

Surveys of hotels, restaurants, dining cars, etc., show that ice cream is now served in such establishments more often than all other desserts combined. Its appearance in take-home packages in grocery stores also indicates its growing popularity.

Some of the factors contributing to the recent development of the ice cream industry are:

1. The perfection of mechanical refrigeration and its application to the food industry.
2. Improved manufacturing methods and equipment such as the homogenizer, overrun testers, continuous freezers, packaging machines, etc.
3. More and better ingredients and more knowledge concerning ice cream making, resulting in a better product.
4. Lower manufacturing costs through mass production.
5. Extensive advertising of the product.
6. A realization of the high food value of ice cream.
7. Changing economic conditions—better wages, more purchasing power, a higher standard of living.
8. Improved storage facilities for ice cream in the home.

The importance of the ice cream industry is further shown by its relation to the other branches of the dairy industry. Table 2 shows that approximately 7.6 per cent of all milk produced in the United States is utilized by the ice cream industry. Over 40 per cent of the ice cream is made during the early summer months when there is a seasonal increase in milk production. Thus the ice cream industry acts as a balance wheel for the dairy industry in supplying a profitable market for the seasonal increase in production.

TABLE 2

UTILIZATION OF MILK IN THE U. S. IN 1959[1]

Product	Per cent of Total Milk Used	Product	Per cent of Total Milk Used
Creamery butter	24.0	Fluid milk & cream	49.0
Cheese	10.4	Calves	2.4
Cond. & evap. milk	4.5	Dry whole milk	0.6
Ice Cream	7.6	Misc.	1.5
		TOTAL	100.0

[1] From Milk Industry Foundation (1960).   Milk Facts, 1961.

The economic importance of the ice cream industry has been established.   The value of ice cream as a food is now realized and much scientific knowledge has been gained in the production and merchandising of ice cream.   Further technological advancement may be expected to accelerate the demand for ice cream.

CHAPTER 2

Food Value

The food value of ice cream obviously depends upon the food value of the products from which it is made. The milk products which go into the mix contain the same constituents as does whole milk, but in different amounts. For instance, ice cream contains 3 or 4 times as much fat, and about 12 to 16 per cent more protein than does milk. In addition it may contain other food products such as fruit, nuts, eggs, and sugar which enhance its nutritive value. However, like milk, it lacks iron and some of the trace minerals.

Calcium Content of Ice Cream. Milk and its products, such as ice cream, are among the richest sources of calcium, phosphorus, and other minerals of vital importance in building good bones and teeth. Recent dietary research shows that large quantities of these products are needed to bring America's health standards above the safety line. Research also indicates that additional amounts of lactose (milk sugar) in a diet favors the assimilation of calcium. Ice cream, which is rich in lactose, should therefore favor the assimilation of greater quantities of the calcium content of the diet which is needed so much by growing children and at least some adults. The calcium and phosphorus content of milk and ice cream are given here in grams per hundred grams of milk and of ice cream.

	Calcium per 100 grams gm.	Phosphorus per 100 grams gm.
Milk	0.118	0.093
Ice Cream	0.122	0.105

The daily human requirements of calcium as recommended by the Committee of Foods and Nutrition, National Research Council, are as follows:

Individual	Calcium, gm.
Normal adult	0.80
Children (up to 20 years)	1.40
Pregnant mother	1.50
Nursing mother	2.00

The ordinary mixed diet of the average American household provides the following amounts of calcium:

Daily Food Intake   *Calcium, gm.*

Regular serving of meat, potato and bread 0.029
Two eggs 0.101
Regular serving of fruits and vegetables 0.158

   The above foods total 0.288
One pint of milk 0.580
One average serving ($^1/_6$ qt.) ice cream 0.122

                                            TOTAL   0.990

This provides a total above the absolute needs of adults. If children and pregnant mothers take another pint of milk daily their calcium intake will be abundantly sufficient.

The protein content of ice cream also rates high, both in amount and in quality. The proteins are mostly derived from milk, a small amount from stabilizers, and from eggs when eggs are used in the mix. The milk and egg proteins are complete; that is, they contain all the amino acids essential to animal life and are especially important sources of tryptophane and lysine which are lacking in many plant proteins, and milk proteins are the most perfect proteins known and are almost completely assimilated by the body tissues. They serve as fine supplements to the protein-deficient foods such as potatoes, cereals, bread, etc. Ice cream provides these valuable proteins in a very palatable form. In fact, ice cream is to many individuals the most palatable source of milk proteins.

TABLE 3

COMPOSITION OF PLAIN ICE CREAM[1]

Protein...............................	3.9 per cent
Fat..................................	13.0 per cent
Carbohydrates........................	20.3 per cent
Fuel value per 100 grams...............	214 calories
Weight of a 100 calorie portion.........	47 grams

[1] Sherman (1946).

Ice Cream Is Also an Excellent Source of Food Energy. As has been stated, the fat content of ice cream is three or four times that of milk, and fully half its total solids content is sugar (including lactose, sucrose, etc.). The fact that these constituents are almost completely assimilated makes ice cream an especially desirable food for growing children and for persons who need to put on weight. For the same reason, its *controlled use* finds a place in the diet of persons who need to reduce or who do not wish to gain weight.

Ice Cream in the Reducing Diet. "Add ice cream to your regular diet and increase your weight; take ice cream as part of your regular diet and reduce your weight." Very often one sees this apparently contradictory statement that ice cream is both a fattening food and a food which can be used to advantage in a reducing diet. This paradox clears up when it is understood that a food may be taken as a supplement to a regular diet, or as a substitute for some other food in the diet. If ice cream is consumed in fairly large amounts in addition to a diet already high in caloric values, the tendency is for the person to put on weight. However, if ice cream is used as one of the regular foods in a diet combination and proper moderation is practiced regarding the richer desserts, there is no reason why it can not be a part of even a slenderizing diet. A study of comparative caloric values indicates that many other desserts are far higher in calories than is ice cream. As an example, a serving of ice cream ranging in size from $1/12$ to $1/6$ of a quart, provides approximately 96 calories in the smaller serving and 200 in the larger serving, while an ordinary serving of lemon pie contains 450 calories.

The Caloric Content of Ice Cream and Related Products. The ice cream manufacturer may often need information regarding the nutritional value of the products he manufactures. School and hospital officials and dietitians often need nutritional data when establishing diets for those whom they serve. The wide variation in the composition of ice cream and related products makes it practically impossible to provide nutritional data that will apply to all products. It is, however, possible to calculate for practical use the food energy value of a given product if the composition is known.

The amount of energy normally expected to be derived from carbohydrates, fats, and protein is as follows:

One gram of carbohydrates yields about 4.0 calories
One gram of fat yields about 9.0 calories
One gram of protein yields about 4.0 calories

These values are the amount of energy released from the food nutrients as heat units or calories and are referred to as physiological fuel values. Proteins and carbohydrates are of equal energy value per gram and fats are 2.25 times as rich in energy.

Minerals or vitamins do not furnish appreciable amounts of energy.

The type of sugar has little relation to the fuel value derived from it, and all sugars may be expected to have about the same energy value.

The lactose content of milk solids-not-fat is about 52 per cent and the protein content of milk solids-not-fat is about 36 per cent.

The total caloric value of ice cream depends on (1) the per cent carbohydrates including lactose, added sweeteners and sugars that may be present in fruit or flavoring, (2) the per cent protein including milk protein

or any other source of protein that may be present in nuts, eggs or stabilizer, and (3) the per cent fat from any source including emulsifier, egg,
cocoa or nut fat that may be in the mix.

In the field of nutrition the composition of a food is expressed as grams
of constituent per 100 grams of product.

The caloric value of 100 grams of vanilla ice cream containing 12.5 per
cent fat, 11 per cent milk solids-not-fat, 15 per cent sugar and 0.3 per cent
gelatin may be calculated as follows:

Calories from

Carbohydrates	$(15 + 11 \times 0.52) \times 4$	=	82.88
Fat	12.5×9	=	112.50
Protein	$(11 \times 0.36 + 0.30) \times 4$	=	15.84
Total calories			211.22

The caloric value of a serving of ice cream varies with the composition
of the mix, overrun and weight of mix per gallon. In determining the
caloric value of a package or serving of ice cream it is necessary to
determine the exact weight of the product contained therein. Calculations may be made readily if the weight in ounces is known since one
ounce is equivalent to 28.35 grams.

Vitamin Content of Ice Cream. Like milk, ice cream is a rich source
of many of the essential vitamins, those food accessories without which
normal health and growth can not be maintained. A brief description of
the better known vitamins may help to emphasize the importance of milk
and ice cream in the diet.

Vitamin A—the anti-infective vitamin—is the principal butterfat vitamin.
It is the most important in building resistance to infection in the respira-
tory tract, in preventing night blindness, and maintaining general good
health. *Ice cream is an excellent source.*

Vitamin B$_1$, or Thiamin—known also as the anti-neuritic vitamin—stimulates appetite, promotes growth, helps maintain normal motility of the
digestive tract, and is largely a preventive of polyneuritis. *Ice cream is a
good source.*

Niacin—anti-pellagra factor of the B complex vitamins (B$_1$, G, and
others less well known)—is very important in the prevention and cure of
pellagra, and in the maintenance of good health in general. *Ice cream is
a fair source.*

Vitamin E—is known as the anti-sterility vitamin since it is concerned
with maintaining normal health of the reproductive organs in laboratory
animals. Its value in human nutrition is not fully understood. *Ice cream
is a fair source.*

Vitamin G—now generally known as riboflavin—ranks with calcium and vitamin A as necessary for nutritional well-being for young and old alike. It is known also as the youth-promoting vitamin and seems to be a factor in extending the "prime of life." *Ice cream is a good source.*

Vitamin C—the anti-scorbutic factor—is most important in prevention of scurvy. It is not stored in the body. Most fruits contain an abundant supply, especially the citrus varieties. Many kinds of ice cream carry 20 to 25 per cent of fruit. These fruits, such as strawberries, pineapple, peaches, oranges, and lemons, in addition to other food values, supply additional amounts of vitamin C. *Fruit ice cream is a fair source.*

Vitamin D—the anti-rachitic or "sunshine" vitamin—prevents rickets in small children and pregnant women by helping to maintain the normal concentrations of calcium and phosphorus in the blood. There are only small amounts in ice cream unless the milk products have been fortified with vitamin D.

Vitamin K. This important vitamin has been found necessary for the proper coagulation of the blood. It is now used extensively to prevent bleeding in operations, and from serious wounds, etc. There is every reason to assume that this vitamin is found in milk and milk serum solids and therefore will also be found in ice cream.

TABLE 4

NUTRIENT CONTENT OF VANILLA ICE CREAM,[1] 100 GRAMS (ABOUT $1/6$ QUART) = 206 CALORIES
(AN AVERAGE SERVING OF ICE CREAM)

Nutrient	Amount gm.	Nutrient	Amount mg.
Protein	3.850	Iron	0.120
Fat	12.060	Vitamin A	548[3]
Carbohydrate[2]	21.310	Thiamin	0.038
Total Mineral	0.810	Riboflavin	0.236
Calcium	0.122	Niacin	0.098
Phosphorus	0.105	Ascorbic Acid	0.000
Potassium	0.090	Sodium	100

[1] Adapted from 1) National Dairy Council, 1957. Nutrition for Every Day Use; 2) H. J. Heinz Co., 1958. Nutritional Data, 3rd Ed., 2nd Revised Printing; 3) U. S. Dept. of Agr., 1959. Food—The Year Book of Agriculture.
[2] Includes milk sugar (lactose) and sweeteners.
[3] International Units, not milligrams.

Digestibility and Palatability of Ice Cream. Many experiments show that homogenized milk is more digestible than milk not so treated. This is based on the fact that the homogenizer has broken the fat globules into very, very minute fat particles which can be more readily acted upon by the digestive juices than can the larger fat globules. The same holds true for the fat in the ice cream mix when it is forced through the homogenizer as is now the practice in commercial ice cream plants. In addition, the high palatability of ice cream stimulates the flow of the digestive juices.

TABLE 5

APPROXIMATE FOOD VALUE OF COMMERCIAL ICE CREAM AND RELATED PRODUCTS. (USUAL VARIATIONS IN COMPOSITION WILL NEITHER INCREASE NOR DECREASE THE VALUES IN THE TABLE BY MORE THAN 10 TO 15 PER CENT)

Product	Amount	Calories	Protein gm.	Calcium gm.	Phosphorus gm.	Iron mgm.	Vit. A I. U.	Thiamin mgm.	Riboflavin mgm.
Vanilla Ice Cream	one quart	1202	23.4	0.784	0.623	0.85	3288	0.229	1.416
	one serving, 1/6 quart[1]	200	3.9	0.131	0.104	0.14	548	0.038	0.236
Raspberry Sherbet	one quart	1544	13.8	0.245	0.233	4.63	...	...	0.091
	one serving, 1/6 quart	257[1]	2.3	0.041	0.039	0.77	...	...	0.015
Vanilla Ice Milk	one quart	936	30.6	1.098	1.002	0.90	1410	0.252	1.716
	one serving, 1/6 quart	156[1]	5.1	0.188	0.167	0.015	235	0.042	0.286
Ice	one quart	881	...	...	...	...	...	...	...
	one serving, 1/6 quart	147[1]	...	...	...	...	...	...	...

[1] The amount accepted as one serving by most dietitians and physicians.

TABLE 6

THE FOOD VALUE OF ICE CREAM AND OF FOODS OFTEN USED SIMILARLY OR SERVED WITH ICE CREAM

Food	Measure Weight	Calories	Protein gm.	Calcium gm.	Iron gm.	Vit. A I.U.	Thiamin mg.	Riboflavin mg.	Ascorbic acid mg.
Vanilla Ice Cream	1/6 qt. 100 gm.	200	3.9	0.131	0.14	548	0.038	0.236	0
Angel Cake	1/10 10" cake 111 gm.	300	9.0	0.006	0.15	...	...	0.129	0
Sugar Cookies	2 cookies 28 gm.	100	1.4	0.004	0.10	200	0.012	0.081	0
Apple Pie	1/8 9" pie 100 gm.	230	2.3	0.009	0.46	115	0.020	0.021	1
Baked Apple (2 T. sugar)	1 medium 158 gm.	260	0.5	0.010	0.45	90	0.034	0.038	2
Chocolate Cup Cake	2 3/4" dia. 51 gm.	200	2.3	0.013	0.30	350	0.018	0.036	0
Brown Betty	1/2 cup 145 gm.	250	2.3	0.012	0.40	450	0.018	0.036	2
Rice Pudding (milk & eggs)	1/2 cup 130 gm.	135	5.8	0.078	0.90	450	0.042	0.189	0
Custard	1/2 cup 111 gm.	130	5.5	0.127	0.80	470	0.054	0.270	0
Chocolate Pudding (milk)	1/2 cup 108 gm.	200	5.0	0.143	0.45	215	0.042	0.252	1
Fruit Cup	1/2 cup 80 gm.	75	0.7	0.011	0.32	85	0.066	0.027	23
Lemon Sherbet (milk)	1/2 cup 131 gm.	200	2.5	0.099	0.32	150	0.036	0.162	12
Milk	1 glass 244 gm.	168	8.5	0.290	0.08	375	0.090	0.410	4

Courtesy of American Dairy Association

FIG. 4. ICE CREAM—THE GREAT AMERICAN DESSERT

A taste-tempting food, rich in energy, vitamins and other food essentials.

a valuable aid to the digestive process. These two factors, together with its sweet flavor, its smooth velvety texture, and its glistening coolness, make it an ideal food for many invalids suffering from throat afflictions or certain stomach ailments, when other foods do not appeal or can not be tolerated. These qualities together with its value as a morale builder have led hospitals to use ice cream extensively in their menus.

It is safe to say that no other food product contributes so much food value in as attractive and appealing a form, or is so universally liked and distributed as ice cream.

Classification of Ice Cream and Related Products

Classification of ice cream, sherbets and ices has been attempted by various authors of ice cream text books and by leading authorities in the industry from time to time over a period of years, but as yet no standard classification has been adopted. The innumerable variations in the composition of ice cream, in the ingredients and the methods of using them, and in the forms in which the finished product is marketed are the source of much confusion in any attempt to make specific rules for definite classes of ice creams. Some authorities have attempted to make groups of the different classes, such as, plain or Philadelphia, French or Neapolitan, and sherbets and ices. However, there is nearly unanimous agreement that all frozen dairy desserts can be classed under the groups given here.

Definition of Ice Cream. The general term *ice cream* is commonly used to denote frozen food made from such a mixture of dairy products as will give the desired percentage of butterfat and non-fat milk solids, together with sugar, flavoring, coloring, and stabilizer, and with or without eggs, fruit, nuts, etc., and usually made smooth by whipping or stirring during the freezing process.

CLASSIFICATION

1. **Plain Ice Cream:** an ice cream in which the total amount of the color and flavoring ingredients is less than 5 per cent of the volume of the unfrozen ice cream. Examples are vanilla, coffee, maple, and caramel ice cream.

2. **Bisque:** ice cream containing appropriate flavorings, and particles of either grapenuts, macaroons, ginger snaps, sponge cake, or other bakery products.

3. **Candy or Confection:** ice cream with appropriate flavorings plus particles of candy, such as peppermint stick, buttercrunch, chocolate chip.

4. **Chocolate:** ice cream flavored with cocoa or chocolate.

5. **Fruit:** ice cream containing fruit, with or without additional fruit flavoring or color. The fruit such as strawberry, apricot, pineapple, etc., may be fresh, frozen-pack, canned or preserved.

6. **Nut:** ice cream containing nut meats, such as almonds, pistachio, walnuts, etc., with or without additional flavoring or color.

7. **Puddings:** ice cream containing a generous amount of mixed fruits, nut meats, and raisins, with or without liquor, spices, or eggs. Examples: Nesselrode and plum puddings.

8. **Custard:** ice cream cooked to a custard before freezing. It contains a generous amount of eggs, with additional flavoring and color.

9. **Parfait:** a frozen custard of high fat content.

10. **Mousse:** whipped cream, plus sugar, color, and flavoring, and frozen without further agitation. Sometimes condensed milk is added to give better consistency.

11. **Rippled ice cream:** a plain vanilla ice cream combined with a syrup such as chocolate, butterscotch, etc., so as to produce a marbled effect in the hardened ice cream.

12. **Rainbow ice cream:** a product made by carefully mixing six or more different colored ice creams as they are drawn from the freezers, to give a marbled or rainbow-colored effect when the product is hardened.

13. **Gelatin cube ice cream:** an ice cream in which colored, fruit-flavored gelatin, cut into small cubes, is used in place of fruits to give color and flavor and a characteristic chewiness.

14. **Ice Milk:** a product containing 2 to 7 per cent fat and with 12 to 15 per cent non-fat milk solids, sweetened, flavored, and frozen like ice cream.

15. **Ices:** made of fruit juice, sugar, and stabilizer, with or without additional fruit acid, color, flavoring, or water, and frozen to the consistency of ice cream. Usually contain 28 to 30 per cent sugar, 20 to 25 per cent overrun, and no dairy products.

16. **Frappé:** an ice made from a mixture of fruit juices and frozen to a slushy consistency; to be served as a drink.

17. **Punch:** a frappé made of mixed fruit juices with or without fruit pulp or additional sugar, water, and spices. Liquors may be used to replace some or all of the fruit juices.

18. **Granite:** water ice frozen with very little agitation.

19. **Sherbet:** made of fruit juices, sugar, stabilizer, and milk products. It is similar to an ice except that milk, either whole, skim, condensed, or powdered, or ice cream mix, is used in place of all or part of the water in an ice.

20. **Soufflé:** a sherbet containing egg yolk or whole eggs.

21. **Lacto:** made from buttermilk or cultured sour milk, eggs, fruit juices, and sugar, and frozen like ices and sherbets.

22. **Fruit Salad:** mixed fruits, in large pieces, in combination with a mixture of whipped cream and mayonnaise, and frozen to be served as a salad. (Mayonnaise may be omitted if desired.)

23. **Fancy Molded Ice Cream includes ice creams (and ices and sherbets):** molded in fancy shapes and composed either of one color and

flavor of ice cream or of a combination of colors and flavors, or specially decorated. This group includes:

a. Brick ice cream in one, two, or more layers, or with fancy centers.
b. Sliced brick with decorative stenciled designs (individual size).
c. Cakes, pies, melon molds, log rolls, sultana rolls, etc.
d. Cake roll—layered ice cream on moist cake, rolled like a jelly roll.
e. Individual or larger molds representing fruits, flowers, animals and other objects, emblems, and designs.
f. Ice cream waffles and tarts.
g. Spumoni: a combination of vanilla ice cream, chocolate ice cream or mousse, cherries, and tutti frutti ice cream or whipped cream combined with fruits, arranged in a spumoni cup, and hardened to serve. Sometimes classed as a parfait.
h. Aufait: two or more layers of ice cream with pectinized fruits or preserves spread thinly between the layers; or the fruits may be stirred gently into the ice cream as it comes from the freezer, to give a marbled appearance.

24. **Novelties:** A novelty ice cream or frozen confection is a specially shaped and usually a low-priced package containing an individual serving whose main appeal consists in its shape, size, color, or convenience for eating. Listed as novelty items are:

a. Eskimo pies, and candy or chocolate-coated ice cream bars with or without sticks.
b. Candy or chocolate-coated ice milk bars, with or without sticks.
c. Ice cream sandwiches—slabs of ice cream pressed between cookies, and wrapped in wax paper and hardened.
d. Popsicles, fudgsicles, and other ice-like mixtures frozen on sticks.

25. **"Soft" ice cream and "Soft" ice milk** (these products are sold as drawn from the freezer without hardening).

26. **Frosted malted milk**—made from milk containing from 4 to 8 per cent butterfat and about 10 per cent non-fat milk solids, sugar, and stabilizer, and flavored with malted milk powder and chocolate. Like "Soft" ice creams it is served from the freezer without hardening.

27. **Imitation Ice Cream:** Imitation ice cream includes products not meeting the legal requirements for ice cream such as those made with vegtable fat and containing milk constituents in insufficient quantity to meet ice cream standards. These may include diatetic or diabetic frozen desserts or other such substandard products.

28. **Mellorine-Type Products:** Mellorine is a product similar to ice cream in which the butterfat has been replaced by a suitable vegetable or animal fat. Such a product is illegal in over three-fourths of the states. The formulas, processing and distribution procedures for ice cream are also applicable to mellorine.

In states which permit the manufacture of a mellorine type frozen dessert the minimum fat standards range from 6 to 10 per cent.

In at least one, standard vegetable fat or oil only is permitted, and in one or two states there is no standard specified but the product is permitted when properly declared. Several states require Vitamin A addition of not less than 8400 U.S.P. units per gallon (with or without Vitamin D concentrate) for 10.0 per cent fat, increasing proportionately. Weight per gallon, minimum milk solids and minimum food solids requirements are similar to those for ice cream but the maximum stabilizer allowed ranges to one per cent.

A few states have standards for a low fat mellorine type product. These products are known in some areas as Olarine or Mellofreeze. The minimum fat requirements for the low fat products range from 3.0 to 4 per cent, minimum total milk solids from 7.75 to 10.8 per cent, minimum weight per gallon of 4.5 lbs.; minimum food solids from 1.0 to 1.3 pounds per gallon and maximum stabilizer ranges to one per cent.

Production data for mellorine type products are indicated in Table 1. (Chapter 1.)

REGULATORY TYPE OF CLASSIFICATION

For regulatory purposes, legislative and administrative officials are finding it desirable to establish a different type of classification. Any classification based upon methods of processing (such as "agitation while freezing"), or upon the kind of ingredients (such as bakery goods), or upon shape is without much meaning from a regulatory enforcement point of view. Some regulatory officials have found it convenient to use a classification based on the concentration of some of the constituents, i.e., milk fat, egg yolk solids, and stabilizer. Table 7 suggests the form of such a classification arranged in the order of decreasing richness of product. This classification is easy to interpret and should be simpler to enforce, it includes all products that are generally prepared by ice cream manufacturers, and is broad enough to include almost any combinations that may become popular. Its chief disadvantage is the fact that it does not suggest names for particular combinations of either ingredients, processing, or shapes. The legal specifications for ice cream in the various states usually include the following requirements: (1) a minimum percentage of fat, (2) a minimum weight per gallon and (3) a maximum percentage stabilizer. In addition one or more of the following may be included: a minimum percentage milk solids, a minimum weight of food solids per gallon, a minimum percentage of total solids or a minimum percentage milk solids-not-fat. In fruit and nut ice cream, a reduction is usually allowed in the fat and milk solids resulting from the addition of flavoring materials to fruit, nut and chocolate flavored ice cream. This often amounts to at least two per cent fat and four per cent milk solids.

The term frozen dairy foods is a general term and includes ice cream, soft frozen products, ice milk, sherbet and ices.

Frozen custard represents the more expensive type of ice cream, including such products as parfait. It may be sold as fancy molded, a molded novelty (such as candy coated), "soft" frozen custard, or bulk frozen custard.

Plain ice cream, defined on page 18, includes the wide range of commercial ice creams even to the high fat ice creams and those containing small amounts of egg yolk solids. A mousse containing no fruit, nuts, etc., would be included as a plain ice cream. These products may be either fancy molded, novelties, or bulk ice cream.

TABLE 7

CLASSIFICATION OF FROZEN DAIRY FOODS BASED UPON THE CONCENTRATION OF CERTAIN CONSTITUENTS

Group	Distinguishing Characteristics	Suggested Regulatory Limitations
I Frozen Custard	High in egg yolk solids which are cooked to a custard before freezing Medium to high in milk fat and milk solids-not-fat With or without fruit, nuts, bakery products, candy, liquor, or spices With or without agitation while freezing	Not more than: 0.5 per cent edible stabilizer 100,000 bacteria per gram Negative coli test Not less than: 1.4 per cent minimum egg solids content for plain and 1.12 per cent for bulky flavors of custard. 10.0 per cent milk fat 20.0 per cent total milk solids 1.6 lb. food solids per gal. of finished product
II Plain Ice Cream	Medium to high in milk fat and milk solids-not-fat With or without egg products With or without agitation while freezing Without visible particles of flavoring material With the total volume of color and flavor less than 5 per cent of the volume of the unfrozen ice cream	Not more than: 0.5 per cent edible stabilizer 100,000 bacteria per gram Negative coli test Not less than: 10.0 per cent milk fat 20.0 per cent total milk solids 1.6 lb. food solids per gal. of finished product
III Composite Ice Cream or Bulky Flavors	Medium to high in milk fat and milk solids not-fat With or without egg products With or without agitation while freezing With the total volume of color and flavor material more than 5 per cent of the volume of the unfrozen ice cream or with visible particles of such products as cocoa, fruit, nut meats, candy, bakery products, liquor or spices.	Not more than: 0.5 per cent edible stabilizer 100,000 bacteria per gram Negative coli test Not less than: 8.0 per cent milk fat 16.0 per cent total milk solids—minimum 1.6 lb. food solids per gal. of finished product

Group	Distinguishing Characteristics	Suggested Regulatory Limitations
IV Ice Milk	Low in milk fat With or without egg products, chocolate, fruit, nut meats, candy, liquor, or spices with or without agitation while freezing	Not more than: 0.5 per cent edible stabilizer 100,000 bacteria per gram Negative coli test Not less than: 3.3 per cent milk fat—2.0 per cent minimum, 7 per cent maximum 14.0 per cent total milk solids—11 per cent minimum 1.3 lb. food solids per gal. of finished product
V Sherbet	Low in milk solids-not-fat Tart flavor Sweetener, water, harmless fruit or fruit juice flavoring, coloring	Not more than: 50,000 bacteria per gram Negative coli test Not less than: 0.35 per cent acidity as determined by titrating with standard alkali, and expressed as lactic acid 4.0 per cent total milk solids—2.0 per cent minimum, 5.0 per cent maximum 6.0 lb. minimum weight per gal. 1.8 lb. food solids per gal. of finished product Citrus fruit flavors 2 per cent, berries 6 per cent and other fruits 10 per cent.
VI Ice	No milk solids Tart flavor Sweetener, water, harmless fruit or fruit juice flavoring, coloring	Sanitary requirements same as for Sherbet
VII Imitation Ice Cream (Mellorine-type Products)	Proper labeling No minimum requirements to not less than 10 per cent food fat No minimum requirements to not less than 20 per cent food solids	Sanitary requirements same as for Ice Milk

Composite ice cream is either ice cream in which the total volume of coloring and flavoring material is more than five per cent of the volume of the unfrozen product, or ice cream containing visible particles of such products as cocoa, fruit, nut meats, candy, bakery products, etc. It may have a high fat content, contain small amounts of egg yolk solids, and be either fancy molded, novelties, or bulk composite ice cream. It includes such ice creams as chocolate, fruit, nut, candy, bisque, and puddings.

Ice milk, defined on p. 19, may be either fancy molded, novelties, or bulk ice milk.

Sherbet, defined on p. 19, may be either fancy molded, novelties, or bulk sherbet, and includes such products as Lacto.

Ices, defined on p. 19, may be either fancy molded, novelties, or bulk ices. This group includes such products as punch, granite, and popsicles. Definitions for fancy molded and novelties can be found on p. 19.

Imitation ice cream includes products such as those made with vegetable fat and containing milk constituents but not meeting ice cream standards. This product obviously cannot be marketed where its use is illegal.

Soft frozen products usually refers to ice milk served in a soft condition with a lower fat content than that required for ice cream. Ice cream, custard, sherbet or imitation ice cream may be served as soft frozen products.

The term **"bulk"** refers to ice cream such as is commonly purchased by retailers for re-packaging, and served directly to the consumer in cones or dishes.

Packaged ice cream refers to ice cream in containers the kind and size in which it reaches the consumer.

FEDERAL ICE CREAM STANDARDS

The Federal Standards (Table 8) for ice cream and related products released by the Food and Drug Administration in the Federal Register Vol. 25, Number 145, July 27, 1960 are presented in full in Chapter 24 (p. 335–347).

TABLE 8

COMPOSITION STANDARDS FOR FROZEN DESSERTS

	Ice Cream	Bulky Flavors	Ice Milk	Fruit Sherbets	Water Ices
Minimum fat, per cent	10	8	2	1	..
Maximum fat, per cent	..	..	7	2	..
Minimum TMS,[1] per cent	20	16	11	2	..
Maximum TMS,[1] per cent	..	..	..	5	..
Min. wt./gal. lb.	4.5	4.5	4.5	6	6
Min. TFS,[2] wt. per gal., lbs.	1.6	1.6	1.3	..	..
Max. stabilizer, per cent	0.5	0.5	0.5	0.5	0.5
Min. acidity, per cent	..	..	..	0.35	0.35

[1] TMS—total milk solids.
[2] TFS—total food solids.

In calculating butterfat, the order permits (regardless of the amount of actual sugar present) a reduction in the case of chocolate or cocoa 1.5 times the weight of the unsweetened chocolate or cocoa, and 1.4 times the weight of unsweetened fruits or nuts.

Frozen Custard Standards are the same as ice cream, except 1.4 per cent minimum egg yolk solids content for plain and 1.12 per cent for bulky flavors.

Ice Milk Standards permit no reduction for bulky flavors. Bulk can be colored or flavored.

Sherbet and Water Ice Standards permit natural and artificial flavors. The minimum fruit contents of sherbets and ices are: citrus 2 per cent (including cold-pressed citrus oil), berries 6 per cent, other fruits 10 per cent.

Labeling Requirements specify that the flavor name on ice cream must be in same size type as name of product and easily read. If artificial flavoring is used, this must be declared on label; i.e.: "Artificially flavored vanilla." If both natural and artificial flavors are used, with natural predominant—label is "vanilla and artificial vanilla flavor" if both are used and the artificial flavor is predominant, label is "Artificial vanilla flavor." Thus only that ice cream carrying 100 per cent of the true flavor or fruit can be designated by that flavor term without using the words "artificial flavor." The same holds true for the ice milk except when artificial color is used—this must also be included on the label.

Artificial coloring or flavoring in sherbets and water ices must be declared on the label. If natural flavors are added to fruit sherbets this must be declared also; i.e.: "Flavoring added" or "With added flavoring" or "————— flavoring added."

Acidity. The final order denies the use of milk alkalies to adjust the acidity and the use of mineral salts to adjust salt balance.

Concentrated Fruit is suitable for use in ice cream.

Whey. FDA opposes the inclusion of whey solids in ice cream. Its use in sherbet is recognized. The final order provides that its label shall bear a statement: "————— added," or "with ————— added," the blank being filled in with the appropriate form of whey such as "concentrated whey."

Caseinates. The standards permit to be added, but not counting toward the 20 per cent total milk solids, sodium, calcium, potassium, and ammonium caseinates.

Stabilizers. The optional stabilizers all of which are limited to 0.5 per cent of the weight of the finished ice cream are agar-agar, algin (sodium alginate), calcium sulfate, gelatin, gum acacia, guar seed gum, gum karaya, locust bean gum, oat gum, gum tragacanth, Irish moss, extract of Irish moss, lecithin, psyllium seed husk, sodium carboxymethylcellulose.

Emulsifiers. Monoglycerides or diglycerides or *both from the glycerolysis of edible fats* are listed as optional ingredients in an amount not more than 2 per cent. This new description of the source of mono and diglycerides is more limited than in the tentative order.

Tween 65 and Tween 80 in a separate food additives order issued are recognized as suitable optional ingredients in all of the standardized products except water ices at levels not to exceed 0.1 per cent.

Novelties. Those products frozen without stirring are considered to be outside the scope of the standard and are not covered nor regulated.

CHAPTER 4

Composition and Properties

Ice cream is composed of a mixture of food materials such as milk products, sweetening materials, stabilizers, flavors or egg products which are referred to as ingredients. The wide variety of ingredients which may be used to produce different kinds of ice cream is apparent from the classification discussed in Chapter 3. Furthermore, any one kind of ice cream may be made by combining the ingredients in any one of several different proportions. However, the effect of these ingredients upon the finished product is due to the constituents of the ingredients. An ice cream mix is the unfrozen blend of the ice cream ingredients and consists of all the ingredients of ice cream with the exception of air and flavoring materials. The composition of ice cream is usually expressed as percentage of its constituents; i.e., percentage of milk fat, milk solids-not-fat, sugar, egg yolk solids, stabilizer and total solids.

Ice cream contains a high concentration of milk solids. Its composition varies in different localities and in different markets. The best ice cream composition for a manufacturer to produce is often difficult to establish. After consideration is given to legal requirements, quality of product desired, raw materials available, plant procedures, trade demands, competition, and cost, there is a choice of a product of minimum, average or high solids composition. Some plants may choose to manufacture only one of these products, others two, and still others all three i.e., an economy brand product, a good average composition product as a trade brand or a deluxe high quality product.

It may be inadvisable for a small manufacturer to produce more than one brand of ice cream. If only one composition is manufactured, it is highly important that every effort be made to produce the best product possible.

In ice cream, the percentage of milk fat varies more than any other constituent. The milk fat content may vary from 8 to 24 per cent, depending upon such factors as state or city requirements, grade, price, competition, etc. As the fat content of ice cream is increased, the milk solids-not-fat must be decreased so as to avoid "sandiness" (i.e., the crystallization of milk sugar or lactose in the finished ice cream). Table 9 suggests compositions which avoid sandiness and permit recognition of particular local preferences as to sugar content, fat content, etc. of commercial ice creams and related products. These local preferences and the quality of the ingredients, as well as the technique of manufacture, are

27

TABLE 9

APPROXIMATE COMPOSITION OF COMMERCIAL ICE CREAM AND RELATED PRODUCTS

Milk Fat Per cent	M.S.N.F. Per cent	Sugar Per cent	Stabilizer and Emulsifier Per cent	Approximate Total Solids Per cent
		Economy Ice Cream		
10	10 to 11	13 to 15	0.30 to 0.50	35.0 to 37.0
12	9 to 10	13 to 15	0.25 to 0.50	
		Good Average Ice Cream		
12	11	15	0.30	
14	8 to 9	13 to 16	0.20 to 0.40	37.5 to 39.0
		Deluxe Ice Cream		
16	7 to 8	13 to 16	0.20 to 0.40	
18	6 to 7	13 to 16	0.25	40.0 to 41.0
20	5 to 6	14 to 17	0.25	
		Ice Milk		
3	14	14	0.45	31.4
		Good Average Ice Milk (Soft Serve)		
4	12.0	13.5	0.40	
5	11.5	13.0	0.40	29.0 to 30.0
6	11.5	13.0	0.35	
		Sherbet		
1 to 3	1 to 3	26 to 35	0.40 to 0.50	28.0 to 36.0
		Ice		
..	...	26 to 35	0.40 to 0.50	26.0 to 35.0

fully as important as the composition in determining the best ice cream for that locality.

Characteristics of a Satisfactory Composition. A satisfactory composition produces an ice cream having the desired combination of cost, food value, flavor, body and texture, cooling effect, color scheme, viscosity, whipping ability, and freezing point. Some of these characteristics are fairly closely associated. For example, a lower freezing point increases the cooling effect and tends toward a more pronounced flavor. Although the methods of processing and freezing influence these characteristics of ice cream, the effect of the constituents supplied by the ingredients is more important. Therefore the role of each constituent (fat, milk solids-not-fat, etc.) should be understood.

THE ROLE OF THE CONSTITUENTS OF ICE CREAM

Milk Fat, the most important constituent of ice cream, is high in food value and high in cost. Its influence on cost is shown by the fact that the cost of ice cream is raised about five cents a gallon for each per cent of increase in fat when the fat costs one dollar per pound. It contributes a characteristic richness and mellowness to produce the full, rich, creamy flavor which ice cream should have. Thus the flavor is improved by additional increments of fat until about 16 per cent is reached. However, the fat must be of fine flavor for if it is even slightly off-flavored, the defect will be more noticeable in rich ice cream. The fat also contributes to the body and melting resistance of ice cream while producing a smoothness of texture that is difficult to obtain by any other means. Since fat gives stability to the ice cream, less stabilizer is necessary in higher fat mixes. Although the viscosity of the mix increases with the fat content, the fat does impair the whipping ability. Since milk fat is in suspension, it has no effect on the freezing point. A satisfactory fat content, as indicated by the experience of numerous manufacturers, is 12 per cent or slightly above.

Milk Solids-not-Fat are the solids of skim milk. They include, the proteins, the milk sugar, and the mineral matter. They are high in food value and inexpensive, but they add very little to flavor, except indirectly by improving the body and texture. The milk sugar adds to the sweet taste largely produced by added sugars, and the minerals tend to carry a slightly salty taste which rounds out the flavor of the finished ice cream. The proteins in the milk solids-not-fat help to make the ice cream more compact and smooth and thus tend to prevent a weak body and coarse texture. Therefore, as much milk solids-not-fat should be added as possible without getting into the danger zone for sandiness. Too high concentrations, however, may impart an objectionable condensed milk flavor. Milk solids-not-fat increase viscosity and resistance to melting but lower the freezing point. Usual variations in concentration of the milk solids-not-fat have no pronounced effect on whipping ability, but variations in their quality do have an important influence on whipping ability.

Sweetening Agents are the sugars used in ice cream.

Sweetening value means the sweetening effect of added sugars expressed as the weight of sucrose necessary to give an equivalent sweet taste. For many years sucrose (cane or beet sugar) was the only sweetening agent added to ice cream; consequently it has been used as a standard in comparing the sweetening effect of other sugars. However, during the last thirty years there has been an increasing tendency to obtain the desired sweetness by blending sucrose with other sugars. This tendency has been due in part to insufficient supplies of sucrose, in part to the gradual improvement in quality of the more economically priced other sugars, and in part to a desire to increase the total solids of some ice creams without exceeding the limit of desirable sweetness of flavor.

It is now accepted that the desired sweetening agent can be obtained only by using some sucrose in the blend. The percentage of the sweetening agent which can be obtained from other sources is influenced mainly by (1) the desired concentration of sugar in the mix, (2) the total solids content of the mix, (3) the effect on the properties of the mix, such as freezing point, viscosity, and whipping ability, (4) the concentration in the sugar source of substances other than sugar; for example, the undesired flavor of honey, or the undesired color of molasses, and the relative inherent sweetening power of the sugars other than sucrose.

The main function of sugar is to increase the acceptance of the product, not only by making it sweeter but more especially by enhancing the pleasing creamy flavor and the desired delicate true fruit flavors. Lack of sweetness produces a flat taste while too much tends to overshadow desirable flavors. The sugar varies from 12 to 20 per cent, while 14 to 16 per cent seems most desirable. The sugars used as a source of sweetening increase the viscosity and the total solids concentration of the mix. This improves the body and texture of the ice cream provided the total solids content does not exceed 42 per cent or the sugar content does not exceed 16 per cent. Above these limits, the ice cream tends to become soggy and sticky. These sugars, being in solution, depress the freezing point of the mix. This results in slower freezing and requires a lower temperature for proper hardening. In addition to their effect on the quality of the ice cream, they are usually the cheapest source of total solids in the mix.

Egg Yolk Solids are high in food value but greatly increase the cost of ice cream. They impart a characteristic delicate flavor which aids in obtaining a desirable blending of other flavors, but even slight off-flavors in egg products are easily noticeable in the ice cream.

They have a pronounced effect in improving the body and texture, have almost no effect on the freezing point, and increase the viscosity. Egg yolk solids, regardless of their source, improve whipping ability, presumably due to lecithin existing as a lecithin-protein complex; and are especially desirable in mixes of low total solids concentration and in mixes where the fat is obtained from such ingredients as butter, butter oil, etc.

Stabilizers are used to prevent the formation of objectionable large ice crystals in ice cream and are used in such small amounts as to have a negligible influence on food value and flavor. They are of two general types, (1) the gelatin type of stabilizers which come from animal sources, such as calf skin, pork skin, bones, etc., and supply certain desirable amino acids; and (2) the vegetable stabilizers, such as sodium alginate, Irish moss, agar-agar, C.M.C. (sodium carboxymethylcellulose) and such other gums as tragacanth, karaya, oat gum, etc. All stabilizers have a high waterholding capacity effective in smoothening the texture and giving body to the finished product. Thus their effect on flavor is indirect. They increase viscosity, have no effect on the freezing point, and with a few exceptions tend to limit whipping ability. Their most important function is to prevent coarsening of texture under temperature fluctuations in retail cabinets. The amount of stabilizer to use varies with its properties, with the solids content of the mix, with the type of processing equipment and other factors.

Emulsifiers are used in the manufacture of ice cream mainly to improve and provide uniform whipping quality of the mix, and the production of a drier ice cream with smoother body and texture. The emulsifying ingredients commonly used in the ice cream industry are monoglycerides or diglycerides or both from the glycerolysis of edible fats. The total weight of these ingredients is not to exceed 0.2 per cent. The use of two polyoxyethylene type emulsifiers, Tween 65 and Tween 80, have been authorized as safe for usage in frozen dairy foods up to 0.1 per cent of the finished product. Use of excessive amounts of emulsifiers may result in slow melting and body and texture defects.

Total Solids replace water in the mix and thereby increase the nutritive value and viscosity, and improve the body and texture of the ice cream. This is especially true when the increase in total solids is due to added dextrine (pro-sugars), sweet cream buttermilk solids or eggs. Egg yolk solids, like sweet cream buttermilk solids, increase the whipping ability and shorten the freezing time. Increasing the concentration of total solids decreases the amount of frozen water and frequently permits a higher overrun while maintaining the minimum of 1.6 pounds of food solids per gallon of ice cream. During hot weather a disadvantage might be that this increase in calorie content somewhat reduces the cooling effect of the ice cream. A heavy, soggy product results when the total solids content is too high, usually when above 40 to 42 per cent.

Ordinary table salt is sometimes used in ice cream. This is usually unnecessary except in special flavors such as custards and nut ice creams. Some believe that a small amount of salt, less than 0.1 per cent improves the flavor of the ice cream. In any case, a salty flavor should be avoided.

Flavor is generally considered the most important characteristic of ice cream. It is easily confused with taste which includes the "feel sensation" of body and texture as well as the true flavor. The flavor of ice cream is the result of blending the flavors of all the ingredients, some of which may not be sufficiently pronounced to be recognizable, although each actually contributes to the final effect. This makes it difficult to forecast the effect of a certain ingredient upon the flavor of the ice cream. Furthermore the desirability of a particular flavor, or more properly "blend of flavors," depends upon the consumer or individual doing the tasting. This is particularly true of the average consuming public and frequently explains why a certain blend of flavors is less desirable at some times than at others.

Flavor has two important characteristics: type and intensity. Flavors that are delicate and mild are easily blended and do not tend to become tiresome even when very intense, while the harsh type of flavors soon become tiresome even in low concentrations. As a general rule, therefore, delicate flavors are preferable to harsh ones, but in any case the intensity of the flavor should be only strong enough to be easily recognized and delicately pleasing to taste.

THE BALANCED MIX

A balanced mix is one in which the proportions of the constituents and ingredients is such as will produce a fine and generally satisfactory ice cream—an ice cream in which the defects, if there still are any, can not be further corrected by any change in the composition or ingredients of the mix.

Defects such as rancid flavor, feed flavor, or uneven color can not be corrected by changing the concentration of the constituents. Therefore, they do not indicate a poorly balanced mix. However, other defects, such as; (1) "lacks flavoring," i.e., insufficient concentration of flavoring, (2) "lacks richness,"—insufficient concentration of fat, (3) "sandiness,"— too high concentration of milk solids-not-fat, or (4) "weak body," i.e., low total solids or low stabilizer, may be corrected by changing the composition of the mix. These defects do, therefore, indicate that the mix is incorrectly balanced.

Conditions Which Limit the Balancing of a Mix. It should, however, be remembered that a mix is balanced to give desirable results under certain limited conditions of processing and handling or even of handling the finished ice cream. For example, a mix may be properly balanced for a finished ice cream that is to have a rapid turnover, but would cause sandiness if the ice cream were to be stored for any length of time. Another mix may be properly balanced for freezing in a batch freezer but not in a continuous freezer. A mix may also be thrown out of balance by changing the source of the constituents. For example, if the fat in the mix is obtained from butter instead of from sweet cream, the mix may need the addition of egg yolk solids to improve its whipping ability and to give it the proper balance, but if made with sweet cream the egg yolk solids would not be necessary. A knowledge of the role of each constituent (pages 28 to 34) together with the outline of the advantages and limitations of the constituents, should be helpful in selecting a desired composition and in properly balancing a mix. Usually an ice cream mix that is properly balanced for average commercial conditions will have (1) between 36 and 42 per cent total solids and (2) between 20 and 26 per cent total milk solids (obtained by adding the percentage fat and the percentage milk solids-not-fat). This does not apply to a mix for ice milk, sherbet, or ice. Furthermore, there has been a tendency to improve the

TABLE 10

ADVANTAGES AND LIMITATIONS OF THE VARIOUS ICE CREAM CONSTITUENTS

I. Milk fat
   A. Advantages: (1) increases the richness of the flavor
                 (2) produces a characteristic smooth texture
                 (3) helps give body to the ice cream
   B. Limitations: (1) cost
                 (2) fat slightly hinders, rather than improves, whipping
                 (3) high fat content may limit the amount of ice cream consumed
                 (4) high caloric value
II. Milk solids-not-fat
   A. Advantages: (1) improve the texture
                 (2) help to give body
                 (3) a higher overrun without snowy or flaky texture
                 (4) a comparatively cheap source of solids
   B. Limitations: (1) a high percentage causes "sandiness"
                 (2) the "condensed milk" flavor may be objectionable
                 (3) may cause salty or cooked flavor
III. Sugar
   A. Advantages: (1) usually is the cheapest source of solids
                 (2) improves the texture
                 (3) enhances the flavor
   B. Limitations: (1) excessive sweetness
                 (2) lowers whipping ability
                 (3) longer freezing time required and the ice cream requires a lower temperature for proper hardening
IV. Stabilizers
   A. Advantages: (1) very effective in smoothening the texture
                 (2) very effective in giving body to the product
   B. Limitations: (1) excess body and melting resistance
V. Egg yolk solids
   A. Advantages: (1) very effective in improving whipping ability
                 (2) produces a smoother texture
                 (3) flavor
   B. Limitations: (1) excessive amounts may produce "foaminess on melting"
                 (2) egg flavor not relished by some consumers
                 (3) cost
VI. Total solids
   A. Advantages: (1) smoother texture
                 (2) better body
                 (3) more nutritious
                 (4) ice cream not as cold
   B. Limitations: (1) heavy, soggy or pasty body
                 (2) cooling effect not high enough
VII. Flavor
   A. Advantages: (1) increases acceptability
   B. Limitations: (1) harsh flavors less desirable
                 (2) intense flavors quickly satisfy desire
VIII. Color
   A. Advantages: (1) improves attractiveness
                 (2) aids in identifying flavor

From Sommer (1946).

nutritive value of ice cream by increasing the concentration of milk solids-not-fat and reducing the fat, sugar and flavor concentrations. Calculations for balancing mixes are given in Chapter 8.

In the foregoing discussion of the constituents of the ice cream mix, their limitations as well as their advantages and beneficial properties have been pointed out. For easy references these advantages and limitations are summarized in Table 10.

IMPORTANT PROPERTIES

Mix properties of practical importance include viscosity, acidity as lactic acid and pH, mix stability and whipping rate.

Viscosity or resistance to flow, has been considered an important property of the ice cream mix, and a certain amount of it seems essential for proper whipping and for retention of air. The viscosity of a mix is affected by:

1. Composition. Viscosity is influenced more by the fat and the stabilizer than by the other constituents.

2. Kind and quality of ingredients. Those carrying the fat are especially important. Also, heat and salts (such as calcium, sodium, citrates, etc.) greatly affect the viscosity due to their effect on the casein and other proteins.

3. Processing and handling of the mix. The steps in processing which have the greatest effect are pasteurization, homogenization, and aging.

4. Concentration (i.e., total solids content).

5. Temperature. Although much has been written about the causes and effects of viscosity, there has been no final answer to the questions: how much is desirable; and how can it be accurately measured? A high viscosity was believed essential at one time, but for fast freezing (rapid whipping) in modern equipment a lower viscosity seems desirable. In general, as the viscosity increases, the resistance to melting and the smoothness of body increases, but the rate of whipping decreases. Viscosity is now considered a phenomenon that frequently accompanies rather than causes good whipping, body and texture. Therefore, the mix should be properly balanced (in regard to composition, concentration, and quality of ingredients) and then properly processed to produce the desired whipping ability, body, and texture. Under these conditions a desirable viscosity is assured.

The normal acidity of mix varies with the percentage of milk solids-not-fat it contains and may be calculated by multiplying the percentage milk solids-not-fat by the factor 0.018. Thus a mix containing 11 per cent milk solids-not-fat would have a normal acidity of 0.198 per cent. The normal pH of ice cream mix is about 6.3. The acidity and pH are related to the composition of the mix and an increase in milk solids-not-fat raises the percentage acidity and lowers the pH. The acidity and pH values for mixes of various solids-not-fat content may be as shown in Table 11.

TABLE 11

ACIDITY AND pH VALUES FOR VARIOUS COMPOSITIONS

Milk solids-not-fat Content of Mix, per cent	Approximate Acidity,[1] per cent	Approximate pH
7	0.126	6.40
8	0.144	6.35
9	0.162	6.35
10	0.180	6.32
11	0.198	6.31
12	0.206	6.30
13	0.224	6.28

[1] As lactic acid.

If fresh dairy products of excellent quality are used, the mix may be expected to have a normal acidity. The normal or natural acidity of ice cream mix is due to the milk proteins, mineral salts and dissolved gases. Developed acidity is caused by the production of lactic acid by bacterial action in dairy products. When the acidity is above normal it indicates that developed acidity is present in the dairy products used in the mix. A high acidity is undesirable as it contributes to excess mix viscosity, decreased whipping rate, inferior flavor and a less stable mix resulting in "cook on" or possible coagulation during the pasteurizing and processing procedure.

Mix stability refers to the stability or resistance to separation of the milk proteins in the ice cream mix. Instability results in separation of the protein particles as coagulated or precipitated material in the mix which may be caused by acidity, heat treatment, milk salts, homogenization pressure or stabilizing material.

High whipping rate describes the property to whip rapidly to a high overrun. It is now definitely known that the differences in whipping ability can not be explained on the basis of viscosity. The present hypothesis is that whipping ability is based on tensile strength and strength of the lamellae or walls around the air cells. Whipping ability is improved by high processing temperatures, proper homogenization, and aging the mix for 2 to 4 hours.

Smaller fat globules and less clumping give increased whipping ability. Mixes made with butter, butter oil, or frozen cream have a less satisfactory dispersion of fat and poorer whipping ability. Egg yolk solids, regardless of their source, and fresh cream buttermilk solids improve whipping ability, presumably due to lecithin existing as a lecithin-protein complex. Emulsifiers, which are described later, also improve whipping ability. Usual variations in concentration of milk solids-not-fat have no pronounced effect on whipping ability, but qualitative variations in the milk solids-not-fat are important. Sugar decreases the whipping ability except when added after homogenizing and then it increases whipping ability. Finally, the construction and operation of the freezer itself determine whether the maximum whipping ability of a given mix is obtained.

CHAPTER 5

Ice Cream Ingredients

Essentials for the manufacture of high quality ice cream are good ingredients mixed and balanced so as to produce a satisfactory composition, together with intelligent processing, freezing, and hardening of the product. All of these factors are important and should be carefully controlled by the ice-cream maker.

The selection of good ingredients[1] is, without doubt, the most important factor in successful ice cream manufacture. A clean, fresh, creamy flavor in ice cream can be secured only by the use of products which have been carefully produced and handled. In general, the more concentrated the dairy product and the longer it is held in storage, the less desirable is the flavor imparted to the ice cream.

A wide choice of ingredients for ice cream is available from various sources. These ingredients may be grouped as dairy products or non-dairy products. The milk products group is the most important, as these products furnish the basic ingredients for good ice cream. Some dairy products supply the major source of fat, others the major source of milk solids-not-fat, and others supply both fat and milk solids-not-fat, while still others supply bulk to the mix. The non-dairy products used in ice cream include: sweetening agents, egg products, stabilizers and emulsifiers, special products, flavoring and colors.

COMPOSITION OF MILK

Since milk is the source of the dairy products used as ice cream ingredients it is important to have an understanding of the composition and properties of milk.

Milk is composed of water, milk fat and milk solids-not-fat. The total solids content of milk includes all the constituents of milk except water. The solids-not-fat constituents are those found in skim milk and include: lactose, protein and minerals. These solids are also referred to as skim milk solids, serum solids (s.s.) or more correctly milk solids-not-fat (m.s.n.f.). The approximate proportions are shown in Table 12.

The composition of milk varies as it is influenced by numerous factors. The solids-not-fat content varies with the fat content of milk. A variation of 0.4 per cent change in solids-not-fat for each per cent change in fat

---

[1] Flavoring and Stabilizers are discussed in Chapters 6 and 7.

TABLE 12

APPROXIMATE COMPOSITION OF MILK

Constituents	Per cent
Water	87.1
Fat	3.9
Protein	3.3
Lactose (milk sugar)	5.0
Ash (minerals)	0.7
	100.0
Solids-not-fat	9.0
Total solids	12.9

may be used in a general way to determine the solids-not-fat content of milk at the various fat levels.

Milk is secreted in the mammary gland from the constituents supplied the gland by the blood. Some constituents may pass through the mammary system and occur in the resulting milk by the process of filtration, but most of them are secreted or produced by the mammary gland and as a result certain of the constituents of milk, including milk fat, casein and lactose are found in major amounts only in milk.

A constituent in colloidal suspension does not affect the freezing point, boiling point or other properties as does the material that is in true solution. Some of the constituents of milk occur in a colloidal state. A colloidal system may be thought of as a system in which a large interface has been attained by the dispersion of one or more of the constituents into units not larger than one micron. A micron is about one-twenty-five thousandth of an inch. The degree of dispersion of the constituents in milk ranges from true solution or molecular size (lactose) through colloidal suspension (casein) to coarse dispersion (milk fat).

The following chart (Table 13) gives the particle size of the milk constituents and of those constituents occurring in ice cream.

The water present in milk is similar to any other water except it has passed through the mammary gland and it is reasonable to assume it has a high degree of purity. Water provides bulk and acts as a dispersion medium for the other constituents holding them in solution, colloidal suspension or emulsion.

Milk fat is found only in milk. It occurs in milk in the form of tiny globules which are held in suspension in the state of emulsion. Normal milk contains about 2.5 billion fat globules per milliliter. The fat globules vary in size from 0.8 to 20 microns in diameter. (See Fig. 5). The size of the globules varies with breed of cow and stage of lactation. The size of the globule affects the rate of the creaming and churning. Fat globules tend to cluster together. This property is responsible for rapid

TABLE 13

PARTICLE SIZE AND STATE OF DISPERSION OF MILK CONSTITUENTS AND CONSTITUENTS OF ICE CREAM

(1 μμ = 1/1000 micron)   (1μ = 1 micron or 1/25000 inch)

1 μμ	10 μμ	100 μμ	1μ 1000 μμ	10 μ	100 μ	1000 μ (1 mm.)
Electron microscope	Ultramicroscope		Microscope		Visible	
Passes filters and membranes	Pass filters but not membranes		Passes neither filters nor membranes			
Molecular movement	Brownian movement		Slow Brownian and gravitational movement			
	Sedimentation and oil globule rise extremely slow		Sedimentation and oil globule rise			
High osmotic pressure	Low osmotic pressure		No osmotic pressure			
True solution	Colloidal suspension		Coarse suspension			

MILK CONSTITUENTS

1 μμ	10 μμ	100 μμ	1μ 1000 μμ	10 μ	100 μ	1000 μ
Lactose and Soluble salts	Whey protein albumin & globulin Colloidal phosphates	Calcium caseinate	Fat globules			

ICE CREAM CONSTITUENTS

1 μμ	10 μμ	100 μμ	1μ 1000 μμ	10 μ	100 μ	1000 μ
Lactose, sucrose corn sugar and soluble salts	Whey protein Albumin Globulin Stabilizers, colloidal phosphates	Casein	Fat globules		Ice crystals Flavoring particles (fruits, nuts, etc.)	

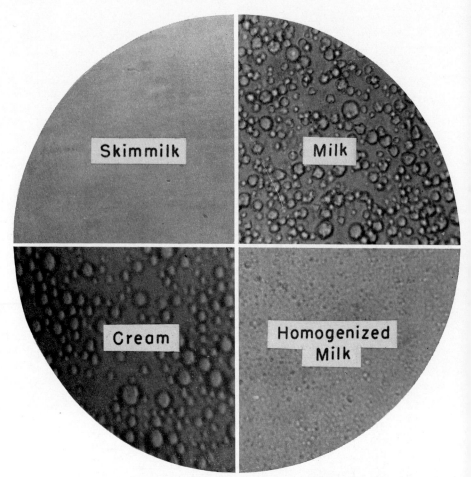

From Maryland Agricultural Experiment Station Bull. 454

FIG. 5. THE MICROSCOPIC APPEARANCE OF FAT GLOBULES

Size—Milk and cream—8–10 microns; homogenized milk—majority less than two microns; skim milk—none.

creaming, viscosity and body characteristics in various manufactured dairy products. The fat globules have on their surface a layer of colloidal substances composed of protein and lecithin. This layer is commonly referred to as the fat globule membrane.

Milk fat is composed of various fatty acids and may contain materials associated with milk fat.

The fatty acids of milk fat exist in combination with glycerol, $C_3H_8O_3$, as fatty glycerides. One molecule of glycerol combines with three molecules of fatty acid, 1 glycerine + 3 fatty acids = $3H_2O$ + 1 fat. When three molecules of the same fatty acid unites with one molecule of glycerine a single glyceride is formed. When the three molecules of fatty-acid are of more than one kind, a mixed glyceride is formed. Milk fat probably contains both simple and mixed glycerides, but the mixed glycerides predominate. Obviously, there is a possibility that a very large number of different combinations of glycerol and fatty acids may exist since milk fat is a mixture of fats, variations in its properties depend upon the proportion and properties of the various fat components present.

Substances associated with milk fat include related compounds, namely the phospholipids, lecithin and cephalin; the sterols, cholesterol and ergosterol; the carotinoids, carotene and xanthophyll and the vitamins, A, D, and E. In phospholipids part of the fatty acids present is replaced by phosphoric acid and a nitrogen base. Lecithin is one of the best known phospholipids. The nitrogen base in lecithin is choline which is a part of the vitamin B complex. Milk contains about 0.075 per cent lecithin and cephalin, and milk fat is about 0.6 per cent lecithin. Cholesterol is the principle sterol in milk. Milk contains about 0.015 per cent cholesterol. Ergosterol, $C_{28}H_{43}OH$, is the precursor of Vitamin D and carotene is the precursor of Vitamin A.

The protein components of milk are casein and the whey protein. The major proteins of casein are a-, b-, and g-casein. The immune globulins, a-lactalbumin, b-lactoglobulin, serum albumin and some minor proteins comprise the whey protein.

Casein is the major protein of milk and it occurs only in milk. It comprises approximately 80 per cent of the total protein. In the pure state casein is white, odorless and tasteless. It occurs in milk in colloidal state. It may be removed by filtration through a porcelain filter and casein particles as they occur in milk can be observed with an ultra-microscope or by use of a dark field attachment. The particle size of casein ranges from 1 to 100 millimicrons, with an average size of 40 to 50 millimicrons. Casein is found in milk in combination with calcium as calcium caseinate. It is precipitated by enzymes, alcohols, heat, various salts and by acids at a pH of 4.6. A temperature of approximately 270°F. is required to coagulate the casein of a high quality milk.

The whey protein particles range in size from 1 millimicron to 20 millimicrons with the average size of about 10 millimicrons. These proteins are not precipitated with acid or with rennin but they are readily precipitated by heat at temperatures about 170°F. These proteins resemble casein in chemical composition.

Lactose or milk sugar is in solution in milk. Lactose is found only in milk and is a major constituent of milk. It is a disaccharide composed of

TABLE 14

GROUPING OF MINERAL CONSTITUENTS AS MINERAL SALTS OF MILK

Grouping	Percentage of Mineral Salts
Sodium chloride, NaCl	10.6
Sodium bicarbonate, $NaHCO_3$	2.4
Potassium chloride, KCl	9.0
Potassium sulfate, K_2SO_4	1.7
Mono-potassium phosphate, KH_2PO_4	10.4
Di-potassium phosphate, K_2HPO_4	9.4
Dicalcium phosphate, $CaHPO_4$	6.5
Tricalcium phosphate, $Ca_3(PO_4)_2$	7.8
Tripotassium citrate, $K_3C_6H_5O_7$	6.5
Trimagnesium citrate, $Mg_3(C_6H_5O_7)_2$	7.4
Tricalcium citrate, $Ca_3(C_6H_5O_7)_2$	17.2
CaO combined with casein	5.7
Sulfur combined with casein, albumin and globulin	3.0
Phosphorus combined with casein, albumin and globulin	2.4
	100.0

two monosaccharides, glucose and galactose linked together. Lactose is a carbohydrate and at favorable temperatures, part of the lactose is converted into lactic acid by the action of certain bacteria usually present in milk thus souring the milk.

The lactose content of milk does not vary widely, it averages about 4.9 per cent. It reduces Fehlings solution forming cuprous oxide, Cu_2O. Lactose is optically active having a specific rotation of 52.53°. It may occur in three forms, two are anhydrous and one a monohydrate. In solution lactose exists in two forms, alpha and beta lactose. There is an equilibrium between the forms, approximately 60 per cent of the lactose is in the beta form, although the exact percentage depends on the temperature of the solution. Crystalline lactose exists in three forms, alpha lactose hydrate, $C_{12}H_{22}O_{11}H_2O$; alpha lactose anhydride, $C_{12}H_{22}O_{11}$ and beta lactose anhydride, $C_{12}H_{22}O_{11}$. Lactose is one-sixth to one-fourth as sweet as sucrose and one-third and one-fourteenth as soluble as sucrose at 32°C., and 212°C. respectively.

The crystals of lactose occur in many forms. The crystalline forms of alpha lactose anhydride have appeared in as many as nine different stages in the development of the same crystal pattern.

Milk ash occurs in milk as mineral salts. Minerals in milk include: calcium, phosphorus, potassium, magnesium, iron, chlorine, copper and traces of other materials. These minerals in the form of citrates, phosphates or oxides are important in influencing the behavior of milk subjected to manufacturing procedures. Milk minerals are of considerable importance as nutrients.

Some of the calcium and phosphorus is combined with casein and is colloidally dispersed. The potassium, chlorine and sodium occur in true solution.

The mineral constituents as they exist in the form of salts in milk may be shown in Table 14.

The mineral content of milk is less variable than most of the other constituents. The ash content of mixed milk averages approximately 0.7 per cent and ranges from 0.65 to 0.75 per cent while the average mineral salts content is about 0.9 per cent.

Other Substances. Milk contains the enzymes, phosphatase, amylase, lipase, cleinase, peroxidase, and others. The gases, carbon dioxide, nitrogen and oxygen are contained in solution in the approximate per cent by volume of 4.5, 1.3 and 0.5 respectively. Milk contains citric acid, lactic acid, leucocytes, epithelial cells and nitrogenous constituents.

The vitamins present include: beta carotene, vitamin A; ascorbic acid, vitamin C; thiamin, vitamin B; vitamin D; riboflavin, vitamin B_2 or G; and many other vitamin-like substances.

MILK PRODUCTS USED IN ICE CREAM

Both the butterfat and the milk solids-not-fat of the milk products used in the mix contribute to the flavor of the ice cream. The butterfat is more important in this respect because the full, rich, and creamy flavor which ice cream should have comes mostly from the butterfat of the mix. The milk solids-not-fat, on the other hand, have a more indirect effect on flavor. The proteins improve the body and texture and tend to prevent a weak body and coarse texture. The milk sugar adds to the sweet taste largely produced by the added sugars, and the milk salts tend to carry a slightly salty taste which rounds out the flavor of the finished ice cream.

Whole milk is very desirable as a source of fat as well as of milk solids-not-fat. Only milk of clean flavor and odor, with a low acidity of 0.2 per cent or less, should be used. A combination of milk and sweet cream is probably the best source of fat for ice cream. Fresh whole milk is seldom used because in many markets it is too expensive a source of fat and milk solids-not-fat.

Fresh sweet cream is the most desirable concentrated source of butterfat for use in the mix. Other concentrated milk products do not impart the same clean, rich, creamy flavor that is carried by a good quality sweet cream. Cream containing 40 per cent fat should not exceed 0.15 per cent acidity and should be free from off-flavors and odors. A butterfat test should be made on each purchase so that the buyer has the assurance that he is receiving the full amount of fat for which he pays. However, sweet cream is relatively expensive as a source of fat, fluctuates considerably in

TABLE 15

APPROXIMATE COMPOSITION AND WEIGHTS PER GALLON OF INGREDIENTS USED IN ICE CREAM MIX

Ingredient	Fat Per cent	M.S.N.F. Per cent	Sugar Per cent	Total Solids Per cent	Weight per Gal. lbs.
Water	0.00	0.00	0.00	0.00	8.3
Skim milk from 3.0% milk	0.00	8.60	0.00	8.60	8.7
Skim milk from 4.0% milk	0.00	9.00	0.00	9.00	8.7
Milk	3.00	8.33	0.00	11.33	8.6
Milk	4.00	8.79	0.00	12.79	8.6
Milk	5.00	9.10	0.00	14.10	8.6
Cream	12.00	7.80	0.00	19.80	8.5
Cream	15.00	7.57	0.00	22.57	8.5
Cream	18.00	7.31	0.00	25.31	8.5
Cream	20.00	7.13	0.00	27.13	8.5
Cream	25.00	6.68	0.00	31.68	8.4
Cream	30.00	6.24	0.00	36.24	8.4
Cream	35.00	5.69	0.00	40.69	8.4
Cream	40.00	5.35	0.00	45.35	8.3
Cream, frozen	50.00	4.45	0.00	54.45	8.2
Cream, plastic	80.00	1.80	0.00	81.80	..
Butter, unsalted	84.00	1.00	0.00	85.00	..
Butter oil	99.00	0.00	0.00	99.00	..
Evaporated milk, canned	8.00	20.00	0.00	28.00	8.9
Evaporated milk, bulk	10.00	23.00	0.00	33.00	9.2
Sweetened condensed whole milk	8.00	23.00	42.00	73.00	9.2
Condensed skim unsweetened	0.00	32.00	0.00	32.00	9.4
Condensed skim sweetened	0.00	27.00	42.00	69.00	9.2
Non-fat dry milk (skim milk powder)	0.00	97.00	0.00	97.00	..
Whole milk powder	26.00	72.00	0.00	98.00	..
Plain condensed whole milk	8.00	20.00	0.00	28.00	8.9
Dry buttermilk solids	5.00	91.00	0.00	96.00	..
Dry whey solids	0.00	93.00	0.00	93.00	..
Special condensed whole milk	19.00	21.00	0.00	40.00	8.9

quality and price, and has the added disadvantage of being difficult to secure in good quality at certain seasons of the year on some markets.

Frozen cream is stored by many companies during the months of surplus and low price. In storing frozen cream only the very best fresh cream should be used. It should be pasteurized at 165° to 175°F. for 15 minutes to inhibit the development of off-flavors. Neither the milk nor the cream should come in contact with exposed iron or copper, as may occur when the tin has worn off separator parts or utensils, or when bronze fittings or bronze pumps are used. Copper, iron, and bronze from these sources dissolve in the cream, producing a tallowy and metallic flavor during storage of the frozen cream. Storage rooms should be about 10°F. below zero, and the cream should be held no longer than six months. While the storing of frozen cream is ordinarily economical, the flavor of such cream after storage is never quite equal to that of good fresh cream. Off-flavors likely to develop in frozen cream are: rancid, fishy, oily, and tallowy flavors. Local regulations may or may not permit the use of cream containing added antioxidants.

When storing cream for use in ice cream, the addition before freezing of 10 per cent by weight of cane sugar is desirable. This cream retains its flavor better, melts more quickly and with less fat separation, and produces a mix with higher whipping ability. However, the addition of sugar ties up additional capital in stored sugar. Moreover, if such cream happens to develop off-flavors there is increased difficulty in finding an outlet for it.

Plastic cream is used to some extent as a source of fat for ice cream. Plastic cream is essentially a very rich cream (80 per cent fat) and is similar to butter in consistency at ordinary temperatures. It is stored and handled commercially like butter.

Unsalted butter (sweet butter) is next to sweet cream in importance as a source of fat. The advantages of butter are that it is a comparatively cheap source of fat, can be transported at low cost, can be stored for months with little deterioration in quality, and is nearly always available in fairly uniform quality. If the butter is of good quality, from 50 to 75 per cent of the fat of the mix can be secured from this source. The unsalted butter should be of a grade that will score 92 or higher and preferably should be made from sweet cream. Such off-flavors as ripened cream, neutralizer, stale, rancid, and tallowy, which are found in butter of low quality, will carry over directly into the mix.

Butter oil[2] is a relatively new source of fat for the ice cream mix. Its quality depends on the quality of the butter or the cream from which it was made. It is convenient and under proper storage conditions will keep better than butter.

The milk products (with the exception of butter oil) which are used primarily as sources of fat also contribute milk solids-not-fat as shown in Table 15.

Fresh skim milk should be used in the mix whenever available at reasonable prices, because it is a cheap source of milk solids-not-fat. It should have a low acidity and a clean flavor. A 40-quart can of skim milk will contain about 7.5 lbs. of milk solids-not-fat. Skim milk when purchased should be bought on the basis of a definite milk solids-not-fat content in order to guard against dilution with water.

When water is used in place of skim milk a larger proportion of condensed or powdered milk is necessary in order to supply the needed milk solids-not-fat. Unless the product is of exceptional quality, this practice usually results in a slightly cooked or "serum solids" off-flavor in the finished ice cream.

---

[2] Butter oil is made by melting butter and removing the curd and salt. The product contains less than one per cent moisture and over 99 per cent of butter fat.

Sweet cream buttermilk is obtained by churning cream that has not developed noticeable acidity; i.e., cream of the same quality as that used in ice cream or retail market cream. A larger supply of sweet cream buttermilk will be available when better methods of storage are developed and continuous churning is more widely practiced. Sweet cream buttermilk has beneficial effects on the whipping ability of the mix and contributes a richness of flavor. The use of sweet cream buttermilk, either as such or in the condensed or powdered form, is especially desirable in ice cream of low fat content or in ice cream made with butter. Sweet cream buttermilk can supply nearly one-fifth of the milk solids-not-fat of the mix; if a larger proportion is used, there is danger of a slight undesirable flavor. The fat content of condensed sweet cream buttermilk will be about 3 or 4 per cent and should of course be considered in calculating the ice cream mix.

Non-fat dry milk is one of the concentrated sources of milk solids-not-fat which is frequently used. There are three forms of non-fat dry milk on the market: spray process powder, drum-dried powder, and flakes. Each contains over 90 per cent milk solids-not-fat. The spray process powders are more soluble than the drum-dried. The skim milk flakes have the advantage of not lumping when added to the mix. A good powder should be of fine flavor, light in color, free from darkened particles, fluffy, and easily soluble. A poor powder often is yellow in color, and granular. Non-fat dry milk should be bought only in such quantities as can be used before the product develops off-flavors, and preferably should be kept in cold storage. Buying in large quantities and storing at room temperatures as frequently practiced is unwise because skim milk powders and flakes have a tendency to become stale, and if in this condition will impart old or storage flavors to ice cream. Modern forms of non-fat dry milk are known as "instant" powders because of their ability to disperse easily and quickly in water without forming lumps.

Powdered whole milk, up to the present time, has not been widely used in the ice cream mix because off-flavors developed fairly rapidly in storage.

Plain condensed skim milk is used more frequently than any of the other condensed milk products. The keeping quality of condensed skim milk is only a little better than that of cream; hence, the product should be used while fresh and sweet. It should be shipped and stored under refrigeration. Condensed skim milk varies from 25 to 35 per cent in milk solids-not-fat.

Superheated condensed skim milk is made by heating the already condensed product to a high temperature which increases the viscosity at ordinary temperature. Its use in ice cream improves the whipping ability. The superheated product when used in ice cream should have that viscosity that will result in the best body, plasticity, and melt-down characteristics in the finished ice cream. It should be free from visible curd specks, and free from a pronounced cooked flavor. Formerly, superheated condensed milk and skim milk were used quite extensively. Since superheated products cost more than plain condensed products, and since they are not always of the desired uniformity, they are now used mostly by manufacturers who omit stabilizers as a point in their sales policy.

Plain condensed whole milk is perfectly satisfactory for use in ice cream. It has not been in general use in the past but more recently is being used extensively as an ingredient in the manufacture of ice cream. It is easily transported and handled in bulk form and for many plants supplies the main source of both fat and milk solids-not-fat. Such a product is prepared to contain approximately 18 to 19 per cent fat and 20 to 21 per cent milk solids-not-fat as specified by the ice cream manufacturer. Then the ice cream mix of the desired composition is readily composed by the addition of sugar and stabilizer.

Sweetened condensed whole milk and skim milk are sometimes used as a concentrated source of milk solids-not-fat. The added sugar (40 to 44 per cent) improves the keeping quality over that of plain condensed milk. The sweetened condensed milk is thick and viscous, hence not so easily handled as the plain condensed. A defect in this milk is the tendency toward crystallization of the milk sugar (lactose) into large crystals. Sweetened condensed milk should be smooth in texture, never "sandy." In judging the quality of a condensed milk product, attention should be centered on flavor—a pronounced cooked flavor will show up in the finished ice cream. Condensed milk should also be free from excessive amounts of copper or iron. These taints will appear as a metallic flavor, which in storage may develop into a tallowy or oxidized fat flavor. The acidity test should also be applied to condensed milk products. When diluted so as to contain the same milk solids-not-fat concentration as skim milk, the acidity should be approximately that of fresh skim milk (about 0.18 per cent).

Special commercial products are sometimes used as constituents of ice cream mix. These products include sodium caseinate, delactosed milk products, modified non-fat milk solids, certain mineral salts or a combination of some of these materials. The functions of these products vary, depending upon their composition and purpose. The products are designed mainly to improve whipping qualities, storage properties, resistance to heat shock, body and texture, to increase the solids content or for mild adjustment of mix acidity.

Sodium caseinate is available for use in a nondesiccated and in a dry form. The amount used of the nondesiccated product ranges from 2.5 to

5 percent by weight of mix and 0.5 to 1.0 per cent of the dehydrated product. These products must be free from excess alkali when used as an ice cream ingredient. The use of sodium caseinate may produce a slight undesirable flavor in the finished ice cream, decrease the mix viscosity significantly, increase the mix acidity about 0.01 per cent for each per cent of sodium caseinate used, improve the texture, and increase the rate of melting in the finished ice cream, but the greatest influence of sodium caseinate is in improving the whipping properties of the mix.

Low lactose milk products have been used in high solids ice cream either to replace a portion of the regular milk solids or to supplement the milk solids-not-fat without the occurrence of sandiness during storage or without the usual lowered effect on the drawing temperature during the freezing process. Approximately 25 per cent of the milk solids-not-fat in a high solids ice cream can be obtained from a low lactose skim milk, or 10 to 12 per cent when a dehydrated low lactose product is used. The use of low lactose products may increase the mix acidity as there is an increase in the mix protein content resulting from their use. There is also an increase in mix viscosity during storage and an improvement in texture and storage quality of the finished ice cream when delactosed products are used. There is little influence on whipping properties or rate of melting.

Non-fat milk solids products such as "Nutrimix" are used to increase the solids-not-fat content 1 to 3.5 per cent with improved body and texture and without the occurrence of sandiness. The product may also be used to replace a portion of the regular milk solids-not-fat. The use of special processed non-fat milk solids products reduces the acidity of the mix, but has little effect on the viscosity and whipping properties of the mix or the melting properties of the ice cream. The usual effect on flavor is desirable and the body, texture and keeping qualities are improved by the use of the special processed non-fat milk solids. The use of several of the special commercial products formerly used in ice cream is not now permitted by the Federal Standards.

Calcium sulfate is used to produce a stiff, dry ice cream as it is delivered from the freezer. The rate of use ranges from 0.08 to 0.16 per cent. The product should be added to the mix before the pasteurization process. The use of calcium sulfate increases the acidity of the mix, produces a dry, stiff ice cream from the freezer and reduces the rate of melting, but has little effect on other properties of the mix or finished ice cream. The degree of these effects may be influenced by the kind of stabilizer used.

Other sources of milk solids-not-fat are not used very extensively in ice cream. **Evaporated milk** imparts a noticeable cooked flavor and caramelized color which is undesirable in most ice creams. **Malted milk** imparts a typical flavor which limits its use. **Powdered whey solids** have been used to supply up to 30 per cent of the milk solids-not-fat content of ice cream mix. Whey solids contain the solids-not-fat portion of milk with the exception of casein. Dried ice cream mix is available and may be reconstituted by adding 5 parts of water to 3 parts of the dried mix. It may be frozen immediately after reconstitution with good results.

SOURCES OF SWEETENING MATERIALS

Many kinds of sweeteners are used in ice cream. These include cane and beet sugar, corn sweeteners, maple sugar, honey, invert sugar, and sugar substitutes. Cane or beet sugars are most commonly used. One-fourth to one-third of the cane or beet sugar may be replaced by corn sugar with good results. The use of a combination or blend of sugars in either dry or liquid forms is a popular practice.

Sugar blends are usually 70 per cent sucrose and 30 per cent corn sweetener. The desired sugar concentration in ice cream is 15 to 16 per cent. The different kinds of sugar do not produce equal sweetening effects although sweetness can neither be exactly defined nor measured. A sweet ice cream is generally desired by the public. In addition to providing sweetness, sugars affect the properties of the mix and the finished product. Sugars depress the freezing point of the mix, produce a thinner mix with a slower whipping rate, and an ice cream with a smoother body and texture with faster melting qualities. Sugar blends may be expected to affect mix and finished product qualities in accordance with the proportion of the kind of sugars in the blend.

Combination corn syrup and corn-syrup solids are used with sucrose as a sweetening agent for ice cream as they affect product cost, body and texture and flavor characteristics, and the shelf life of the finished product.

Sucrose, commonly known by such trade names as granulated sugar, cane sugar, and beet sugar, is the most widely accepted source of sugar. Although sucrose depresses the freezing point (see Fig. 6), its concentration in ice cream is limited only by its sweetening effect. It is not satisfactory as the only source of sugar in ices and sherbets since it may crystallize out at the surface. This defect in ices and sherbets can be avoided by using one part of dextrose to three and a half parts of sucrose.

Brown sugar and maple sugar are nearly 100 per cent sucrose, but they contain characteristic flavoring materials which limit their use in ice cream. For example, only 6 per cent of maple sugar in the mix will produce a good maple flavor. Furthermore, these sugars are usually more expensive than other sources of sweeteners.

Corn sweeteners of three major types are available for use in ice cream as follows: (1) refined corn sugar (dextrose), a dry crystalline product; (2) dried corn syrup or corn-syrup solids; and (3) corn syrup, a liquid.

Corn syrup solids or corn syrup imparts a firmer and heavier body to the finished ice cream, provides an economical source of solids, and improves the shelf life of the finished products.

Dextrose, cerelose, dextrose hydrate and corn sugar are trade names commonly applied to the most refined sugar obtained by the hydrolysis of corn starch. These products owe their sweetness to dextrose, i.e., d-glucose. Commercially the term glucose is incorrectly applied to a variety of products which contain some dextrose. Dextrose is now quite extensively used in ice cream and is considered necessary to sherbets and ices, where it inhibits the crystallization of sucrose on the surface. Since it is only about 80 per cent as sweet as sucrose, it requires 1.25 lb. of dextrose to obtain the sweetening effect obtained from 1.0 lb. of sucrose. Dextrose causes a lower freezing point than does sucrose because its molecular weight is lower. This effect on the freezing point limits the amount of dextrose which can be used to about 25 per cent of the total desired sugar. Usually dextrose is more economical than sucrose as a source of sweetness. Dextrose has a slightly greater tendency than cane or beet sugar to become lumpy when exposed or stored in slightly moist air.

Corn syrup solids, such as "Frodex" and "Dri-sweet" are among the products obtained in the hydrolysis of corn starch. They contain the sugars dextrose and maltose together with dextrine (pro-sugar), but usually contain no starch. They are white granular solids and about equal to cane sugar in their tendency to become lumpy when exposed to moist air. They usually have been more economical than cane sugar, but because of their lower sweetening effect it requires about 2.1 lb. of Frodex or corn syrup solids to produce the sweetness obtained from 1.0 lb. of sucrose. The dextrins which they contain actually raise the freezing point slightly. These dextrins also increase the total solids of the mix and supply some stabilizing effect against coarseness. The effect on the freezing point and smoothness seems to give corn syrup solids an advantage over dextrose not only in sherbets and ices but also in ice creams of low total solids concentration. Usually not more than one-fourth to one-third of the total sweetener is supplied by corn syrup solids.

The four major types of corn syrups used in ice cream based on degree of conversion are: (1) Low conversion 30 to 37 D.E.,[1] (2) Regular con-

---

[1] Dextrose Equivalent—The dextrose equivalent (D.E.) is a measure of reducing-sugar content calculated as dextrose and expressed as percentage of the total dry substance. Pure dextrose has a D.E. of 100. Corn syrups and corn-syrups solids are available in the D.E. range of 28 to 62. The approximate composition of corn syrup and corn-syrup solids is shown in Table 16.

version 38 to 49 D.E., (3) Intermediate conversion 50 to 57 D.E., (4) High conversion 58 D.E. or higher.

Corn syrup, frequently incorrectly called "glucose," is made either by acid hydrolysis or by enzyme hydrolysis of corn starch. It contains no sucrose, but does contain a variable amount of dextrose and maltose with some impurities depending upon the degree of refining used in its manufacture. It may be considered as a source of dextrose. While its sugar content and also total solids content vary considerably, it is usually safe to assume that 1.5 lb. of corn syrup will replace 1.0 lb. of sucrose. The effect on the freezing point is similar to that of corn syrup solids.

"Sweetose" is a trade name for corn syrup made by the enzyme hydrolysis of corn starch. It is generally marketed at about 43° Baumé and a sugar concentration that gives a sucrose equivalent of 67 per cent, therefore it will require 1.5 lb. of sweetose to replace 1.0 lb. of sucrose in the ice cream mix. Composition and properties of corn derivatives are shown in Table 16.

Other syrups, such as honey, malt syrup, etc., are rarely used in ice cream because of their characteristic and pronounced flavor.

Saccharin, the first so-called "artificial sweetener" to be used commercially, is not a sugar, but a product derived from coal tar. It has a sweetening effect up to 550 times that of sucrose. The Federal food laws (U. S. Dept. Agr., Food Inspection Decision 135) prohibit the use of saccharin in foods since the continued consumption of more than 0.3 gram per day is liable to impair digestion because of its antiseptic power and preservative action. However, special permission is sometimes granted for its use in making so-called "diabetic ice cream." In such cases, as little as ten grams or less of saccharin per 100 pounds of mix will approximate 15 per cent sugar. Thus it is necessary to use a high concentration of fat to supply the needed total solids, and about 4 to 5 per cent glycerin to reduce the firmness of the ice cream. Such a product is a poor substitute for real ice cream but does offer some variety to a restricted diet.

"**n-Propoxy**" is a trade designation for 1-n-propoxy-2 amino-4-nitrobenzene, a benzene derivative and not a sugar. Its sweetening properties were reported about 1940–45 by Prof. P. E. Verkade of the Netherlands as 4000 times that of sucrose. It is easily obtained in the pure state as crystals which are orange in color and very slightly soluble in water. Its use in ice cream should be subject to the same supervision and restriction as that placed on saccharin.

"**Dulcine**" (p-phenetyl-urea, or $NH_2CONH \ C_6H_4OC_2H_5$) is also rarely used in ice cream even though it is supposed to be from 70 to 250 times as sweet as sucrose. Its use should be subject to supervision and restrictions similar to those for saccharin.

TABLE 16[1]

APPROXIMATE CARBOHYDRATE COMPOSITION OF CORN SYRUP AND CORN-SYRUP SOLIDS (DRY-SUBSTANCE BASIS)[1]

	Per cent Saccharides							
	Mono-	Di-	Tri-	Tetra-	Penta-	Hexa-	Hepta-	Higher
Low (32 D.E.)	11.5	10.2	9.2	8.6	7.5	6.2	5.3	41.5
Regular (42 D.E.)	18.5	13.9	11.6	9.9	8.4	6.6	5.7	25.2
Intermediate (52 D.E.)	27.5	17.2	13.1	9.9	7.7	5.7	4.7	14.2
High Conversion (62 D.E.) (acid or enzyme)	38.8	28.1	13.7	4.1	4.5	2.6	..	8.2[2]

Approximate Physical Constants of Corn Syrups

Baumé	Specific Gravity	Per cent Solids	Pounds Per Gallon	Pounds Solids Per Gallon
		Low-Conversion Corn Syrup—32. D.E.		
42	1.4049	77.64	11.700	9.084
43	1.4184	79.59	11.813	9.402
44	1.4322	81.53	11.928	9.725
45	1.4463	83.51	12.045	10.059
46	1.4605	85.49	12.163	10.389
		Regular-Conversion Corn Syrup—42 D.E.		
42	1.4049	78.30	11.700	9.161
43	1.4184	80.27	11.813	9.482
44	1.4322	82.25	11.928	9.811
45	1.4463	84.25	12.045	10.148
46	1.4605	86.26	12.163	10.492
		Intermediate-Conversion Corn Syrup—52 D.E.		
42	1.4049	78.94	11.700	9.236
43	1.4184	80.94	11.813	9.561
44	1.4322	82.96	11.928	9.895
45	1.4463	84.98	12.045	10.236
46	1.4605	87.03	12.163	10.586
		High-Conversion Corn Syrup—62 D.E.		
42	1.4049	79.59	11.700	9.312
43	1.4184	81.62	11.813	9.642
44	1.4322	83.67	11.928	9.980
45	1.4463	85.72	12.045	10.325
46	1.4605	87.80	12.163	10.679

[1] Courtesy, Corn Industries Research Foundation, Inc.
[2] Includes heptasaccharides.

Sugar-Saving Suggestions. In times of sugar shortage the following suggestions should be helpful to the ice cream manufacturer in stretching his allotment of cane and beet sugar:

1. Use more of other sources of sugar such as corn sugar and corn syrup solids, better known as Frodex, Sweetose, corn syrup, etc. As stated elsewhere in this chapter these products can be used to replace as much as one-fourth to one-third of the sugar required in the formula. Many ice

cream makers are coming to believe that a finer quality of ice cream is produced when part of the sucrose is replaced by corn syrup solids.

Maple sugar, maple syrup, honey, and sorghum, when available and not too high priced, also can take the place of a limited amount of cane or beet sugar in the mix.

2. Reduce the sugar content in the ice cream, by replacing part of it with milk solids. Research carried on by the Bureau of Dairy Industry of the U. S. Department of Agriculture revealed the fact that sweetness of ice cream depends upon the concentration of sugar in the water of the mix. Therefore if part of the free water content of the mix is absorbed by the addition of milk solids, obviously there will be less volume of water to dissolve the sugar, and this higher concentration will taste sweeter. It was found that a saving of as much as 20 per cent of sugar can be made without lowering the degree of sweetness of the ice cream.

3. Invert up to one-third of the cane or beet sugar required in the mix. Since invert sugar tastes sweeter its use in time of sugar scarcity is recommended even though some additional labor and expense is involved in the inversion process.

Sugars in the form of syrups may also be used as a source of sugar. This form of sweetener is coming into general use as liquid sugar products. These products sometimes contain two or more sugars. Sucrose can be purchased as a liquid product containing 67 per cent sucrose solids. Liquid sugar products have favorable handling and price advantages. Blends of sucrose with corn sweeteners are available in various combinations.

The total solids concentration of sucrose syrups is usually measured by "degree Brix" which is the percentage of sucrose assuming all the solids to be sucrose. This is a safe assumption for practical purposes. Corn syrup, and many others, are often labeled with a Baumé reading. This reading is based on the specific gravity of the syrup and therefore is a measure of the total solids concentration. However, it does not indicate the kind or amounts of the various sugars and dextrins present in the syrup. Baumé and Brix are not the same. Brix gives the percentage sweetening effect only for sucrose syrups. Baumé readings have to be calculated into terms of specific gravity from which the total solids concentration can be calculated.

Baumé readings and percentage total solids should not be called "sweetness," "per cent sweet," nor confused with the sweetening effect which depends upon the kind and concentration of sugar present.

Liquid sugar or No. 1 syrup are trade designations for the colorless sucrose syrup used by ice cream manufacturers (see Table 17). The bill and delivery slip generally specify the Brix reading which is not only the percentage of sucrose (i.e., the percentage sweetening effect) but also the percentage of total solids of the syrup. The effect on the freezing point is the same as that of the sucrose it contains. As yet, deliveries of liquid sugar are made only in tank cars and tank trucks, so its use has been restricted to ice cream manufacturers having special facilities for this type of delivery. Blended syrups are used in the manufacture of ice cream in many areas. A typical commercial blend is one containing 70 per cent sucrose (66.5 Brix) and 30 per cent corn syrup. This blend has approximately 70 per cent solids.

TABLE 17

RELATION OF BAUMÉ TO CONCENTRATION OF SUCROSE (CANE OR BEET SUGAR) SYRUP

Degrees Baumé[1]	Degrees Brix[2]	Weight[3] per Gal. 68°F.	Sugar per Gal.	Water per Gal.
		lbs.	lbs.	lbs.
33.0	61.0	10.78	6.58	4.20
33.5	62.0	10.83	6.71	4.12
34.0	63.0	10.88	6.85	4.03
34.5	63.9	10.92	6.98	3.94
35.0	64.9	10.97	7.12	3.85
35.5	65.9	11.02	7.26	3.76
36.0	66.9	11.07	7.41	3.66
36.5	67.9	11.13	7.56	3.57
37.0	68.9	11.18	7.70	3.48
37.5	69.9	11.23	7.85	3.38
38.0	70.9	11.28	8.00	3.28
38.5	71.9	11.33	8.15	3.18
39.0	72.9	11.39	8.30	3.09
39.5	73.9	11.44	8.45	2.99
40.0	74.9	11.49	8.61	2.88

[1] Sp. gr. $= \frac{145}{145-d}$ where specific gravity of the liquid is compared with water at 39° F. and d is the Baumé hydrometer reading at 68° F.
[2] Degrees Brix = per cent sucrose by weight for *sucrose* syrups.
[3] One U. S. gallon of water at 68°F. weighs 8.322 lb.

Invert sugar is a mixture of equal parts of glucose and fructose resulting from hydrolysis of sucrose and is generally obtained in the form of a syrup. It is sweeter than sucrose and the increased sweetness obtained by hydrolyzing a given weight of sucrose is sufficient to justify the inversion process at a time of sugar scarcity. Even though this invert sugar syrup contains from 25 to 30 per cent water, one pound of invert sugar syrup will produce almost as much sugar as one pound of sucrose. However, it is similar to dextrose in depressing the freezing point and therefore should be used to supply not more than one-third of the total sugar in the mix.

Invert sugar may be prepared by the following procedure: Heat 26 lb. of water to 180°F. and slowly add 74 lb. of sucrose to avoid having much undissolved sugar present at any one time. When the syrup is at 180°F.

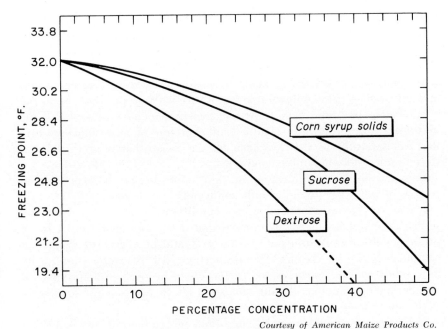

Courtesy of American Maize Products Co.

Fig. 6. Freezing Point Relationships of the Various Sugar Solutions

shut off the heat and add 36.3 ml. hydrochloric acid (40 per cent, sp. gr. 1.20) with suitable stirring to distribute it evenly. There will be a temperature rise due to the chemical action. After the acid has acted 15 minutes, cool promptly, and when the temperature is down to about 140°F., add sodium bicarbonate at the rate of 1 1/3 oz. per 100 lb. of syrup, to neutralize the acid and then continue cooling. This procedure will give approximately 95 per cent complete inversion (Sommer 1946).

Lactose, the sugar that is found only in milk, is not as sweet as sucrose and is much less soluble. When the water portion of the mix contains as much as 9 per cent lactose, the lactose may separate out in crystals large enough to be discernible and produce an undesirable "sandy" feel in the mouth. This property definitely limits the concentration of lactose to be used in ice cream. The source of lactose is the milk solids-not-fat of dairy products, and about 54 per cent of these solids is lactose. Therefore, the maximum concentration of lactose that can be safely used also establishes the maximum concentration of milk solids-not-fat.

This maximum concentration of milk solids-not-fat to avoid sandiness varies somewhat with conditions under which ice cream is produced and stored. For instance, if ice cream is frozen at the higher temperatures generally prevailing in batch freezers, or if excessive amounts of corn syrup solids are used in the mix; if there is much fluctuation in storage temperatures, and if the ice cream is likely to be held in customer's cabinet for longer periods (14 days or more), before it is consumed, such ice cream may be considered as being subjected to rather severe conditions and any or all of these unfavorable factors are likely to produce sandiness. Where such conditions have to be met experiments have proved that the maximum concentration of lactose (and therefore of milk solids-not-fat) that can safely be used is less than for ice cream that is produced and stored under more favorable conditions.

This maximum concentration of milk solids-not-fat is expressed in pounds of water per pound of milk solids-not-fat as follows:

1. For ice cream produced under conditions as severe as those described above it has been determined that if the mix contains 6.4 lb. of water per lb. of milk solids-not-fat there should be very little danger of sandiness in the ice cream. This proportion (6.4 lbs. water plus 1.0 lb. milk solids-not-fat) becomes the **factor 7.4** to be used in a formula for calculating the amount of milk solids-not-fat to be used for ice cream subjected to these rather severe conditions.

2. Under average commercial conditions where there is less danger of sandiness a concentration of 5.9 lb. water per lb. milk solids-not-fat can ordinarily be used. *The factor then becomes 6.9,* (i.e., 5.9 plus 1.0).

3. For ice cream to be consumed within a week after it is placed in the retailer's cabinet, in which time sandiness rarely develops, the normal concentration is 5.4 lb. water per lb. milk solids-not-fat and the *factor is 6.4*

The foregoing factors are used as follows in:

Formula for calculating the per cent of milk solids-not-fat to use in an ice cream mix.

$$\frac{100 - X}{\text{Factor}} = \text{per cent milk solids-not-fat to use under conditions for which}$$

the Factor applies

In the equation $100 =$ total mix; $x =$ (the sum of the percentages of all solids except milk solids-not-fat).

Example: If a mix contains 12 per cent fat, 14 per cent sugar, 0.5 per cent egg yolk solids, and 0.5 per cent stabilizer, what would be the maximum percentage of milk solids-not-fat which could be safely used under average commercial marketing conditions?

Substituting in the formula:

$$\frac{100 - (12 + 14 + 0.5 + 0.5)}{6.9} = 10.58 \text{ per cent milk solids-not-fat}$$

This means that 10.58 per cent milk solids-not-fat is the maximum concentration of milk solids-not-fat that would not be likely to cause "sandiness" even under rather severe commercial marketing conditions.

The ratio of fat to milk solids-not-fat for the proper blend under practical use may be as in Table 18.

TABLE 18

FAT AND MILK SOLIDS-NON-FAT RATIOS IN ICE CREAM

Fat in Mix Per cent	Milk Solids Not-fat Per cent
10	11.0 to 12.0
12	10.5 to 11.0
14	8.5 to 10.5
16	7.0 to 9.5
18	6.5 to 8.5
20	6.0 to 7.5

The properties of the formulated mix should be such that the mix has the proper viscosity, stability and handling properties. The finished ice cream should meet the conditions which prevail in the plant where it is to be produced. Properties of various sweetness are given in Table 19.

SOURCES OF EGG YOLK SOLIDS

Fresh eggs are seldom used in ice cream except in rich ice creams, such as puddings. The cost of fresh eggs is generally such that they can be economically used only in ice cream retailing at higher than average prices.

Frozen egg yolks and powdered egg yolk are used by many ice cream makers because the egg yolk solids improve the whipping ability of the mix. Usually not more than 0.5 per cent of egg yolk solids in the mix is needed for this purpose. Egg yolk solids are especially desirable in mixes in which butter or butter oil is used as a main source of fat. Investigations have shown that the egg yolks improve the rate of whipping more if they are sweetened with 10 per cent of sugar before they are frozen.

The use of egg yolk solids produces the following beneficial effects:

1. Increased rate of whipping, particularly for slow whipping mixes.
2. Firmer ice cream at a given drawing temperature.
3. Less change in percentage overrun while unloading the freezer.
4. Improved appearance while ice cream is melting.
5. Slightly improved texture.
6. Increased food value.

The disadvantages are the cost of the egg yolk and the fact that frequently it may be slightly off-flavored.

TABLE 19

SOURCES OF SWEETENING AGENTS IN ICE CREAM

Approximate data to serve as a guide in calculating mixes.

Commercial Product	Physical Appearance	Type of Sugar	Per cent Sugar Content	Pounds to Equal 1.0 lb. of Sucrose	Per cent of Total Sugar it Can Supply[1]	Per cent Total Solids	Weight per Gallon
Sugar Granulated sugar (Cane or Beet)	Dry crystals	Sucrose	100	1.00	100	100	lbs. 7.5
Dextrose Cerelose Dextrose hydrate Corn sugar	Dry crystals	Glucose	80	1.25	35	92	...
Corn syrup solids Frodex, Dri-Sweet, Clintose, etc.	Dry crystals	Dextrose & Maltose	47	2.10	35	96.5	...
Liquid Sugar[2]	Liquid	Sucrose	67	1.50	100	67.0	11.1
Liquid sugar (80/20) blend (Sucrose 67 Brix, Corn Syrup 43 D.E.)	Liquid	Sucrose	68	1.58	100	68	11.2
Invert sugar syrup[3]	Liquid	Dextrose & Levulose	95	1.05	33	74.0	11.5
Corn Syrup[4] Sweetose[4]	Liquid	Dextrose & Maltose	67	1.50	35	83.0	9.5
Honey	Liquid	Dextrose Levulose Sucrose	75	1.40	30[5]	82.0	...

[1] The recommended maximum amount. For example: dextrose should supply no more than 35% of all the sugar in the mix.
[2] The usual liquid sugar (67%) employed by ice cream makers.
[3] Assuming 95% complete inversion with a 74% sucrose solution.
[4] The usual commercial syrup of 43° Baumé.
[5] Assuming a mild flavored honey, less if strong flavored.

It is necessary to use egg products in custard type ice cream and the amount of eggs added to custard ice cream is usually equivalent to the yolks from 4 to 5 dozen eggs per 100 pounds of mix. One dozen eggs yields approximately 1.2 pounds edible portion or 0.5 pounds of yolks. One pound of dried yolks requires approximately four dozen eggs. The manufacturer of ice cream can justify the use of egg products from a quality improvement and improved handling properties standpoint in mixes made from butter and non-fat dry milk solids, regardless of whether the mix is frozen by a continuous or batch freezer. The use of eggs also improves mixes made of fluid dairy products when the mix is frozen by a batch freezer. The value of the use of eggs under other conditions is more questionable and must be justified by the policies which prevail in the individual plant.

TABLE 20

APPROXIMATE DATA ON EGG PRODUCTS TO SERVE AS A GUIDE IN CALCULATING MIXES

Egg Product	Pounds per Dozen Eggs	Eggs per Lb. of Egg Product	Egg Yolk Solids Per cent	Egg Fat Per cent	Total Solids Per cent
Fresh eggs (edible portion)	1.17	10.0 to 10.6	20.0	10.5	26.3
Egg yolk	0.50	24	50.5	33.3	50.5
Egg white	0.67	18	. . .	0.2	13.8
Dried whole egg	0.33	36	55.0	40.0	94.0
Dried egg yolk	0.25	48	94.0	62.5	94.0
Dried egg white	0.083	144	. . .	1.4	96.0

FOOD ADDITIVES

If a substance is found by the Food and Drug Administration as safe for its intended use in a food product, it will be classed in a category of generally recognized as safe (GRAS). Other substances may be proposed for this category. Use limits and restrictions are also specified (see Chapter 24).

Flavor, stabilizer, emulsifier, sweetener and acid materials are some of those classed as additives for ice cream.

Approximately 150 natural flavorings are classed as GRAS and about 650 artificial flavors are being considered.

The Food and Drug Administration has found the following stabilizer, emulsifier, sweetener and acid substances to be in the indicated categories along with limits and use restrictions.

Stabilizers

The U. S. Food and Drug Administration has found the following stabilizers to fall into one of the categories shown in Table 21:

TABLE 21

ADDITIVES—STABILIZERS (GRAS)

Product	Limits	Specific Uses or Restrictions
Agar-agar	None	None
Carob bean gum (locust bean gum)	None	None
Carragheenin	None	None
Guar gum	None	None
PROPOSED AS GENERALLY RECOGNIZED AS SAFE		
Acacia (gum arabic)	None	None
Ammonium alginate	None	None
Calcium alginate	None	None
Tragacanth (gum tragacanth)	None	None
Sterculia gum (karaya gum)	None	None
Sodium alginate	None	None
Lecithin	None	None
Sodium carboxymethylcellulose[1]	None	None

[1] (The sodium salt of carboxymethylcellulose, (CMC) not less than 99.5 per cent on a dry-weight basis, with maximum substitution of 0.95 carboxymethyl groups per anhydro-glucose unit, and with a minimum viscosity of 25 centipoises for 2 per cent by weight aqueous solution at $77°F$.)

TABLE 22

ADDITIVES—EMULSIFIERS (GRAS)

Product	Limits	Specific Uses or Restrictions
Propylene glycol ester of methylcellulose	None	Thickener, stabilizer, protective, colloid, suspending agent, emulsifier, and film former in foods.
Polyoxyethylene (20) sorbitan monooleate	0.1 per cent	In frozen desserts (other than water ices), as an emulsifier.
Polyoxyethylene (20) sorbitan monooleate	0.1 per cent	In imitation ice cream, as an emulsifier.
Polyoxyethylene (20) sorbitan tristearate	0.1 per cent	In frozen desserts (other than water ices), as an emulsifier.
Polyoxyethylene (20) sorbitan tristearate	0.1 per cent	In imitation ice cream, as an emulsifier.

TABLE 23

ADDITIVES—SWEETENERS OTHER THAN SUGAR (GRAS)

Product	Limits	Specific Uses or Restrictions
Sorbitol	7 per cent	In special dietary foods
Mannitol	5 per cent	In special dietary foods
Saccharin	None	Nonnutritive sweeteners
Calcium saccharin	None	Nonnutritive sweeteners
Sodium saccharin	None	Nonnutritive sweeteners
Ammonium saccharin	None	Nonnutritive sweeteners
Calcium cyclohexyl sulfamate	None	Nonnutritive sweeteners
Sodium cyclohexyl sulfamate	None	Nonnutritive sweeteners
Magnesium cyclohexyl sulfamate	None	Nonnutritive sweeteners
Potassium cyclohexyl sulfamate	None	Nonnutritive sweeteners

Emulsifiers

The only emulsifiers which have been found to be "generally recognized as safe" (GRAS) are: Mono- and diglycerides from the glycerolysis of edible fats and oils.

The emulsifiers, along with limits and restrictions are shown in Table 22.

Sweeteners

The following non-sugar sweeteners have been found to be safe by the U. S. Food and Drug Administration. Tolerance and restrictions are given in Table 23.

Acids

The following acids (Table 24) which are commonly used in the dairy industry and have been found to be either GRAS or proposed GRAS are as follows:

TABLE 24

ADDITIVES—ACIDS (GRAS)

Product	Limits	Specific Uses or Restrictions
Ascorbic	None	None
Citric	None	None
Lactic	None	None
Phosphoric	None	None
Tartaric	None	None
PROPOSED AS GENERALLY RECOGNIZED AS SAFE		
Malic	None	None

CHAPTER 6

Stabilizers and Emulsifiers

The primary purposes of using stabilizers[1] in ice cream are to produce smoothness in body and texture, retard or reduce ice crystal growth during storage, provide uniformity of product and resistance to melting. Stabilizers function through their ability to form gel structures in water or their ability to combine with water as water of hydration.

An emulsifier is a substance which will produce an emulsion of two liquids which do not naturally mix. The function of an emulsifying agent in the manufacture of ice cream lies mainly in improving the whipping quality of the mix, the production of a smooth texture, giving a dry stiff product at the time it is drawn from the freezer and a more exact control during the various manufacturing processes.

Excellent ice cream can be made and considerable amounts are made without the use of a stabilizer or emulsifier. Since milk and milk products contain natural stabilizing and emulsifying materials (milk protein, fat, lecithin, phosphates, and citrates) mixes of certain composition and processing treatment may be stabilized by the effect of these natural materials.

Among the stabilizers used in the making of ice cream and related products are gelatin and modified gelatin; algin derivatives including: sodium alginate and its modified form Dariloid; C.M.C. (sodium carboxymethylcellulose)—a cellulose derivative; Irish moss derivatives; pectin derived chiefly from citrus fruits; carob bean gum; guar gum; mucilaginous extracts from quince seed, psyllium seed, etc.: gum exudates such as tragacanth, karaya, arabic and others. Algin derivatives have gained an important place as stabilizers in the ice cream industry.

Gelatin, the first of the commercial stabilizers is still used. Its advantages lie in its ability to form a gel in the mix during the aging period as well as during the freezing process, and even after the frozen product is placed in the hardening room. Its peculiar gel structure and its great affinity for water prevent the formation of large ice crystals in ice cream, and contribute to smoothness in texture, and firmness in body of the frozen product. Although not a complete protein its amino acids do contribute slightly to the food value. It is generally thought less satis-

---

[1] J. H. Frandsen in 1915 used the word "stabilizer" to designate a group of substances which at that time were generally referred to as "holders," "colloids," "binders," and "fillers." Frandsen and Markham (1915).

factory than vegetable stabilizers for sherbets and ices because it has a tendency to produce too high an overrun which is often associated with poor body and texture in these products.

The amount of gelatin to use depends on many factors such as the source of the gelatin, whether from calf or pork skins or bone material, its gel strength as measured by the Bloom Test, its viscosity value, the composition of the mix, etc. In general the amount to use is approximately the amount required to produce a melt-down (in the evenly-melted ice cream) of about the same consistency as aged 40 per cent sweet cream. This amount usually is between 0.25 and 0.5 per cent for a 250 Bloom gelatin.

Tests for Gel Strength.[2] Several tests have been developed to determine the gel strength and to serve as guides to the amount to be used in the mix. Among these are the Bloom Test[3] for Gel Strength, the Dahlberg Test (see chapter 21) and the "Protein-Nitrogen Content" Test developed at University of Illinois. In a general way it may be said that, other factors being equal, the gelatin that carries the greatest gel strength per unit of cost is the one to select. Good quality gelatin should have low bacteria count and should be practically odorless and colorless or, if made from calf products, of light amber color. "Vesterine," a modified gelatin, is composed of gelatin and a monoglyceride or a monostearate. It stabilizes the fat emulsion and improves the whipping quality of the mix and the texture of the finished product.

Sodium alginate and a modified form sold under the trade name of "Dariloid" are rather widely used vegetable stabilizers. Their basic stabilizing principle, algin, is extracted from a giant ocean kelp growing on the shores of California and Japan. Dariloid seems to consist almost entirely of sodium alginate, with small amounts of sugar and sodium citrate added to assist its solubility and to standardize its stabilizing properties. This product improves whipping ability and leaves a slightly cleaner flavor in the mouth—two distinct advantages. Dariloid dissolves properly only when added to the mix at about 155° to 160°F., which may be a disadvantage in certain methods of processing. A slightly smaller amount of Dariloid is needed to give the same stabilizing effect as gelatin.

Irish moss and a modified form sold under the trade name of "Krageleen" contain the basic stabilizing principle carrageenin. This is extracted from carrageen (Irish moss) a seaweed growing on the coast of

---

[2] These tests are not too satisfactory but they may be considered as a fairly good guide as to the strength of the gelatin.

[3] This test is accepted by the Gelatin Research Society of America, Inc., as a standard for gel strength.

Massachusetts, France and Ireland. In stabilizing value these products are comparable to a 250 Bloom Test gelatin, and (it is claimed) can be added to the mix as easily as gelatin.

Agar-agar. A product extracted from red algae growing on the Pacific coast has been recommended in combination with gums or gelatin for use as a stabilizer in sherbets and ices. Although it swells and absorbs large quantities of water and thus prevents coarseness in the finished product, it is not easily dispersed in the mix and tends to produce a crumbly body. It is also high in cost.

C.M.C., the trade name for sodium carboxymethylcellulose, forms the basis of stabilizers which are now being accepted by the ice cream industry. It has high water-holding capacity and is easily dissolved in the mix—two qualities of a fine stabilizer—and it acts also as an emulsifier. The amount to use is slightly less than of gelatin. It does not form as firm a gel as gelatin and some of the vegetable stabilizers but seems to have merit for use in ice cream, and especially in sherbets and ices.

Pectin is a carbohydrate obtained mainly from citrus fruit. It is especially desirable as an ingredient in the syrups and fruits used in making aufaits and rippled effects in ice cream, and is also effectively used in sherbets and ices. However, it is not very satisfactory as a stabilizer for ice cream. Purified sugar beet pectin forms a weaker and less brilliant gel than citrus pectin.

Carob (locust) bean gum, a product imported from Europe, is an ingredient of stabilizers sold mainly for use in sherbets and ices. Its principal advantage in these products is that it inhibits overrun. Since it has a tendency to cause curdling of the milk proteins, its use in ice cream is limited, and heating to temperatures above 100°F. should be avoided.

Guar gum is a complex carbohydrate obtained from a legume grown in India. Its use in ice cream has occurred only recently and it is often used in combination with carrageenin. Guar gum is readily soluble in cold solutions and is used as a stabilizer for mixes to be pasteurized by high temperatures for short times or continuous pasteurization.

Other Gums such as tragacanth, arabic, karaya, or India gum are exudates from incisions made in the bark of certain trees and plants growing usually in the warmer regions of the earth. They find their chief use as ingredients in stabilizers for use in ices and sherbets and in the so-called Ice Cream Improvers. The mucilaginous extracts from some plant seeds (quince and psyllium) are less widely used.

"Ice Cream Improvers" are used by some manufacturers to improve the body and texture of ice cream. Some of these improvers consist mainly of the gum type of stabilizer (one or a mixture of two or more gums) and are sold as ice cream improvers under various trade names. Other improvers contain an enzyme such as rennin (rennet extract) or pepsin, capable of coagulating casein. Partial coagulation of the casein by these enzymes affects the body and texture of the ice cream. Therefore care must be taken to check the coagulation at the right time. If such an improver is used it seems preferable to add it to the mix before pasteurization since the heat will destroy the enzyme and thus prevent too much coagulation and wheying-off. Unless the enzyme is destroyed by heat it will continue to work slowly even during the hardening period, and as a result the ice cream may shrink in the can or package. Ice creams containing improvers often have a curdled appearance when melted, due to a slight excess in the coagulation of the casein. The benefit of improvers is questionable except possibly in ice cream of low total solids content.

Antioxidants are substances which inhibit the development of "oxidized" flavor, often a troublesome defect in ice cream. They are successful only when added before the objectionable flavor develops. Several substances are known to have this effect. Some of these are oat flour (a somewhat modified oat flour is being marketed under the trade name, Avenex), an extract of oat flour, an extract of lettuce leaves, some vitamins, tannin, etc. The oat flour products are also credited with some merit as stabilizers. Although these products are frequently found in foods, their use in ice cream is illegal in some states.

The selection of a suitable stabilizer for use in the mix is influenced by many factors. One of the most important factors to consider is the adaptability of the product to the particular needs of the plant. Besides preference, availability, cost and freedom from toxicity, other factors must be considered such as: effect of the product on the properties of the mix, whether or not an aging period is necessary, kind of product being manufactured and method of processing. Additional factors including: the effect on flavor, body and texture characteristics, melting and storage properties of the ice cream, must be considered also.

The use of stabilizers changes the acidity of the mix slightly in some cases, produces a decided increase in mix viscosity, and increases the surface tension and whipping time slightly. In the finished ice cream, stabilizers have little effect on flavor, produce a smoother more resistant body and texture, may increase the rate of melting slightly and improve storage qualities.

The amount of stabilizer used depends on the kind of stabilizer and the quality necessary to produce the desired stabilizing effect in the product being manufactured. There are four common ways of determining the amount of stabilizer to be used in the ice cream mix, namely:

TABLE 25

TABLE 25

A GUIDE TO THE USE OF STABILIZERS

| | Percentage Used | |
Stabilizer	Ice Cream	Sherbet, Ice and Soft Ice Cream
Gelatin −150 bloom	0.50	0.50
Gelatin −200 bloom	0.42	0.45
Gelatin −250 bloom	0.35	0.40
Sodium alginate (Dariloid)	0.27	0.33
C.M.C. (sodium carboxymethylcellulose)	0.16	0.20
Irish Moss	0.10	0.25
Locust Bean Gum	0.25	0.25
Guar gum	0.25	0.25
Pectin	0.15	0.18

the fat content of the mix; the total solids content of the mix; the kind of freezer used; and the use of a constant percentage which may range from 0.15 to 0.50 per cent.

The amount of the basic stabilizers to use may range as in Table 25.

The method of incorporating stabilizers and emulsifiers in the mix may be by mixing with 4 to 5 parts of sugar and adding before or during the heating process, or dispersed by gently adding to the mix without special

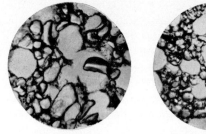 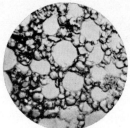 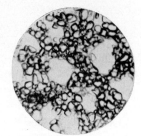

No stabilizer
or emulsifier   Stabilizer plus
                       Stabilizer   emulsifier

FIG. 7.   EFFECT OF THE USE OF STABILIZERS AND EMULSIFIERS ON THE INTERNAL STRUCTURE OF ICE CREAM

The details of the internal structure of ice cream are explained in Chapter 12.   See also Fig. 21, p. 158.

handling, or, in the case of algin stabilizers, suspended in cold water and added to the mix when the mix temperature is 160°F., or using a hopper and a pump or other special arrangement.

When the batch method of pasteurization is employed the stabilizer may be added to the cold or hot mix and there is more latitude for the selection of the stabilizer.   In the high temperature short time process of pasteurization the stabilizer must be added to the cold mix ingredients and should disperse readily at a low temperature. The algin, guar, and C.M.C. (sodium carboxymethylcellulose) type products are commonly used in this method of processing.

Proprietary stabilizers contain a combination of the various stabilizer and emulsifier materials with sugar as a carrier and salts. These combinations may be more effective in producing the characteristics desired than some of the stabilizing materials used alone.

Typical stabilizer combinations are: C.M.C. and gelatin; C.M.C. and Irish Moss; gelatin, C.M.C. and Irish Moss; and C.M.C., Locust Bean and Irish Moss.

Figure 7 shows the effects of the use of stabilizers and emulsifiers on the internal structure of ice cream.

EMULSIFIERS

Emulsifiers are substances which tend to concentrate in the interface between the fat and the plasma and reduce the surface tension of the system.

The value of emulsifying agents in the manufacture of ice cream lies mainly with the improved whipping quality of the mix, the production of a drier ice cream with a smoother body and texture having superior drawing qualities at the freezer, and more exact control which can be maintained in the various manufacturing processes.

Although emulsifiers such as mono- and diglycerides are more recently recognized products, milk contains certain natural emulsifying constituents including: milk proteins, fat lecithin, phosphates, and citrates. Egg yolk products are high in lecithin and have long been used in ice cream. These products produce results similar to, but not as pronounced as, those produced by the commercial emulsifiers. Emulsifiers are available in liquid, semi-solid and powder forms and may include glycerides, lecithin and fatty acid esters. The mono- and diglyceride products have gained general popular approval. In general, emulsifiers have little effect on the acidity, pH or viscosity of the ice cream mix, but they tend to lower the surface tension and improve the whipping properties.

A significant reduction in whipping time is encountered when any emulsifier is used. The effect of emulsifiers on surface tension is most significant, and the determination of surface tension may be of value in estimating the effectiveness of an emulsifier product. The use of emulsifiers decreases the rate of melting in the finished ice cream. Structure measurements show that emulsifiers produce somewhat smaller ice crystals more evenly distributed and smaller air cells that result in a smoother ice cream.

Many factors may affect the action of an emulsifier. Among these are the ingredients of the mix, procedure of processing, freezing and hardening, and the amount of emulsifier used. Emulsifiers must be used judiciously as regulated by prevailing plant conditions and practices.

Typical of the effect of emulsifiers on the properties of the mix and the finished ice cream are the following data (Table 26) for a mix stabilized with gelatin and a heavily emulsified mix respectively:

TABLE 26

PHYSICAL EFFECTS OF EMULSIFIERS

Property	Mix Stabilized With Gelatin	Mix Stabilized With Gelatin and Heavily Emulsified
Surface tension—dynes	51.9	48.3
Time to reach 90% overrun—min.:sec.	8:30	4:45
Per cent melted by weight when exposed at 85°F. for 45 min.		
Frozen in batch freezer	23.7	5.2
Frozen in continuous freezer	31.4	13.8
Air cell size-diameter in microns	204	146
Ice crystal size—length and width in microns	44 × 32	40 × 30
Texture comments	Very slightly coarse	Smooth

Some disadvantages in the use of emulsifiers are: homogenization of the mix is essential to obtain best results; their use is illegal in some states; and some investigators think that they tend to favor the development of the defect called "shrinkage."

Excessive emulsification may cause a short body and texture characteristic, slow melting, and a curdy meltdown in the finished ice cream.

The correct use of emulsifiers produces a mix which is more adaptable to general processing procedures, enhances the whipping properties of the mix, and generally improves the body and texture of the finished ice cream.

CHAPTER 7

Flavoring and Coloring Materials

Frozen desserts are valued mainly for their pleasing flavor and their cooling and refreshing effects. Since there are so many kinds of flavoring material and since they are sold under so many brands and grades, it is well to understand their sources and to select and buy with great care. Among the flavoring substances that play a more or less important part in frozen desserts are vanilla, chocolate and cocoa, fruits and fruit extracts, nuts, spices, and sugars. In the selection of flavoring materials it is important to consider the quality of the ice cream mix in which they are to be used since slight off-flavors in it may obscure the delicate flavor of the flavoring material to be added. Local preference of consumers is also important since they may not appreciate the finer, delicate flavors, but prefer the stronger, harsher ones (See Table 27).

VANILLA

Vanilla is without exception the most popular flavor for ice cream. Records show that about 75 per cent of all ice cream contains vanilla flavoring. This flavoring material is usually obtained in extract form, but there is a rapidly growing demand for vanilla concentrates and paste, and for powdered vanilla and sugar preparations.

The finest vanilla has traditionally been obtained from the fruits of an orchid plant, *Vanilla fragrans,* indigenous to Southeastern Mexico where it was used by the Aztecs to season their chocolate.

The plant has been introduced into other tropical countries: the islands in the Madagascar area, now providing 80 per cent of the world's supply; Indonesia; certain islands in the West Indies and other parts of Central America. The product of Tahiti in the French Oceania, is derived from *Vanilla tahitensis,* an inferior variety whose fruits impart a harsh flavor. The fruits of *Vanilla pompona* are known as vanillons and are similar to the Tahiti beans in flavor.

Vanillin is the principal flavoring essential in vanilla. However, there is no free vanillin in the beans when they are harvested, but it develops gradually during the curing period from glucosides which break down during the fermentation and "sweating" of the beans. (See Figs. 8 and 9.) The sweating process consists of alternately drying the beans in the sun and wrapping them up at night so that they heat and ferment. This process, which is continued until the flavor and aroma are developed, takes four weeks to four months and reduces the beans to sufficient dry-

69

TABLE 27

ICE CREAM SALES FLAVOR ANALYSIS IN THE UNITED STATES—BY DISTRICTS

Flavor	United States		North Atlantic		Central Eastern		Middle Western		Southern		Western	
	Rank	Per cent	Rank	Per cent	Rank	Per cent	Rank	Per cent	Rank	Per cent	Rank	Per cent
Vanilla	1	51.42	1	46.34	1	54.68	1	59.43	1	51.05	1	57.21
Chocolate	2	12.27	2	15.86	2	8.61	2	7.49	3	11.59	2	9.41
Strawberry	3	8.66	3	7.95	3	7.33	3	5.54	2	14.93	3	9.13
Variegated Chocolate	4	3.61	5	3.72	6	2.94	6	2.42	4	5.44	4	3.35
Cherry Vanilla	5	2.95	4	3.80	5	4.29	9	1.85	7	1.97	10	1.01
Butter Pecan	6	2.74	6	3.59	4	4.72	19	0.25	5	2.39	13	0.72
Peach	7	1.77	8	2.82	12	1.05	25	0.17	6	1.97	16	0.51
Maple Nut	8	1.51	10	1.06	9	1.64	7	2.32	11	0.91	6	2.46
Coffee	9	1.46	7	3.15	38	0.03	38	0.02	33	0.05	34	0.13
Variegated Strawberry	10	1.25	27	0.23	16	0.73	4	4.16	9	1.16	5	2.58
Variegated Butterscotch	11	1.19	9	1.07	7	2.57	10	1.44	25	0.16	11	0.93
Chocolate Marshmallow	12	1.06	12	0.94	8	1.70	13	1.09	28	0.08	7	1.49
Cherry	13	0.73	16	0.57	10	1.60	15	0.61	10	0.95	20	0.36
Butter Brickle	14	0.69	34	0.14	19	0.43	5	3.65	31	0.06	12	0.90
Variegated Raspberry	15	0.64	29	0.20	14	0.92	12	1.10	15	0.40	8	1.45
Chocolate Chip	16	0.62	17	0.49	17	0.71	11	1.38	22	0.20	14	0.72
Black Walnut	17	0.60	32	0.18	11	1.07	17	0.46	8	1.83	15	0.51
Banana	18	0.53	15	0.61	13	1.04	21	0.21	17	0.35	28	0.22
Caramel	19	0.51	11	1.03	34	0.04	22	0.20	40	0.01	38	0.08
French Vanilla	20	0.45	13	0.72	23	0.19	14	0.83	38	0.02	44	0.02
Pineapple	21	0.42	14	0.69	27	0.11	23	0.17	14	0.45	35	0.12
Butter Almond	22	0.38	19	0.39	15	0.73	33	0.06	30	0.06	18	0.48
Cherry Nut	23	0.35		. . .	24	0.18	8	2.18	20	0.24	22	0.31
Orange Pineapple	24	0.26	28	0.20	18	0.50	32	0.06	13	0.57	36	0.10
Pecan Crunch	25	0.25	43	0.02	32	0.05	34	0.04	18	0.35	9	1.07

Flavor	U.S. Rank	U.S. %	%	Rank	%	Rank	%	Rank	%	Rank	%	Rank
Peppermint	26	0.23	0.19	30	0.25	21	0.47	16	0.07	29	0.27	26
Black Raspberry	27	0.21	0.37	20	0.12	26	0.12	28			0.08	37
Chocolate Mint	28	0.21	0.45	18					0.02	39		
Egg Nog	29	0.20	0.35	21	0.03	39	0.03	37	0.15	26	0.08	39
Lemon	30	0.19	0.27	25	0.23	22	0.24	20	0.03	37	0.06	41
Raspberry	31	0.18	0.29	23	0.07	30			0.23	21	0.03	42
Banana Nut	32	0.17	0.06	38	0.01	41	0.11	29	0.75	12	0.22	30
Lemon Custard	33	0.17	0.04	40	0.29	20	0.12	27	0.40	16	0.29	23
Frozen Pudding	34	0.17	0.34	22	0.03	36			0.03	35	0.03	43
Holiday Fruit	35	0.12	0.01	45	0.07	31	0.17	24	0.27	19	0.34	21
Burnt Almond	36	0.12	0.27	24	0.05	33	0.11	30			0.01	46
Chocolate Almond	37	0.12	0.15	33	0.09	29	0.02	39	0.05	32	0.18	32
Pistachio	38	0.12	0.19	31	0.10	28	0.27	18	0.19	23	0.07	40
Tutti-Frutti	39	0.11	0.04	39							0.15	33
Mint Chocolate Flake	40	0.11	0.24	26							0.01	47
Texas Pecan	41	0.09	0.13	35	0.01	43	0.12	26	0.17	24		
Chocolate Malt	42	0.09							0.10	27	0.50	17
Banana Bisque	43	0.07	0.07	37	0.14	25	0.03	36	0.03	34	0.41	19
Butterscotch	44	0.07	0.02	44	0.02	40	0.04	35			0.01	45
Almond Toffee	45	0.07									0.29	24
Coconut Pineapple	46	0.06			0.03	35	0.07	31	0.01	41	0.27	25
English Toffee	47	0.05	0.03	42	0.03	37			0.03	36	0.20	31
Mint	48	0.05	0.03	41	0.01	42					0.22	29
Macaroon Bisque	49	0.05	0.11	36								27
Spumoni	50	0.04									0.24	
All Other Flavors		0.61	0.58		0.56		0.95		0.28		0.77	
Total		100.00	100.00		100.00		100.00		100.00		100.00	
Per Cent of U. S. Total		100.00	45.19		14.22		10.98		12.32		17.29	

Flavor Preference and Other Products Sold Analysis—1952.   Special Bul. No. 87 IAICM Dec. 1953.

Fig. 8.   Vanilla Vine and Green Beans

Courtesy of David Michael and Co.

ness so that they will not mold.   Beans are sometimes artificially dried but this produces a product of inferior quality.

At the end of the curing period the pods are carefully sorted into various grades based on their quality.

Artificial or synthetic vanillin as made in the laboratory is a product of slightly different flavor but the same general composition as that which occurs naturally in vanilla beans.   Tests have shown that $1^{1}/_{8}$ oz. of vanillin are equivalent in flavoring strength to one pound of vanilla beans. It has also been stated that a 0.7 per cent solution of vanillin is equal in strength of flavor to single strength vanilla extract.   The formula for vanillin is $C_8H_8O_3$.

The amount of vanilla used in flavoring ice cream depends on the concentration of the vanilla flavoring material and the composition of ice cream.   Vanilla flavoring is available in liquid or powder forms as pure vanilla, reinforced vanilla with vanillin and imitation vanilla.   Concentration ranges from single strength (extractive from 13.35 oz. of vanilla beans per gallon extract) to a ten fold or higher concentrate.   Vanilla may be used at rates ranging from one-eighth oz. to 5 or 6 oz. per ten gallons of ice cream depending upon the extract concentration.

The amount of vanilla required decreases with decreased fat content of the mix; increases with increased milk solids-not-fat content of the mix and a low sugar level requires a higher vanilla level.

The flavoring material used should always be in sufficient amounts and of the best quality.   Careful selection of fine natural flavoring material will do much to maintain the desired delicate natural flavor in the finished ice cream.

Classification of Vanilla Flavorings

Vanilla flavorings of which there are many variations on the market may be grouped into these general classes: True Vanilla Flavorings, Compound Vanilla Flavorings, and Imitation Vanilla Flavorings. Other comments follow:

True Vanilla Flavorings

True vanilla extract is prepared by the extraction of finely cut vanilla beans by a solution containing not less than 35% alcohol.

Courtesy of David Michael and Co.

FIG. 9. SUNNING GREEN VANILLA

Curing helps develop the vanilla flavor.

The present *Federal Standard for vanilla extract* calls for the soluble matters from not less than 10 grams of vanilla beans in 100 ml. of alcohol, with or without added sugar, glycerine, or coloring matter. This amounts to 13.35 oz. of beans to make a gallon (128 fl. oz.) of extract. These true vanilla extracts are generally of such a strength that 5 or 6 oz. of the extract are required to flavor 5 gallons of ice cream mix.

Concentrated vanilla extract is made by distilling off a large part of the solvent, usually in vacuum, until the strength reaches the desired concentration which is then specified as "fourfold," "fivefold" or whatever the actual strength. Each "fold" must correspond to an original 13.35 oz.

of beans in the starting extract before concentration. The maximum strength of a direct extraction, without concentration, is two pounds of vanilla beans in one gallon of solvent. The amount used, of such products, should be slightly higher than the number of the "fold" divided into the amount used of a standard vanilla extract.

True vanilla powders are made (a) by mixing finely ground vanilla beans with sugar, or (b) by incorporating the vanilla extractives with a dry carrier, evaporating the solvent and drying. The amount used would correspond by weight to the number of ounces used of a standard strength extract.

Vanilla paste is made by mixing the concentrated extractives with a dry carrier to form a paste. The amount used would be the same as for powders.

True vanilla flavor conforms to the same standards as for vanilla extract except that it contains less than 35% alcohol, propylene glycol or other solvent being used as the carrier.

Compound Vanilla Flavorings

Vanilla and Vanillin. Not less than half of the flavor must be derived from the vanilla bean content. Not more than one ounce of vanillin may be used in conjunction with 13.35 oz. of vanilla beans. This type is also available in various degrees of concentration.

Imitation Vanilla Flavorings

Blends of true vanilla extract, flavor or powder with added synthetics where less than half of the flavor is derived from the vanilla beans.

Preparations that contain no vanilla bean extractives and which are made up entirely of any combination of substances such as synthetics and natural extractives other than from vanilla beans. These preparations may contain added water, alcohol, propylene glycol, vanillin, caramel color, etc.

For those who wish to economize on vanilla costs a suggested reinforcement for a vanilla extract is two ounces of vanillin to the gallon.

A highly reinforced vanilla should not exceed eight ounces of vanillin per gallon as addition to the pure vanilla base.

An artificial flavoring extract strong enough so that one-half ounce is sufficient to flavor ten gallons of ice cream usually contains 12 to 14 ounces of vanillin to the gallon. Fortunately, these imitations are seldom used exclusively in ice cream.

Other materials may be added to vanilla to produce a vanilla-like flavor. These may include such substances as the synthetic vanilla-like flavoring material, propenyl guaethol (0.0132 gm. to 0.0166 gm. per 10 gal. mix), ethyl vanillin, anisyl aldehyde, heliotropine (piperonal) and other substances.

CHOCOLATE AND COCOA

Chocolate and cocoa rank second only to vanilla as flavoring for ice cream. They are obtained from the cacao bean, the fruit of the tree, *Theobroma cacao,* growing in such tropical regions as Mexico, Central America, Ecuador, Venezuela, Brazil, West Indies, the African Gold Coast, and the East Indies.

The almond-sized cacao beans or seeds develop in a large pulpy pod— 20 to 30 beans to the pod. The ripened pods, rich golden red in color, are cut from the trees, gathered in piles and left to ripen further for about 48 hours after which they are slashed open, the beans removed and placed in vats or bags to heat and ferment for about ten days, or until the characteristic flavor and cinnamon-red color develop. The beans are then washed clean of the dried pulp, are dried slowly and sufficiently to prevent mold growth, and are then sorted and graded prior to shipment to manufacturers of chocolate and cocoa.

Processing the Cocoa Beans. At the factory the beans are first mechanically cleaned. Then they are roasted to drive off the moisture and to bring out the special chocolate flavor and aroma. The roasted beans are then cooled quickly by forced air, and are next run through a winnowing machine which crushes them into small pieces and separates the shells from the nibs, the seed part which is made into chocolate and cocoa. These nibs, containing approximately 50 per cent of the fat of the bean, are then placed between heavy stone grinders or mills which reduce them to a liquid by the heat created by the friction of milling.

Chocolate Liquor or Pure Bitter Chocolate is the trade name for the liquid chocolate produced by the processes described above. This liquor may then be cooled in molds and put up in large slabs, or in one-half pound packages such as are sold in grocery stores as bitter cooking chocolate, or it may be further processed into cocoa.

Sweet Milk Chocolate may be made from the chocolate liquor by adding the necessary proportions of sugar, milk, and cocoa butter, with or without vanilla flavoring. The blending of these ingredients requires a considerable amount of skill and special machinery.

Natural Process Cocoa is made from chocolate liquor by subjecting the liquid to high pressure in hydraulic presses. This process removes a large amount of the cocoa (fat) butter, usually about 38 to 40 per cent of the total, and leaves a hard, dry cake which normally contains about 22 per cent fat, though some cocoas contain more and some less. It also contains nearly all the flavoring material from the cocoa bean. The fat is practically tasteless. This cocoa cake is then put through a number of processes known as milling which result in the finely sifted cocoa.

Dutch Process Cocoa is made just as is the natural process cocoa, except in one particular. In the Dutch process the beans are treated with certain alkalis at the time of roasting to break up the cell structure. This alkali treatment makes the cocoa more soluble and gives it the desired darker color which distinguishes Dutch process from natural cocoa. It also aids in bringing out the full fine chocolate flavor when the cocoa is used in the finished product. Because the alkalis counteract the puckery acid taste which is found in natural cocoa, the Dutch process cocoa leaves no bitter taste when used as flavoring in ice cream.

A defect which sometimes appears in chocolate ice cream made with Dutch process cocoa is the formation of a greenish-black coloration where the ice cream comes in touch with exposed iron on the inner surface of the packing cans, as is the case if the cans are rusty or the tinning is scratched or worn off. In the "Dutching" of the cocoas, the tannins which they contain are made soluble by the added alkalis, and they react with the iron to form ferric tannate which gives the greenish-black discoloration to the ice cream. This discoloration can be avoided by using well-tinned cans, paper can-liners, or paper containers.

Concentration of Flavor in Cocoa. Cocoa is more concentrated for ice cream flavoring than chocolate liquor because it contains a higher percentage of the real chocolate flavor. The fat which has been removed is nearly tasteless and adds very little flavor to the ice cream mix. This is shown in the following equation:

100 lbs. of cocoa contains 78 lbs. flavor plus 22 lbs. fat.
100 lbs. chocolate liquor contains 48 lbs. flavor plus 52 lbs. fat.

It is evident, therefore, that in 100 lbs. of cocoa there is approximately 30 lbs. more of real chocolate flavor than in 100 lbs. of chocolate liquor. Due to the prevailing high price of cocoa butter, it is more economical for the ice cream manufacturer to use cocoa rather than chocolate liquor.

The color of cocoa is the resultant of several factors such as:

1. The blend of beans
2. The fat content
3. Treatment (Dutching)
4. Rate of chilling

The rate of chilling is an important factor and influences color by affecting the size of the fat globules in the cocoa. This influence is lost when the cocoa is used.

Chocolate products used in flavoring ice cream are cocoa (20 to 25 per cent cocoa fat), chocolate liquor (50 to 53 per cent cocoa fat), cocoa and chocolate liquor blends (36 to 40 per cent cocoa fat), and chocolate syrups. The use of 3 per cent cocoa, 4 per cent of blend of cocoa (two and one-half) and chocolate liquor (one and one-half), or 5 per cent chocolate liquor is very acceptable.

Cocoa Is Seldom Adulterated. Sugar, starch, cocoa shells, ground wood fiber, or iron oxide, which at one time were often used as adulterants, are seldom found in cocoas now. Some companies do, however, add to cocoa some aromatic substance such as cinnamon, oil of cloves, oil of bitter almond, or vanillin. Some of these substances in small quantities will give cocoa a higher, pleasant aroma.

The amount of cocoa or chocolate liquor to use in ice cream depends upon several factors, such as consumer preference, color desired in ice cream, strength of flavor, fat content of flavor, etc. The usual recommendation is sometimes as much as 4 lbs. of cocoa or 6 lbs. of chocolate liquor to 100 lbs. of mix. Extra sugar should be added to compensate for the bitter flavor of the cocoa, the usual recommendation being the same weight of sugar as of cocoa or chocolate. The tendency seems to be to flavor chocolate ice cream too highly. It is apparent that a better product could be made by reducing the amount of flavor and using instead a finer grade of cocoa or chocolate liquor.

Preparing the Chocolate Syrup. The small ice cream manufacturer usually prefers to flavor chocolate ice cream by adding syrup at the freezer. Desirable results may be expected by using a formula of 20 lbs. cocoa, 20 lbs. sugar and enough water to make 10 gallons of finished syrup. Five to seven pounds of this syrup may be used to five gallons of mix. The syrup should be made up in a chocolate kettle or double boiler. Mix the sugar and cocoa or chocolate together and add enough water to make a heavy paste. Heat gradually and add water slowly as necessary. (The final syrup should contain enough water so that it will pour when cooled.) The syrup should be heated to the boiling point, and cooled before using so as not to prolong the freezing operation.

When to Add. Wherever possible, an entire chocolate mix should be made by adding the cocoa (or chocolate) and extra sugar to the mix, along with the other dry ingredients, before pasteurization. The temperature of pasteurization is sufficient to incorporate the flavor properly. A chocolate mix made in this way whips more rapidly than plain mix plus syrup at the freezer, and gives a better flavored, more uniform product, freer of dark specks.

The best chocolate ice cream is made when the chocolate mix is compounded and processed. A typical formula is as follows: Fat, 10 per cent; milk solids-not-fat, 10 per cent; sugar, 18 per cent;

cocoa, 2.5 per cent; chocolate liquor, 1.5 per cent; stabilizer, 0.2 per cent; and total solids, 42.2 per cent.

Freezing Characteristics. Chocolate ice cream is one of the most difficult to freeze because it whips very slowly. This is due to the fact that chocolate mix is viscous. The viscosity may be reduced and whipping time improved by adding one pound of citrates or phosphates to 1,000 lbs. of mix.

FRUITS IN ICE CREAM

The ice cream trade is one of the chief markets for fresh, frozen and canned (pie grade) fruits. Strawberry ice cream ranks third among flavors, being about eight per cent of the total amount of ice cream made. Other fruit flavors are popular in season and are consumed more or less throughout the year.

Fruit flavors are available as (1) extracts prepared from the fruit, (2) artificial compounds, and (3) true extracts fortified artificially. These

TABLE 28

AMOUNT AND PREPARATION OF FRUITS AND NUTS FOR ICE CREAM

Flavor	Fruit-Sugar Ratio	Quantity of Fruit Per cent of Mix	Kind of Preparation	Color
Apple	7 to 1	20 to 25	Sliced	Lt. yellow green
Apricot	3 to 1	20 to 25	Sliced, diced or puree	Lt. orange yellow
Banana	none	18 to 20	Puree	. . .[1]
Blackberry	3 to 1	20	Crushed or puree	Slight red
Blueberry	4 to 1	20	Crushed or puree	Light blue
Cherry	5 to 1	15 to 20	Whole or crushed	Light red
Fruit Salad	3 to 1	15	Sliced or diced	. . .[1]
Grape	none	25	Juice	Light purple
Peach	4 to 1	20 to 25	Sliced, diced or puree	Light
Pineapple	4 to 1	12 to 15	Diced or crushed	. . .[1]
Plum	4 to 1	25	Puree	Light red
Raspberry	2 to 1	10 to 12	Crushed or puree	Light purple
Strawberry	3:1 to 4:1	15 to 20	Sliced, crushed or puree	Pink
		Sugar pack may range from 2:1 to 9:1		
Almond		3 lbs. per 10 gal. mix	Broken	. . .[1]
Chocolate		2.7 to 3.5 lbs. cocoa		
		3.5 to 4.5 lbs. cocoa-liquor blend	Syrup	. . .[1]
		4.5 to 5.5 lbs. chocolate liquor per 10 gal. mix		
Pecan		3 lbs. per 10 gal. mix	Broken	
Pistachio		4 lbs. per 10 gal. mix	Whole & broken	Light green
Walnut		4 lbs. per 10 gal. mix	Broken	. . .[1]
Orange	5 to 1	14–18 oz. per 10 gal. mix	Puree	Orange
Lemon	5 to 1	10–14 oz. per 10 gal. mix	Puree	Yellow green
Lime	5 to 1	8–12 oz. per 10 gal. mix	Puree	Green

[1] Natural—no color added.

Courtesy of Rietz Mfg. Co.

FIG. 10. ANGLE DISINTEGRATOR

All stainless steel construction for chopping and puréeing of fruits
used in ice cream production and in toppings.

flavors supplement the fruits in cases where it is necessary to avoid excessive amounts of fruit, but they are quite generally inferior to the flavor
obtained from the fruit itself and do not supply the desired fruit pulp.

A special mix need not be used for fruit ice cream unless the basic mix
contains more than 16 per cent sugar. With a 16 per cent sugar content a
3:1 fruit pack should be used. If the mix contains 15 per cent sugar or
less, the 2:1 pack is usually preferred.

Since fruit ice cream contains a higher percentage of sugar than plain
ice cream it should be drawn from the freezer at about 1°F. colder. A
drawing temperature of 23°F. for the batch freezer or 20°F. for the continuous freezer is satisfactory under most conditions.

Fresh fruit must be considered the best source of flavor when available at sufficiently low prices. Fresh fruit ice creams also have a special sales appeal. The fruit should be washed and hulled or peeled and then mixed with sugar in the ratio of 2 to 7 lbs. fruit to 1 lb. sugar (see Table 28) and held at about 40°F. for 12 to 24 hours before using. During this aging period a large part of the juice and flavor of the fruit will combine with the sugar, by osmotic action, to form a fruit syrup. This syrup will impart to the ice cream the full flavor of the fruit much more effectively than would the fresh fruit used immediately. Strawberries need not be mashed or sliced. This is merely a waste of time and does not enhance their flavoring ability. Very seedy fruits such as raspberries should be pureed so that about three-fourths of the seeds are removed. Peaches should be sliced.

Fresh fruit and fresh frozen fruit are most desirable flavoring materials. The aged fruit-sugar mixture used at the rate of 15 to 20 per cent produces good results with many fruits. The fruit-sugar ratio may vary from 2 parts fruit to 1 part sugar to as high as 9 parts fruit to 1 part of sugar. Fruits may be used whole, sliced, crushed, diced, pureed (coarse, medium or fine) or as juice. The use of whole or large slices of fruit sometimes results in coarse texture which reduces the consumer acceptance of the finished product. A greater amount of fruit is often required to obtain the desired flavor intensity when a puree is used.

Good results from the standpoint of fruit distribution, appearance, and desirable texture and flavor characteristics result from the use of diced fruit or coarse puréed fruit. A combination of sliced fruit and fruit purée is sometimes used with success.

Kind of Pack to Use. Fresh or frozen packs are preferable for fruits such as strawberries whose distinctive flavor is easily impaired by heating; while fruits like cherries or pineapple, whose flavors are relatively stable or improved by heating, are usually heat-preserved, that is, canned. For strawberries the 2:1 and 3:1 frozen packs are the most popular, with the tendency toward the latter. Peaches should also be frozen, the 3:1 pack being preferred. Raspberries are very satisfactory frozen, although they withstand heating much better than strawberries. Cherries are usually canned although the frozen fruit is satisfactory. The 2:1 ratio pack should be used in both cases. Generally the maraschino process cherries are used. Frozen pineapples are used occasionally and have a very fine flavor but the canned fruit flavor is also very popular.

The amount of fruit required to impart the desired flavor varies with the characteristic intensity of the flavor. This amount varies from 10 to 25 per cent of the weight of the finished product. In every case fruit ice cream should contain not less than 3 per cent by weight of clean,

Courtesy of Rietz Mfg. Co.

FIG. 11. STAINLESS STEEL DISINTEGRATOR

Produces fresh fruit purée or juice for sherbet or ice cream mixes.

mature, sound fruits or the juice thereof. This minimum value is desirable and is already a legal requirement in some states. It is usually desirable also to have pieces of the fruit or pulp large enough so they can be easily recognized in the finished ice cream.

For strawberries the optimum amount seems to be about 15 per cent of 2:1 or 3:1 pack. For cherry ice cream, as well as pineapple, 12 to 15 per cent is satisfactory. When these fruits are high in price, less fruit is often used, and enough true fruit extract added to produce a flavor approximately the same as the natural fruit flavor. A little artificial color is added to give the delicate tints associated with these fruits. Raspberries are generally rather expensive so about 10 per cent of fruit plus enough good raspberry extract to bring out the desired flavor should be used. For best results with peaches about 20 per cent of frozen pack fruit should be used along with a good peach brandy syrup. Of the mixed fruits and fruit combinations, about 15 per cent seems to be the desirable amount to use.

Fruit Concentrates and Essences. Considerable results have been obtained on the technology of utilizing concentrated fruit juice and essences in ice cream and related frozen dairy foods. The most desirable use levels and best formulas have been established for peach, blueberry, grape, apple, red raspberry and strawberry flavor concentrates. In most cases, the supplemental use of 3.5 to 10 per cent fruit equivalent of concentrates improved flavor properties. The amount of flavoring material, composition of the ice cream mix and the sugar-acid ratio are factors that have been controlled in obtaining the most desirable flavor. Adjustment of the acidity and the sugar content of the mix produced desirable effects for the flavors studied except for apple products where acidity adjustment did not produce an improvement. Fruit concentrates and essences have been found to be valuable products in improving fruit ice cream and sherbet flavors either when used to supplement the use of fruit or in some cases when used as the sole source of flavor.

The results indicate that the established flavors of ice cream can be improved by the addition of concentrated fruit juice i.e., peach or blueberry, and that the use of fruit concentrates or essences offers the possibility of the development of new flavors of ice cream i.e., grape or Montmorency cherry.

Candied or Glacéd fruits such as cherries, pineapple, and citron, and such candied fruit peels as orange, lemon, and grapefruit are very good flavoring materials. They are used chiefly in rich types of ice cream— puddings, aufaits, mousses—and as decorative material for fancy molded ice creams, and sherbets and ices.

Dried fruits such as apricots, figs, prunes and raisins make tasty ice creams. Although of slightly different flavor than the corresponding fresh fruit, they usually are less expensive and often can be obtained at times when fresh fruit is very scarce or in places where it is practically unobtainable. Dates, figs, and raisins, particularly, have long been used in frozen puddings, but recently there has been a tendency to use these and other dried fruits as flavoring material for ice cream either separately or in combinations.

NUTS

Nut meats and nut extracts are quite extensively used as flavorings in ice cream. Pecans, walnuts, almonds, pistachios, filberts, and peanuts are among the most popular. Nut meats should be sound and clean and free from rancid flavors. They should be stored in tight containers in a cool place until used. Considerable care should be used in preparing them for the ice cream mix, to make certain that no foreign material, such as pieces of shell or pieces of wood and nails from containers, get into the mix. Some nuts such as almonds, filberts, and pistachios should be blanched to remove their dark outer skin.

Since nut meats are often high in bacteria count and sometimes are not hygienically handled, they may contaminate the mix and be the source of high count and sometimes pathogenic bacteria count in the ice cream unless they receive special heat treatment. Some manufacturers dry-heat the nuts to pasteurizing temperatures or above, while others have found that they can greatly reduce bacterial count, and improve the flavor of some nut meats by dipping them in a boiling, slightly salted sugar solution for a few seconds. To prevent sogginess, the meats are afterwards dried for three or four minutes at 250° to 300°F. All nut meats should be chopped into very small pieces before they are added to the mix.

SPICES AND SALT

Spices such as cinnamon, cloves, nutmeg, allspice, and ginger are used to a limited extent as flavorings in ice cream, sherbets, and ices. Ginger ice cream is a favorite in some localities. Cinnamon, nutmeg, or cloves are often used to enhance or vary the flavor of chocolate ice cream, and they are used in combination with fruits or fruit extracts in such frozen products as puddings, eggnog, and punch.

Spices may be purchased either in dried and finely ground form or as extracts. Their flavors are very pungent and therefore only small amounts are required to produce the desired flavoring effect.

Salt, although not a spice, is often used in very small quantities to enhance the flavor of ice creams, especially in mixes containing eggs—custards and rich puddings—and in nut ice cream.

VARIEGATED OR RIPPLED ICE CREAM

Variegated ice cream is becoming increasingly popular. This product is produced by injecting approximately 10 per cent of a prepared base into the ice cream. Most popular flavors of variegated ice cream are chocolate, butterscotch, marshmallow, fudge, strawberry, pineapple, raspberry, and caramel. This type of ice cream provides almost unlimited possibilities for flavor combinations.

A base may be prepared for fruit flavor syrup by using 55 lbs. sugar, 2.5 lbs. stabilizer (pectin gives very desirable results) and sufficient water to make 100 lbs. of base syrup. The syrup may then be prepared by using one-third fruit puree and two-thirds base syrup. The addition of 0.3 lb. of citric acid per 100 lbs. of syrup may be used with good results for fruit flavors.

COLOR IN ICE CREAM

Ice cream should have a delicate, attractive color which suggests or is readily associated with the flavor. Only colors certified by the Food and Drug Administration should be used.

Almost All Flavors of Ice Cream Should Be Slightly Colored. Enough yellow color is generally added to vanilla ice cream to give it the shade of natural cream produced in the summer months. Fruit ice creams need to be colored because about 15 per cent of fruit, the maximum commonly used, produces only a slight effect on color. Chocolate ice cream is one of the exceptions. It rarely needs to be colored, for the required amount of a Dutch processed cocoa will produce sufficient color.

Most Colors Are of Chemical Origin. A weak alkaline solution annatto color is about the only vegetable color used in ice cream. However, this does not produce a good egg-shade yellow, but rather a pinkish tinge. Therefore, the bulk of colors used are chemical in origin. Most ice cream makers purchase the desired colors in liquid or paste form.

Preparation of Coloring Solutions. It is more economical to purchase food colors in powder form and dissolve them in boiling water as needed. Blending of these "primary colors" to give desired shades requires some artistic ability and experience. Such coloring solutions if contaminated will become very high in bacteria count. In this way the bacteria content of the ice cream is increased and the growth of the organisms partially destroys the color pigment. Therefore color solutions should not be prepared in large amounts, should be boiled, and should be stored in a cool place. A good practice is to add 0.1 per cent of sodium benzoate to the solution to keep it sterile.

Permitted Coal Tar Food Colors. The following (Table 29), coal-tar dyes are now accepted for certification under the authority of the Federal Food, Drug and Cosmetic Act:

TABLE 29

FOOD COLORS FOR ICE CREAM

Previous Name	Current Listing
Red Colors:	
80 Ponceau 3R	
184 Amaranth	F.D and C Red No. 2
773 Erythrosine	F.D and C Red No. 3
Ponceau SX	F.D and C Red No. 4
Green Colors:	
666 Guinea Green B	F.D and C Green No. 1
670 Light Green SF Yellowish	F.D and C Green No. 2
Fast Green FCF	F.D and C Green No. 3
Blue Colors:	
Brilliant blue FCF	F.D and C Blue No. 1
1180 Indigotine	F.D and C Blue No. 2
Yellow Colors:	
10 Naphthol Yellow S	F.D and C Yellow No. 1
640 Tartrazine	F.D and C Yellow No. 5
Sunset Yellow FCF	F.D and C Yellow No. 6

The numbers preceding the names refer to the colors as listed in the Colour Index published in 1924 by the Society of Dyers and Colourists of England, which gives the composition of these dyes. Names not preceded by numbers are not listed in the Colour Index. The Food, Drug and Cosmetic numbers listed are those in current use by the Food and Drug Administration. The composition of such dyes will be furnished on application to the Food and Drug Administration.

Color solutions of a strength commonly used may be prepared by dissolving 4 ounces of a primary or basic color per gallon of water or one-half ounce per pint to make a liquid solution of about three per cent. Use one ounce of this liquid solution to 5 gallons of mix.

CHAPTER 8

Calculation of Ice Cream Mixes

The Importance of Calculations. Since the palatability, quality, body and texture, and cost of the ice cream hinges upon the ice cream maker's ability to select and use, in the right proportion, the various ingredients from those that are available, it becomes highly desirable for him to learn to calculate accurately the amount of each ingredient that goes into the mix that he desires to make. In other words the ice cream maker needs to know the answer to such questions as: How much does it cost to make a gallon of ice cream? How much ice cream can be made from a gallon of mix? How much cream, sugar, etc., are needed to make one hundred pounds (or any other number of pounds) of mix? Answers to such questions can be obtained only if he has the "know how" to make at least simple, although time-consuming, calculations.

A knowledge of calculations is also helpful in properly balancing a mix, and especially in establishing and maintaining uniform quality, and in producing ice cream that conforms to the necessary legal standards. Some authorities think that the ice cream maker's knowledge concerning the making of ice cream is in direct proportion to his ability to make the necessary calculations.

The method and procedure of making calculations are demonstrated by a few typical problems. These demonstrations are presented in detail for the benefit of the reader who might be confused by figures alone—i.e., without explanation of the processes involved. However, the presentation here attempts to focus attention on *the method* and *the procedure* with a minimum of effort in performing the necessary arithmetic. It is assumed that the reader is most interested in learning a quick and easy way to arrive at the correct answer and therefore little explanation is given of the mathematics involved in deriving the formulas or the logic in setting up the equations.

Much practice is usually necessary to develop speed and accuracy in making calculations. This practice can be obtained by using the demonstrated problems as a pattern for setting up and solving many similar problems.

Ice cream mixes may be divided into two groups, namely; simple and complex. Simple mixes require the least calculations and are made of ingredients each of which supplies one constituent. Complex mixes are more difficult to calculate. They include mixes where at least one constituent is obtained from two or more products. Simple mixes may be figured by multiplication, addition, subtraction or division while complex mixes require the use of the *Pearson Square Method,* the *Serum Point Method* or *Algebra.*

MATHEMATICAL PROCESSES MOST FREQUENTLY USED

Briefly the discussion in this chapter on calculating ice cream mixes, assumes a knowledge of arithmetic, especially decimals and percentages. Even so, it may be helpful to state the following mathematical facts that will be used frequently:

1. A fraction indicates the process of division. Thus:

$\dfrac{2.25}{5}$ means that 2.25 is divided by 5 to give 0.45, or

$$\frac{2.25}{5} = 2.25 \div 5 = 0.45$$

and $\dfrac{2.25}{94\%}$ indicates that 2.25 is divided by 0.94, or

$$\frac{2.25}{94\%} = 2.25 \div 0.94 = 2.39$$

and $\dfrac{63}{100\%}$ indicates that 63 is divided by 1.00, or

$$\frac{63}{100\%} = 63 \div 1.00 = 63$$

2. When a percentage figure is used in division or multiplication, the per cent sign is dropped and the decimal point is moved two places to the left. Thus, 10 per cent becomes 0.10, 25.5 per cent becomes 0.255, and so on.

3. When the lbs. of milk (or cream) and the test are given, the lbs. of fat are obtained by multiplication, thus:

$$50 \text{ (lbs. milk)} \times 4\% \text{ (fat)} = 50 \times 0.04 = 2.00 \text{ lbs. fat}$$

4. When the lbs. of fat and the test are given the lbs. of milk (or cream) are obtained by division, thus:

$$\frac{2.00 \text{ lbs. fat}}{4\%} = 50 \text{ lbs. milk}$$

5. When the lbs. of fat and the lbs. of milk (or cream) are given the test is obtained by division, thus:

$$\frac{2.00 \text{ lbs. fat}}{50 \text{ lbs. milk}} = 0.04 \text{ or } 4\%$$

This chapter also contains certain abbreviations and terms, some of which are widely accepted, while others are new and are introduced here for the sake of brevity and convenience. The following abbreviations are widely accepted:

ABBREVIATIONS AND SPECIAL TERMS

lb.—pound, or **lbs.**—pounds

serum—that portion of the mixture containing the water and milk solids-not-fat.

m.s.n.f.—milk solids-not-fat, the moisture-free non-fat milk solids which includes protein, lactose and minerals.

stab.—stabilizer

t.s.—total solids—moisture-free—, and not to be confused with dried products such as powdered milk, cocoa or gelatin, all of which contain some moisture, in spite of their dry appearances.

s.n.f.—solids-not-fat.

Other terms may be used as follows:

plain condensed skim milk—condensed skim milk, usually having 28–30 per cent m.s.n.f., containing no added sugar, and not superheated.

egg yolk solids—total solids contained in egg yolk product but does not include sugar if present.

non-fat dry milk solids—refers to powdered skim milk.

sweetened condensed milk—condensed skim milk with approximately 42 per cent sugar addition.

sugar—refers to the cane sugar or sucrose equivalent.

DECIDE ON ESSENTIALS OF MIX

Before a mix can be calculated it is necessary first to decide upon the composition desired in the finished product, i.e., the percentage fat, milk solids-not-fat, sugar, stabilizer, and egg yolk solids. Second, the amount of mixture, generally referred to as "mix," to be made at one time is also important and this is usually fairly constant in any one factory. However, it is often more convenient to calculate the amount of each ingredient needed to prepare one hundred pounds of finished product, and these amounts can then readily be increased proportionately for large batches. The third decision concerns the choice of ingredients that are available and the composition of each ingredient. Approximate compositions are found in Table 15, but accurate results can best be obtained when the calculations are based on the exact analysis of the ingredients actually used in making the ice cream. The relation of cost to quality desired should also be considered. The above information needed before a mix can be calculated can be briefly summarized as follows:

1. Decide upon composition of the mix to be made.

2. Decide on amount of mix in the batch to be made at one time. Whatever the amount, it may be calculated on the basis of 100 lbs. if so desired.

3. Choose from the available ingredients those that will give the desired quality, characteristics, and composition at lowest cost.

4. Be familiar with the composition (i.e. the analysis) of ingredients to be used. See Table 15, page 44.

5. When the above information has been obtained, the mix can be classified either as a *simple mix* or a *complex mix* and calculations can be made accordingly.

6. Prepare proof sheet and record each succeeding calculation.

7. Calculate the amount of each ingredient which supplies only one constituent to the mix. (Usually sugar and stabilizer).

8. Calculate the amounts of products supplying concentrated serum solids or fat as the case may be. Record the amounts of the various constituents supplied.

9. Calculate the amounts of remaining dairy products needed. Record the amounts of the various constituents supplied by these products.

10. Total each constituent column and check "needed" column against "total" column.

SIMPLE MIXES

Simple mixes require the least calculation and include such mixes as one made of stabilizer, sugar, and cream, and condensed skim milk or non-fat dry milk solids; or one made from ingredients each of which supply only one constituent. Mixes having two sources of one constituent are more complex, but sometimes the calculation may be reduced to the same simple procedure which is used for the simplest mixes.

Problem 1

How much 30 per cent cream, non-fat dry milk solids testing 97 per cent milk solids-not-fat, cane sugar, dried egg yolk, stabilizer and water will be needed to make 450 lbs. of mix testing 10 per cent fat, 11 per cent m.s.n.f., 14 per cent sugar, 0.5 per cent egg yolk solids, and 0.5 per cent stabilizer?

SOLUTION:

Step 1.—List the available ingredients and the number of pounds of each constituent in the desired mix, thus:

Available Ingredients	Desired Mix
Stabilizer 90% t.s.[1]	Fat, 10% of 450 lbs. = 45 lbs.
Dried egg yolk, 62.5% fat 94% t.s.	M.s.n.f. 11% of 450 lbs. = 49.5 lbs.
Cane sugar, 100% sugar	Sugar, 14% of 450 lbs. = 63 lbs.
Non-fat dry milk, 97% t.s. 97% m.s.n.f.	Egg yolk solids, 0.5% of 450 lbs. = 2.25 lbs.
Cream, 30% fat, 6.24% m.s.n.f.	Stab.,[2] 0.5% of 450 lbs. = 2.25 lbs.
Water	

[1] The composition of the ingredients is preferably obtained from laboratory analyses, but approximate figures are available in Table 15 on page 44.

[2] Stabilizer in these calculations means the moisture-free part of the stabilizer. Stabilizer as used in these calculations refers to the stabilizer product and may include emulsifiers also. Although egg products are not used extensively in ice cream manufacture they are included in these calculations for illustration purposes.

Step 2.—If desired, make a proof sheet and enter the weight and percentage of each constituent of the desired mix in the lines labeled "desired wt. and %" columns (from step 1). Enter the information obtained in each succeeding step. (See completed proof sheet, p 92.)

Step 3.—Compute the amount of each ingredient which supplies only one constituent. In this problem these will be the stabilizer product, supplying all of the stabilizer, and the cane sugar, supplying all of the sugar.

The stabilizer contains 90 per cent total solids, and therefore 90 per cent of the number of lbs. of stabilizer needed must equal 2.25 lbs., the desired amount of stabilizer (the moisture-free part of the stabilizer). From this it follows that:

$$\frac{2.25}{0.90} = 2.50 \text{ lbs. stabilizer needed}$$

Enter 2.50 in weight column of proof sheet and enter 2.25 in the stab. and the total solids columns. Cane sugar is 100 per cent sugar and so

$$\frac{63}{1.00} = 63 \text{ lbs. cane sugar needed}$$

Enter this figure (63) in the wt., sugar, and total solids columns of the proof sheet.

Step 4.—Compute the amount of those ingredients which supply more than one constituent of the mix but which are the only remaining source of some one constituent—in this problem, the dried egg yolk which is the only source of egg solids.

$$\text{lbs. dried egg yolk needed} = \frac{2.25 \text{ lbs.}}{94\%} = 2.39 \text{ lbs.}$$

Enter in proof sheet.

Enter 2.25 lbs. in the "egg solids" and "total solids" columns of proof sheet.

Also calculate the amount of other constituents supplied by the dried egg yolk, namely fat.

$$2.39 \text{ lbs.} \times 62.5 \text{ per cent} = 1.49 \text{ lbs. fat}$$

Enter in proof sheet. This 1.49 lbs. of fat is part of the 2.25 lbs. of egg solids or total solids. Frequently the fat supplied by the eggs is disregarded, but sometimes, as in this problem, it is considered as a part of the fat which is desired in the mix. Thus the 45 lbs. of fat desired less the 1.49 lbs. of fat supplied by the dried egg yolk leaves 43.51 lbs. of fat to be supplied by other ingredients, in this case, the cream.

$$\text{Hence the lbs. 30 per cent cream needed} = \frac{43.51 \text{ lbs.}}{30\%} = 145.03 \text{ lbs.}$$

Enter in proof sheet. This cream furnishes not only fat but also milk solids-not-fat and the amount of the latter is computed as follows:

145.03 lbs. 30 per cent cream $\times$ 6.24 per cent =
$$9.05 \text{ lbs. milk solids-not-fat.}$$

Enter in proof sheet. The total 49.5 lbs. of milk solids-not-fat desired less the 9.05 lbs. m.s.n.f. supplied by the cream leaves 40.45 lbs. of milk solids-not-fat to be obtained from the remaining ingredients, namely the non-fat dry milk. Therefore it follows that:

$$\frac{40.45 \text{ lbs. m.s.n.f.}}{97\%} = 41.70 \text{ lbs. non-fat dry milk solids needed.}$$

Enter in proof sheet. Enter 40.45 lbs. in milk solids-not-fat and total solids columns of proof sheet.

Finally, the above calculated amounts of each ingredient are totaled, and this sum is subtracted from the total 450 lbs. of mix desired. The difference represents the amount of water needed, thus:

$$450.00 - (2.50 + 2.39 + 63.00 + 145.03 + 41.70) =$$
$$450.00 - 254.62 = 195.38 \text{ lb. of water needed}$$

Enter in proof sheet.

Step 5.—At this time it may also be desirable to compute the cost of the mix by entering in the proof sheet the actual cost of the ingredients used. See problem 9, page 130. Cost figures are assumed, not actual.

Step 6.—Find the percentage (test) of each constituent in the mix. If a proof sheet is used, each column should now be totaled. The calculated test for any constituent is obtained by dividing the total of that column by the total weight of the ingredients. For example, the calculated m.s.n.f. test is obtained by dividing 49.50 lbs. milk solids-not-fat (the total of the column "m.s.n.f., lbs.") by 450 lbs., the total weight of the ingredients, giving the answer 11.0 per cent. Similarly 160.51 lbs., the total of the column "t.s. lbs.," is divided by 450 lbs., the total weight of the ingredients, to give 35.67 per cent total solids. In similar manner find the percentage of each of the remaining constituents, and enter the figures in their respective columns in proof sheet.

Step 7.—Determine the correctness of the calculation from the proof sheet by comparing the "calculated percentage" for each constituent with the corresponding desired test. When the difference between these two percentages is less than one-tenth, the mix is assumed to be correctly calculated.

The completed proof sheet for Problem 1 appears as follows:

Ingredients Used	Weight	Fat	M.s.n.f.	Sugar	Egg Solids	Stab.	T.s.	Cost
	lbs.	lbs.	lbs.	lbs.	lbs.	lbs.	lbs.	$
Stabilizer	2.50	...	...	...	...	2.25	2.25	
Dried egg yolk	2.39	1.49	...	...	2.25	...	2.25	
Cane sugar	63.00	...	...	63.00	...	...	63.00	
Cream, 30%	145.03	43.51	9.05	...	...	...	52.56	
Non-fat dry milk solids	41.70	...	40.45	...	...	...	40.45	
Water	195.38	...	...	...	...	...	...	
Total, lbs.	450.00	45.00	49.50	63.00	2.25	2.25	160.51	
Calculated, %		10.00	11.00	14.00	0.50	0.50	35.67	
Check with desired wt.	450.00	45.00	49.50	63.00	2.25	2.25	162.00	
and %		10.0	11.0	14.0	0.50	0.50	36.00	

Calculated Constituents

COMPLEX MIXES

Complex mixes, according to our classification, include all mixes, except those classed as simple mixes, and mixes made in a vacuum pan. They can usually be identified by the fact that at least one constituent is obtained from two or more ingredients. These complex mixes are most rapidly calculated by using formulas in the following steps:

1. List the available ingredients and the number of pounds of each constituent of the desired mix.

2. Make a proof sheet as on p. 94, and enter in it the information obtained in Step 1 and also in each succeeding step.

3. Compute the amount of each ingredient which is the only source

of some one constituent of the mix, and enter this in the proof sheet. This usually includes the stabilizer, egg products, and sugar substitutes.

4. Calculate the needed amount of condensed or powdered dairy product by either formula No. I or II.

5. Calculate the amount of sugar needed.

6. Calculate the needed amount of cream, or butter by formula No. III.

7. Calculate the needed amount of sweet whole milk or sweet skim milk.

8. Total each column and compute the "calculated percentages," especially the total solids test.

9. Examine for accuracy, by comparing with weights and percentages in the desired mix.

10. Compute the cost of the mix, if desired.

FORMULAS FOR CALCULATING COMPLEX MIXES

FORMULA NO. I[1]

To find lbs. of $\left\{ \begin{array}{c} \text{non-fat dry milk solids} \\ \text{or} \\ \text{condensed skim milk} \end{array} \right\}$ when using fresh whole milk or skim milk.

$$\frac{\text{lbs. m.s.n.f. needed} - (\text{lbs. serum of mix}[2] \times 0.09[3])}{\text{lbs. m.s.n.f. in 1 lb. non-fat dry milk solids}}$$
$$= \text{lbs. non-fat dry milk solids}[4]$$

FORMULA NO. II

To find lbs. of $\left\{ \begin{array}{c} \text{condensed whole milk} \\ \text{or condensed skim milk} \end{array} \right\}$ when using fresh whole milk or skim milk.

$$\frac{\text{lbs. m.s.n.f. needed} - (\text{lbs. serum of mix}[2] \times 0.09[3])}{\text{lbs. m.s.n.f. in 1 lb. cond. milk} - (\text{lbs. serum in 1 lb. cond. milk} \times 0.09[3])}$$
$$= \text{lbs. condensed milk needed}$$

---

[1] Although this formula is not absolutely accurate when butter is the source of fat, it gives results that are sufficiently accurate for practical operation.

[2] Serum of mix = lbs. of mix − sum of lbs. fat, gelatin, egg and sugar source. Serum is the milk solids-not-fat plus water.

[3] This figure represents the percentage of total solids in 1.00 lb. of skim milk in this case, 9.0 per cent. However if skim milk tests 8.8 per cent total solids, then for accurate calculation the figure used would be 0.088.

[4] Condensed skim milk can be substituted for non-fat dry milk solids.

To find lbs. of cream needed when using fresh whole milk. This same formula may be used to find the lbs. of butter needed if the word "butter" is substituted for the word "cream" in the formula.

$$\frac{\text{lbs. fat needed}[5] - (\text{lbs. milk and cream needed}[6] \times \% \text{ fat in milk})}{\text{lbs. fat in 1 lb. cream} - \text{lbs. fat in 1 lb. milk}}$$

$$= \text{lbs. cream needed}$$

Sample Proof Sheet

Ingredients Used	Weight	Fat	M.s.n.f.	Sugar	Stab.	T.s.	Cost
	lbs.	lbs.	lbs.	lbs.	lbs.	lbs.	$
. . . .							
. . . .							
. . . .							
. . . .							
. . . .							
. . . .							
Total, lbs.							
Calculated, %							
Check with desired wt.							
and %							

This proof sheet is useful in calculating the mix and especially helpful in examining the accuracy of the calculations.

Problem 2: In which the Milk Solids-Not-Fat Are Obtained From Three Sources

Calculate the amount of ingredients needed to make 200 lbs. of mix testing 14 per cent fat, 9 per cent milk solid-not-fat, 13 per cent sugar, and 0.5 per cent stabilizer. The available ingredients are 40 per cent cream, 4 per cent milk, condensed skim milk (27 per cent milk solids-not-fat, 27 per cent total solids), cane sugar, and stabilizer.

SOLUTION:

This is a complex mix since the milk solids-not-fat will be obtained from three sources (condensed skim milk, cream, and milk). Therefore it is most rapidly calculated by using formulas No. I and No. III.

---

[5] Lbs. fat needed = lbs. fat in the milk needed plus lbs. fat in the cream needed.

[6] Lbs. milk and cream needed = lbs. mix — sum of lbs. of all ingredients except milk and cream.

Step 1.—

Available Ingredients	Desired Mix
Stabilizer, 90% t.s.[1]	Fat, 14% of 200 lbs. = 28 lbs.
Cane sugar, 100% sugar	M.s.n.f., 9% of 200 lbs. = 18 lbs.
Condensed skim milk, 27% t.s. 27% m.s.n.f.	Sugar, 13% of 200 lbs. = 26 lbs.
Cream, 40% fat, 5.35% m.s.n.f.	Stabilizer, 0.5% of 200 lbs. = 1 lb.
Whole milk, 4% fat, 8.79% m.s.n.f.	

[1] The composition of the ingredients is preferably obtained from laboratory analyses, but approximate figures are available in Table 15 on page 44.

*Step 2.—*Make proof sheet and enter information from step 1.

*Step 3.—*In this problem, there is only one source of stabilizer, and it contains 90 per cent t.s., the balance being water. Therefore 90 per cent of the number of lbs. of stabilizer needed must equal 1.0 lb., the desired amount of stabilizer.

It follows that $1.0/0.90 = 1.11$ lbs., the amount of stabilizer needed. This figure (1.11) is entered in the weight column of the proof sheet.

Since the 1.1 lb. of stabilizer product supplies 1.00 lb. of dry stabilizer, also 1 lb. total solids—enter these figures in the stabilizer and total solids columns respectively.

In this problem, no egg products are used and no sugar substitutes are used, therefore, these require no calculation.

Also, in this problem, cane sugar happens to be the only source of sugar, therefore, it can be calculated either here or in step 5.

*Step 4.—*To find the amount of condensed skim milk needed, it will be necessary to use formula No. I. The figures to substitute in the formula are obtained as follows:

lbs. m.s.n.f. needed = 18 lbs. (from proof sheet or step 1)
lbs. serum of mix = 144.89 lbs., obtained by calculation as follows:
First find the sum of:

28.00 lbs. fat (from step 2)
1.11 lbs. stabilizer (from step 3)
26.00 lbs. sugar source since it is all sucrose (from step 2)

55.11 lbs. total

then subtract this 55.11 lbs. from the desired total weight of the mix, in this problem, 200.00 lbs. This leaves 144.89 lbs. the amount of serum of the mix.

lbs. m.s.n.f. in 1 lb. condensed skim milk = 0.27, obtained by multiplying the 1.0 lb. by 27 per cent which is the milk solid-not-fat.

These figures are substituted in formula No. I to give:

$$\frac{18 \text{ lbs. m.s.n.f. needed} - (144.89 \text{ lbs. serum} \times 0.09)}{0.27 - 0.09} = \text{lbs.}$$

condensed skim milk needed.

The formula is solved by making the computation, thus:

$$\frac{18 \text{ lbs.} - (144.89 \text{ lbs.} \times 0.09)}{0.27 - 0.09} = \frac{18 - 13.04}{0.27 - 0.09} = \frac{4.96}{0.18} =$$

27.56 lbs. condensed skim milk needed.

This figure is entered in the weight column of the proof sheet. Also enter in their respective columns of the proof sheet, the lbs. milk solids-not-fat and the lbs. total solids supplied by the 27.56 lbs condensed skim milk They are obtained by multiplication as follows:

$$27.56 \times 27\% \text{ m.s.n.f.} = 7.44 \text{ lbs. m.s.n.f.}$$

$$27.56 \times 27\% \text{ t.s.} = 7.44 \text{ lbs. t.s.}$$

Step 5.—To calculate the amount of sugar needed, divide the remaining lbs. of sugar by the percentage of sugar in the sugar. In this problem all of the 26 lbs. of sugar remain to be furnished by cane sugar, since there is only one source of sugar. Therefore, it follows that $26/1.00 = 26$, the lbs. of sugar needed. This can be entered in the proof sheet under weight, sugar, and total solids because cane sugar is practically 100 per cent total solids.

Step 6.—The amount of cream needed is calculated with the aid of formula III. The figures to substitute in the formula are obtained as follows:

lbs. fat needed = 28 (from step 2)
lbs. of milk and cream needed = 145.33 lbs., calculated as follows:
first find the sum of:

    1.11 lbs. stabilizer (step 3)
    27.56 lbs. condensed skim milk (step 4)
    26.00 lbs. sugar (step 5)
    ―――
    54.67 lbs. total

then subtract 54.67 lbs. from the desired total weight of the mix, 200 lbs., which leaves 145.33 lbs., the amount of milk and cream needed.

lbs. fat in 1 lb. of 40 per cent cream = 0.40 lb. obtained by multiplication:

1 lb. cream $\times$ 40 per cent fat $= 0.40$ lb. fat

lbs. fat in 1 lb. of 4 per cent milk $= 0.04$ lb. obtained by a similar multiplication.

These figures are substituted in the formula to give:

$$\frac{28 \text{ lbs.} - (145.33 \text{ lbs.} \times 4\%)}{0.40 - 0.04} = \text{lbs. } 40\% \text{ cream needed}$$

In the process of solving, the formula becomes

$$\frac{28 \text{ lbs.} - 5.813 \text{ lbs.}}{0.36} = \frac{22.187}{0.36} = 61.63 \text{ lbs. } 40\% \text{ cream needed}$$

This (61.63 lbs.) is entered in the weight column of the proof sheet. Also enter in their respective columns of the proof sheet, the lbs. of fat, milk solids-not-fat and total solids which are contained in the 61.63 lbs. of cream.

$$61.63 \text{ lbs.} \times 40\% = 24.65 \text{ lbs. fat}$$

$$61.63 \text{ lbs} \times 5.35\% = 3.30 \text{ lbs. m.s.n.f.}$$

$$24.65 \text{ lbs. plus } 3.30 \text{ lbs.} = 27.95 \text{ lbs. t.s.}$$

Step 7.—The lbs. of milk needed are computed by subtraction thus:

145.33 lbs. milk and cream needed (from step 6)

less: 61.63 lbs. cream needed (from step 6)

leaves: 83.70 lbs. milk needed.

This 83.70 lbs. is entered in the weight column of the proof sheet, and also the lbs. fat, lbs. milk solid-not-fat, and lbs. total solids are entered in their respective columns.

$$83.70 \text{ lbs.} \times 4\% = 3.35 \text{ lbs. fat}$$

$$83.70 \text{ lbs.} \times 8.79\% = 7.36 \text{ lbs. m.s.n.f.}$$

$$3.35 \text{ lbs. fat plus } 7.36 \text{ lbs. m.s.n.f.} = 10.71 \text{ lbs. total solids}$$

Step 8.—Each column of the proof sheet is now totaled and these totals should agree with the corresponding figure of the desired mix. In other words, the total weight of all ingredients should equal the desired weight of the mix, the total fat supplied by all ingredients should equal the fat desired in the mix, and so on. However, if the decimals are not carried far enough, these totals may sometimes be slightly higher or slightly lower than the corresponding figure of the desired mix. This apparent error may be insignificant, as shown by step 9. The calculations in this book (Chapters 8, 9, & 10) were made by using four decimal places throughout, although in most cases only two are recorded. In practical work, it is not necessary to use more than two decimal places. One unit in the second decimal place is equivalent to only about one-sixth of an ounce.

The total solids test is computed by division, thus:

$$\frac{73.10 \text{ lbs. t.s.}}{200 \text{ lbs. mix}} = 0.3655 \text{ or } 36.55\% \text{ t.s.}$$

Similar divisions will compute the calculated % for each of the constituents, thus:

$$\frac{18.10 \text{ lbs. m.s.n.f.}}{200 \text{ lbs. mix}} = 0.0905 \text{ or } 9.05\% \text{ m.s.n.f.}$$

Step 9.—The correctness of the calculations may be determined by comparing the calculated percentage for each constituent with the corresponding test of the desired mix. For example: in this problem, the calculated percentage of milk solids-not-fat is 9.05 per cent (see step 8), which is compared with the 9.0 per cent milk solids-not-fat of the desired mix. Since the difference between these two percentages is less than 0.1, it is not significant. Similar comparisons for each constituent show no significant differences, and therefore the calculations are correct.

Step 10.—Since the actual cost depends upon many factors, the figures are not included in this problem but the methods of calculating an assumed cost is demonstrated in problem 9, page 130.

The completed proof sheet for Problem 2 appears as follows:

| Ingredients Used | Weight | Calculated Constituents | | | | | Cost |
		Fat	M.s.n.f.	Sugar	Stab.	T.s.	
	lbs.	lbs.	lbs.	lbs.	lbs.	lbs.	$
Stabilizer	1.11	. . .	. . .	. . .	1.00	1.00	
Cane sugar	26.00	. . .	. . .	26.00	. . .	26.00	
Condensed skim milk	27.56	. . .	7.44	. . .	. . .	7.44	
Cream, 40%	61.63	24.65	3.30	. . .	. . .	27.95	
Milk, 4%	83.70	3.35	7.36	. . .	. . .	10.71	
Total, lbs.	200.00	28.00	18.10	26.00	1.00	73.10	
Calculated, %	. . .	14.00	9.05	13.00	0.50	36.55	
Check with desired wt.	200.00[1]	28.00	18.00	26.00	1.00	73.00	
and %		14.0	9.0	13.0	0.5	36.50	

[1] Includes the lbs. total solids and water which sometimes can be correctly stated only after calculating the mix.

Problem 3: In Which There Is More Than One Source of Sugar, M.s.n.f. and Fat

Calculate the amount of ingredients needed to make 900 lbs. of mix testing 12 per cent fat, 10 per cent milk solids-not-fat, 14 per cent sugar, and 0.4 per cent stabilizer. The available ingredients are 40 per cent cream, 4.0 per cent milk, Frodex to supply one-fourth of the sugar, sweetened condensed skim milk (42 per cent sugar, 30 per cent milk solids-not-fat), cane sugar and stabilizer.

SOLUTION:

This complex mix has three sources of sugar, three sources of milk solids-not-fat and two sources of fat. Therefore the calculations will be made by formulas No. II and No. III.

Step 1.—

Available Ingredients	Desired Mix
Stabilizer, 90% t.s. Frodex, 47% sugar, 96.5% t.s. Sweetened condensed skim milk, 42% sugar, 30% m.s.n.f. Cane sugar Cream, 40% fat[1] Milk, 4% fat	Fat, 12% of 900 lbs. = 108 lbs. M.s.n.f. 10% of 900 lbs. = 90 lbs. Sugar, 14% of 900 lbs. = 126 lbs. Stabilizer, 0.4% of 900 lbs. = 3.6 lbs.

[1] When percentage composition of ingredients is not given, use data from Table 15 on page 44.

*Step 2.—*Proof Sheet Form:

Ingredients Used	Weight	Calculated Constituents					Cost
		Fat	M.s.n.f.	Sugar	Stab.	T.s.	
	lbs.	lbs.	lbs.	lbs.	lbs.	lbs.	$
Stabilizer							
Frodex							
Sweetened condensed skim milk							
Cane sugar							
Cream, 40%							
Milk, 4%							
Total, lbs.							
Calculated, %							
Check with desired wt.	900.00[1]	108.00	90.00	126.00	3.60	327.60	
and %		12.0	10.0	14.0	0.4	36.4	

[1] Includes the lbs. total solids and water which sometimes can be correctly stated only after calculating the mix.

*Step 3.—*In this problem there is only one source of stabilizer, and, as previously stated, it contains 90 per cent total solids. Therefore, 90 per cent of the number of lbs. needed equals 3.6 lbs., the desired amount of stabilizer, (from Step 1). It follows that 3.6 lbs./0.90 = 4.0 lbs. stabilizer needed. This figure (4.0) is entered in the weight column of the proof sheet. Enter 3.6 lbs. in the stab. column of the proof sheet, and also in the total solids column.

Frodex, corn syrup solids, is used to supply one fourth of the desired sugar. Therefore

$$\frac{126 \text{ lbs. sugar}}{4} = 31.50 \text{ lbs.}$$

sugar to be obtained from Frodex which contains only 47 per cent sucrose equivalent. It follows that

$$\frac{31.5 \text{ lbs. sugar}}{0.47} = 67.02 \text{ lbs.,}$$

the amount of Frodex needed.

This figure (67.02) is entered in the weight column of the proof sheet. Enter the 31.5 lbs. of sugar in the sugar column. Multiplying, 67.02 × 96.5 per cent (per cent total solids in Frodex) gives 64.67 lbs. total solids to enter in the total solids column of the proof sheet.

Step 4.—To find the amount of sweetened condensed skim milk needed, use formula No. II. The figures to substitute in the formula are obtained as follows:

lbs. milk solids-not-fat needed = 90 lbs. (from proof sheet or step 1)
lbs. serum of mix = 626.48 lbs., obtained by calculations as follows:

first find the sum of:
    108.00 lbs fat (step 1 or 2)
      4.00 lbs. stabilizer (step 3)
     67.02 lbs. Frodex (step 3)
     94.50 lbs. sugar not supplied by Frodex (126 − 31.5 = 94.50 lbs.)
    ──────
    273.52 lbs. total

then subtract 273.52 lbs. from the desired total weight of the mix: 900.00 − 273.52 = 626.48 lbs. serum of the mix.

lbs. m.s.n.f. in 1 lb. sweetened condensed milk = 0.30, obtained by multiplying the 1 lb. by 30 per cent (the m.s.n.f. test).

lbs. serum in 1 lb. sweetened condensed milk = 0.58 lb. obtained by calculation as follows: first multiply 1 lb. sweetened condensed skim milk by 42 per cent sugar to get 0.42 lb. sugar. Then subtract the 0.42 lb. from the 1 lb. sweetened condensed skim milk. This leaves 0.58 lb. serum which includes only the water and milk solids-not-fat in the 1 lb. sweetened condensed skim milk.

These figures are substituted in formula No. II thus:

$$\frac{90.00 \text{ lbs. m.s.n.f.} - (626.48 \text{ lbs.} \times 0.09)}{0.30 - (0.58 \times 0.09)} \text{ lbs. sw. cond. skim milk needed}$$

The formula is solved by making the computations, thus:

$$\frac{90.00 \text{ lbs. m.s.n.f.} - (626.48 \text{ lbs.} \times 0.09)}{0.30 - (0.58 \times 0.09)} = \frac{90 - 56.38}{0.30 - 0.052} = \frac{33.62}{0.248} =$$

135.56 lbs. sweetened condensed skim milk needed.

This figure (135.56) is entered in the weight column of the proof sheet. Also, enter in their respective columns of the proof sheet the lbs. milk solids-not-fat, lbs. sugar, and lbs. total solids, which the 135.66 lbs. sweetened condensed skim milk contain. These are obtained by multiplication as follows:

$$135.56 \times 30\% \text{ m.s.n.f.} = 40.67 \text{ lbs. m.s.n.f.}$$

$$135.56 \times 42\% \text{ sugar} = 56.94 \text{ lbs. sugar}$$

$$135.56 \times 72\% \text{ t.s.} = 97.60 \text{ lbs. t.s.}$$

Step 5.—To calculate the amount of sugar needed, divide the remaining lbs. of sugar by the percentage of sugar in the sugar. In this problem, a total of 126 lbs. of sugar is desired, and in step 3 Frodex was calculated to supply 31.5 lbs. of this sugar. Also in step 4, the sweetened condensed skim milk was found to furnish 56.94 lbs. of sugar, making 88.44 lbs. of sugar supplied by the Frodex and the sweetened condensed skim milk. Subtracting the 88.44 lbs. from the 126 lbs. leaves 37.56 lbs. to be obtained from cane sugar which is 100 per cent sugar. Therefore it follows that 37.56/1.00 = 37.56 lbs. the amount of cane sugar needed. This figure can be entered in the proof sheet under weight, sugar and total solids.

Step 6.—The amount of cream needed is calculated with the aid of formula III. The figures to substitute in the formula are obtained as follows:

lbs. fat needed = 108 (from step 2)
lbs. milk and cream needed = 655.80 lbs., obtained by calculation as
  follows:
first find the sum of:
    4.00 lbs. stabilizer (step 3)
    67.02 lbs. Frodex (step 3)
    135.56 lbs. sweetened condensed skim milk (step 4)
    37.56 lbs. cane sugar (step 5)

    244.14 lbs. total

then subtract this 244.14 lbs. from the 900 lbs. desired weight of the mix. This leaves 655.86 lbs., the amount of milk and cream needed.

lbs. fat in 1 lb. cream = 0.40 lb., obtained by multiplying 1 lb. cream × 40%

lbs. fat in 1 lb. milk = 0.04 lb., obtained by a similar multiplication.

These figures are substituted in the formula to give:

$$\frac{108.00 \text{ lbs.} - (665.86 \text{ lbs.} \times 4\%)}{0.40 - 0.04} = \text{lbs. } 40\% \text{ cream needed}$$

In the process of solving, the formula becomes:

$$\frac{108.00 \text{ lbs} - 26.23 \text{ lbs.}}{0.36} = \frac{81.77}{0.36} = 227.13 \text{ lbs. } 40\% \text{ cream needed}$$

This number is entered in the weight column of the proof sheet. Also enter in their respective columns in the proof sheet, the lbs. fat, lbs. milk solids-not-fat, and lbs. total solids which are contained in the cream, thus:

$$227.13 \text{ lbs} \times 40\% \text{ fat} = 90.85 \text{ lbs. fat}$$

$$227.13 \text{ lbs} \times 5.35\% \text{ m.s.n.f.} = 12.15 \text{ lbs. m.n.s.f.}$$

$$90.85 \text{ plus } 12.15 = 103.00 \text{ lbs. t.s.}$$

Step 7.—The lbs. of milk needed are obtained by subtraction, thus:

	655.86 lbs. milk and cream (see step 6)
less:	277.13 lbs. cream (see step 6)
leaves:	428.73 lbs. milk needed

This 428.73 lbs. is entered in the weight column of the proof sheet. Also enter in their respective columns in the proof sheet, the lbs. fat, lbs. milk solids-not-fat and lbs. total solids contained in the milk.

$$428.73 \text{ lbs.} \times 4\% \text{ fat} = 17.15 \text{ lbs. fat}$$

$$428.73 \text{ lbs.} \times 8.79\% \text{ m.s.n.f.} = 37.68 \text{ lbs. m.s.n.f.}$$

$$17.15 \text{ plus } 37.68 = 54.83 \text{ lbs. t.s.}$$

Step 8.—Each column of the proof sheet is now totaled, and these totals should agree with the corresponding figure of the desired mix. In other words, the total weight of all the total fat supplied by all ingredients should equal the fat desired in the mix, and so on. However, if the decimals are not carried far enough, these totals may sometimes be slightly higher or slightly lower than the corresponding figure of the desired mix. This apparent error may be insignificant as shown by Step 9.

The percentage of total solids is computed by division, thus:

$$\frac{361.28}{900 \text{ lbs. mix}} = 0.4014 = 40.14\% \text{ t.s.}$$

Similarly compute the percentages of the remaining constituents, thus:

$$\frac{90.50 \text{ lbs. m.s.n.f.}}{900 \text{ lbs. mix}} = 0.1006 = 10.06\% \text{ m.s.n.f.}$$

and so on until the percentages for all the constituents in the mix are calculated.

Step 9.—The correctness of the calculations may be determined by comparing the calculated percentages for each constituent with the corresponding test of the desired mix. For example, in this problem, the calculated percentage of milk solids-not-fat is 10.06 per cent (see step 8), which is compared with the 10 per cent milk solids-not-fat of the desired mix. Since the difference between these two percentages is less than 0.1, it is not significant. Similar comparisons for each constituent show no significant differences, and therefore, the calculations are correct.

Step 10.—At this time it may be desirable to compute the cost of the mix by entering in the proof sheet the actual cost of each ingredient. Since the actual cost depends upon many factors, the figures are not included in this example.

The completed proof sheet for Problem 3 appears as follows:

Ingredients Used	Weight	Calculated Constituents					Cost
		Fat	M.s.n.f.	Sugar	Stab.	T.s.	
	lbs.	lbs.	lbs.	lbs.	lbs.	lbs	$
Stabilizer	4.00	. . .	. . .	. . .	3.60	3.60	
Frodex	67.02	. . .	. . .	31.50	. . .	64.68	
Sweetened condensed skim milk	135.56	. . .	40.67	56.94	. . .	97.61	
Cane sugar	37.56	. . .	. . .	37.56	. . .	37.56	
Cream, 40%	227.13	90.85	12.15	. . .	. . .	103.00	
Milk, 4%	428.73	17.15	37.68	. . .	. . .	54.83	
Total, lbs.	900.00	108.00	90.50	126.00	3.60	361.28	
Calculated, %		12.00	10.06	14.00	0.40	40.14	
Check with desired wt.	900.00[1]	108.00	90.00	126.00	3.60	327.60[2]	
and %		12.0	10.0	14.0	0.4	36.4	

[1] Includes the lbs. total solids and water which sometimes can be accurately stated only after calculating the mix.

There are times when it is necessary to use up odd lots of products which result from variation from the planned production schedule. The odd lots may include ice cream mixes of different composition cream, condensed milk, whole milk, skim milk or other products. These products may best be utilized in making a mix of desired composition. The calculations shown in Problem 4 illustrate such a case.

Problem 4: In Which Left-Overs Are Used

A 900 lbs. mix testing 12 per cent, 10 per cent milk solids-not-fat, 14 per cent sugar, 0.5 per cent egg solids, and 0.3 per cent stabilizer is desired. The following materials are "left-overs" to be used to avoid loss: 40 lbs. frozen 50 per cent cream, 90 lbs. 30 per cent cream, 25 lbs. sweetened condensed skim milk (42 per cent sugar, 28 per cent milk solids-not-fat), 100 lbs. 3 per cent milk, and 30 lbs. Sweetose.

The following ingredients are also available: stabilizer, cane sugar, frozen egg yolk (33 per cent fat, 50 per cent t.s.), condensed skim milk (32 per cent t.s.), 40 per cent cream, and 4 per cent milk.

The use of odd lots or leftovers as referred to in problem 4 does not imply in any way the use of inferior quality products. It should be understood that the odd lots of products used in ice cream mixes should be of the highest quality. Accurate information of the composition of such products must be available if these small lots are to be used to the best advantage.

SOLUTION:

This problem shows how to make use of "left-overs" or relatively small amounts of several ingredients. The procedure can also be used when there are several lots of cream, none large enough to make the entire batch of mix.

Step 1.—

Available Ingredients	Desired Mix
Frozen cream, 50% fat, 4.45% m.s.n.f.	Fat, 12% of 900 lbs. = 108 lbs.
Cream, 30% fat, 6.24% m.s.n.f.	M.s.n.f., 10% of 900 lbs. = 90 lbs.
Sweetened condensed skim milk, 28% m.s.n.f., 42% sugar	Sugar, 14% of 900 lbs. = 126 lbs.
Milk, 3% fat, 8.33% m.s.n.f.	Egg solids, 0.5% of 900 lbs. = 4.50 lbs.
Sweetose, 67% sugar, 83% t.s.	Stabilizer, 0.3% of 900 lbs. = 2.70 lbs.
Stabilizer, 90% t.s.	
Frozen egg yolk, 33% fat, 50% t.s.	
Cane sugar	
Condensed skim milk, 32% m.s.n.f., 32% t.s.	
Cream, 40% fat, 5.35% m.s.n.f.	
Milk, 4% fat, 8.79% m.s.n.f.	

Step 2.—Proof Sheet Form:

Ingredients Used	Weight	Calculated Constituents						Cost
		Fat	M.s.n.f.	Sugar	Egg Solids	Stab.	T.s.	
	lbs.	lbs.	lbs.	lbs.	lbs.	lbs.	lbs.	$
Frozen cream								
Cream, 30%								
Sweetened condensed skim milk								
Milk, 3%								
Sweetose								
Stabilizer								
Frozen egg yolk								
Cane sugar								
Condensed skim								
Cream, 40%								
Milk, 4%								
Total, lbs.								
Calculated, %								
Check with desired wt.	900.00[1]	108.00	90.00	126.00	4.50	2.70	331.20	
and %		12.0	10.0	14.0	0.5	0.3	36.8	

[1] Includes the lbs. total solids and water which sometimes can be accurately stated only after calculating the mix.

Step 3.—Since there are several ingredients to be completely used, enter the amount of each of these immediately in the weight column of the proof sheet. Then compute the lb. of each constituent contained in each ingredient and enter these amounts in their respective columns of the proof sheet. For instance, 40 lbs. frozen cream multiplied by its fat test (50%) gives 20 lbs. fat, and multiplied by its milk solids-not-fat test (4.45%) gives 1.78 lbs. milk solids-not-fat and multiplied by its total solids test (54.45%) gives 21.78 lbs. total solids. Similar multiplications are made for the 30 per cent cream, sweetened condensed skim milk, 3 per cent milk, and Sweetose.

When these data have been entered in the proof sheet it is apparent that no stabilizer has been obtained, and that 2.7 lbs. is needed. In this problem there is only one source of stabilizer, and it contains 90 per cent total solids. It follows that 2.7 lbs./0.90 = 3.0 stabilizer product is needed. This figure (3.0) is entered in the weight column of the proof sheet. The 2.7 lbs. of stabilizer is entered in the stabilizer column, and also in the total solids column of the proof sheet.

Again referring to the partially completed proof sheet, it is apparent that 4.50 lbs. of egg solids must be obtained from the frozen egg yolk which is 50 per cent total solids and therefore 50 per cent egg solids. It follows that

$$\frac{4.50 \text{ lbs.}}{0.50} = 9.00 \text{ lbs. the amount of frozen egg yolk needed.}$$

This figure (9.0) is entered in the weight column of the proof sheet. The following multiplications give the amount of each constituent furnished by the frozen egg yolk:

$$9.0 \text{ lbs.} \times 33\% \text{ fat} = 2.97 \text{ lbs. fat}$$
$$9.0 \text{ lbs.} \times 50\% \text{ egg solids} = 4.50 \text{ lbs. egg solids}$$
$$9.0 \text{ lbs.} \times 50\% \text{ t.s.} = 4.50 \text{ lbs. t.s.}$$

These amounts of fat, egg solids, and total solids are entered in their respective columns of the proof sheet.

Once again refer to the partially completed proof sheet. It now appears that all of the stabilizer and all of the egg solids have been provided for. Also, it appears that the sweetened condensed skim milk and the Sweetose will furnish 30.60 lbs. of sugar leaving some to come from the cane sugar which is the only remaining source of sugar. By subtracting the 30.60 lbs. from the desired 126 lbs. leaves 95.40 lbs. sugar to be obtained from cane sugar which is 100 per cent sugar. It follows that 95.40 lbs./1.00 = 95.40 lbs., the amount of cane sugar needed. This figure (95.40) is entered in the weight, the sugar, and total solids columns of the proof sheet.

By adding each column as it now stands, it appears that provision has been made for 392.4 lbs. total weight, 52.97 lbs. fat, 22.73 lbs. milk solids-not-fat, 126 lbs. sugar, 4.50 lbs. egg solids, and 2.7 lbs. stabilizer. Subtracting each of these from its corresponding figures in the desired mix leaves 507.60 lbs. total weight, 55.03 lbs. fat, and 67.27 lbs. milk solids-not-fat. These figures will be used in the following steps:

Step 4.—To find the amount of condensed skim milk needed, it will be necessary to use formula No. I. The figures to substitute in the formula are obtained as follows:

lbs. m.s.n.f. needed = 67.27 (see end of step 3).
lbs. serum of mix = 452.57 lbs., obtained by substraction as follows:

507.60 lbs. total weight
less: 55.03 lbs. fat
_____
leaves: 452.57 lbs. serum

lbs. m.s.n.f. in 1 lb. condensed skim milk = 0.32, obtained by multiplying 1 lb. × 32% which is the m.s.n.f. test.

These figures are substituted in the formula, thus:

$$\frac{67.27 \text{ lbs. m.s.n.f.} - (452.57 \text{ lbs.} \times 0.09)}{0.32 - 0.09} =$$

lbs. condensed skim milk needed

The formula is solved by making the computations, thus:

$$\frac{67.27 - (452.57 \times 0.09)}{0.32 - 0.09} = \frac{67.27 - 40.73}{0.23} = \frac{26.54}{0.23} =$$

115.39 lbs. cond. skim needed.

Therefore 115.39 condensed skim milk is entered in the weight column of the proof sheet. Also enter in their respective columns of the proof sheet, the lbs. milk solids-not-fat and the lbs. total solids which are contained in the condensed skim milk. These are obtained by multiplication as follows:

$$115.39 \text{ lbs.} \times 32\% \text{ m.s.n.f.} = 36.92 \text{ lbs. m.s.n.f.}$$

$$115.39 \text{ lbs.} \times 32\% \text{ t.s.} = 36.92 \text{ lbs. t.s.}$$

Step 5.—The amount of sugar was calculated as part of Step 3.

Step 6.—To find the amount of cream needed, it will be necessary to use formula No. III. The figures to substitute in the formula are obtained as follows:

lbs. fat needed = 55.03 (see end of step 3).

lbs. milk and cream needed = 392.21 lbs., obtained by subtraction as follows:

	507.60 lbs. total weight
less:	115.39 lbs. cond. skim
leaves:	392.21 lbs. milk and cream

lbs. fat in 1 lb. cream = 0.40 lb., obtained by multiplying 1 lb. × 40% = 0.40 lb. fat.

lbs. fat in 1 lb. milk = 0.04, obtained by a similar multiplication.

These figures are substituted in the formula, thus,

$$\frac{55.03 \text{ lbs. fat} - (392.21 \text{ lbs.} \times 4\%)}{0.40 - 0.04} = \text{lbs. } 40\% \text{ cream}$$

In the process of solving, the formula becomes:

$$\frac{55.03 - 15.69}{0.40 - 0.04} = \frac{39.34}{0.36} = 109.28 \text{ lbs. } 40\% \text{ cream needed.}$$

Therefore this figure (109.28) lbs. 40 per cent cream is entered in the weight column of the proof sheet. Also enter in their respective columns of the proof sheet, the lbs. fat, lbs. milk solids-not-fat and lbs. total solids contained in the cream. These are obtained by the following multiplications:

$$109.28 \text{ lbs.} \times 40\% \text{ fat} = 43.71 \text{ lbs. fat}$$

$$109.28 \text{ lbs.} \times 5.35\% \text{ m.s.n.f.} = 5.85 \text{ lbs. m.s.n.f.}$$

$$109.28 \text{ lbs.} \times 45.35\% \text{ t.s.} = 49.56 \text{ lbs. t.s.}$$

Step 7.—The lbs. of milk needed are computed by subtraction thus:

	392.21 lbs. milk and cream (from step 6)
less:	109.28 lbs. cream (from step 6)
leaves:	282.93 lbs. milk needed

This figure (282.93) lbs. 4 per cent milk is entered in the weight column of the proof sheet. The following multiplications give the lbs. fat, lbs. milk solids-not-fat, and lbs. total solids which the milk contains, so that these figures may be entered in their respective columns of the proof sheet.

$$282.93 \text{ lbs.} \times 4\% \text{ fat} = 11.32 \text{ lbs. fat}$$

$$282.93 \text{ lbs.} \times 8.79\% \text{ m.s.n.f.} = 24.87 \text{ lbs. m.s.n.f.}$$

$$282.93 \text{ lbs} \times 12.79\% \text{ t.s.} = 36.19 \text{ lbs. t.s.}$$

Step 8.—Each column of the proof sheet is now totaled and these totals should agree with the corresponding figure of the desired mix. In other words, the total weight of all ingredients should equal the desired weight of the mix, the total fat supplied by all ingredients should equal the fat desired in the mix, and so on. However, if the decimals are not carried far enough, these totals may sometimes be slightly higher or slightly lower than the corresponding figure of the desired mix. This apparent error may be insignificant, as shown by step 9.

The total solids test is computed by division, thus:

$$\frac{333.40 \text{ lbs. t.s.}}{900 \text{ lbs. mix}} = 0.3704 \text{ or } 37.04\% \text{ t.s.}$$

$$\frac{90.37 \text{ m.s.n.f.}}{900 \text{ lbs. mix}} = 0.1004 \text{ or } 10.04\% \text{ m.s.n.f.}$$

and similarly calculate the percentages of fat, sugar, egg solids and stabilizer.

Step 9.—The correctness of the calculations may be determined by comparing the calculated percentage for each constituent with the corresponding test of the desired mix. For example, in this problem, the calculated percentage of milk solids-not-fat is 10.04 per cent (see step 8) which is compared with 10 per cent m.s.n.f. of the desired mix. Since the difference between these two percentages is less than 0.1, it is not significant. Similar comparisons for each constituent show no significant differences, and therefore the calculations are correct.

Step 10.—Since the actual cost depends upon many factors, cost figures are not calculated in this problem.

The completed proof sheet for Problem 4 appears as follows:

Ingredients Used	Weight	Calculated Constituents						
		Fat	M.s.n.f.	Sugar	Egg solids	Stab.	T.s.	Cost
	lbs.	lbs.	lbs.	lbs.	lbs.	lbs.	lbs.	$
Cream, Frozen 50%	40.00	20.00	1.78	...	...	...	21.78	
Cream 30%	90.00	27.00	5.62	...	...	...	32.62	
Sweetened condensed skim milk	25.00	...	7.00	10.50	...	...	17.50	
Milk 3%	100.00	3.00	8.33	...	...	...	11.33	
Sweetose	30.00	...	...	20.10	...	...	24.90[2]	
Stabilizer	3.00	...	...	...	...	2.70	2.70	
Egg yolk, frozen	9.00	2.97	..	...	4.50	...	4.50[2]	
Cane sugar	95.40	...	...	95.40	...	...	95.40	
Condensed skim milk	115.39	...	36.92	...	...	...	36.92	
Cream, 40%	109.28	43.71	5.85	...	...	...	49.56	
Milk, 4%	282.93	11.32	24.87	...	...	...	36.19	
Total, lbs.	900.00	108.00	90.37	126.00	4.50	2.70	333.40	
Calculated, %	...	12.00	10.04	14.00	0.50	0.30	37.04	
Check with desired wt.	900.00[1]	108.00	90.00	126.00	4.50	2.7	331.20	
and %		12.0	10.0	14.0	0.5	0.3	36.8	

[1] Includes the lbs. total solids and water which sometimes can be accurately stated only after calculating the mix.

[2] The apparent total solids discrepancies in the Sweetose and frozen egg items are due to the fact that (1) Sweetose contains more solids than cane sugar equivalent because the solids are less sweet than cane sugar, and (2) the fat in the frozen eggs was counted twice in the "fat" and "egg solids" columns but not in the total solids column.

CHAPTER 9

Restandardizing and Calculating Some Unusual Mixes

RESTANDARDIZING A MIX OR CORRECTING MIXES HAVING AN UNDESIRED COMPOSITION

Sometimes when a mix has been made it is found by analysis to have a composition different from that which is desired, and it should be designated "incorrect mix." This condition can easily be corrected by restandardizing; i.e., by adding sufficient quantities of one or several ingredients, to give the desired composition. This obviously increases the total amount of the mix and requires a vat large enough to hold the added ingredients, plus the incorrect mix so that they may be properly blended. Usually the total weight of all the added ingredients will not be more than one-third of the weight of the incorrect mix. For example: the total amount of sugar, cream, stabilizer, etc., necessary to restandardize 900 pounds of incorrect mix will usually be less than 300 pounds.

If the vat space is limited, it may be convenient to store a part (usually half) of the incorrect mix while the other part is used as one ingredient of the next batch of mix, thus distributing the incorrect mix between the two next batches. This method is illustrated by problem 5.

If vat space is available, the entire incorrect mix may be used as one ingredient of a batch having a total weight approximately one-third larger than the weight of the incorrect mix. In this manner the calculations will be similar to problem 5, and a smaller amount of added ingredients will be used.

Problem 5: Restandardizing an Incorrect Mix

Calculate the amount of ingredients required to make 1800 lbs. of mix testing 14 per cent fat, 10 per cent milk solids-not-fat, 14 per cent sugar and 0.3 per cent stabilizer. We want to use 900 lbs. (half of a batch not correctly made) of mix testing 10 per cent fat, 11 per cent milk solids-not-fat, 14 per cent sugar, 0.5 per cent stabilizer and 35.5 per cent total solids. In addition to this mix there is available 40 per cent cream, 4 per cent milk, sweetened condensed skim milk (42 per cent sugar, 30 per cent milk solids-not-fat), cane sugar and stabilizer.

SOLUTION:

This problem is solved in the same manner as problem 4, using the formulas and procedure steps that are used for other complex mixes.

110

Step 1.—

Available Ingredients	Desired Mix
Incorrect mix, 10% fat, 11% m.s.n.f. 14% sugar, 0.5% stab., 35.5% t.s. Stabilizer, 90% t.s. Sweetened condensed skim milk, 30% m.s.n.f., 42% sugar Cane sugar Cream, 40% fat, 5.35% m.s.n.f. Milk, 4% fat, 8.79% m.s.n.f.	Fat, 14% of 1800 lbs. = 252 lbs. M.s.n.f., 10% of 1800 lbs. = 180 lbs. Sugar, 14% of 1800 lbs. = 252 lbs. Stab., 0.3% of 1800 lbs. = 5.4 lbs.

Step 2. Proof Sheet Form:

Ingredients Used	Weight	Calculated Constituents					Cost
		Fat	M.s.n.f.	Sugar	Stab.	T.s.	
	lbs.	lbs.	lbs.	lbs.	lbs.	lbs.	$
Incorrect mix							
Stabilizer							
Sweetened condensed skim milk							
Cane sugar							
Cream, 40%							
Milk, 4%							
Total, lbs.							
Calculated, %							
Check with desired wt.	1800.00[1]	252.00	180.00	252.00	5.40	689.40	
and %		14.0	10.0	14.0	0.3	38.3	

[1] Includes the lbs. total solids and water which sometimes can be accurately stated only after calculating the mix.

Step 3.—Since 900 lbs. of incorrect mix is all going to be used in this problem, it may be entered in the proof sheet immediately. The amount of each constituent contained in the incorrect mix is obtained by the following multiplications and entered in their respective columns of the proof sheet.

$$900 \text{ lbs.} \times 10\% \text{ fat} = 90.00 \text{ lbs. fat}$$

$$900 \text{ lbs.} \times 11\% \text{ m.s.n.f.} = 99.00 \text{ lbs. m.s.n.f.}$$

$$900 \text{ lbs} \times 14\% \text{ sugar} = 126.00 \text{ lbs. sugar}$$

$$900 \text{ lbs.} \times 0.5\% \text{ stabilizer} = 4.50 \text{ lbs. stab.}$$

$$900 \text{ lbs.} \times 35.5\% \text{ t.s.} = 319.50 \text{ lbs. t.s.}$$

Now subtract each of these amounts from the corresponding figure of the desired mix, which leaves 900 lbs. mix, 162 lbs. fat, 81 lbs. milk solids-not-fat, 126 lbs. sugar, 0.9 lb. stab.   Now proceed to calculate the amounts of the remaining ingredients needed to make 900 lbs. of mix containing 162 lbs. fat, 81 lbs. milk solids-not-fat, 126 lbs. sugar and 0.9 lb. stabilizer.

There is only one source of stabilizer and it contains 90% t.s.   Therefore the 0.9 lb. of needed stabilizer will require 1.0 lb. stabilizer (0.9/0.90 = 1.0 lb.)   This figure (1.0) is entered in the weight column of the proof sheet.   Also enter 0.9 lb. in the stabilizer column, and in the total solids column of the proof sheet.

Step 4.—To find the amount of sweetened condensed skim milk needed, it will be necessary to use formula No. II.   The figures to substitute in the formula are obtained as follows:

Lbs. m.s.n.f. needed = 81 (see step 3)
Lbs. serum of mix = 611 lbs., obtained by the following calculations:
first find the sum of:
162 lbs. fat (see step 3)
126 lbs. sugar (see step 3)
  1 lb. stabilizer (see step 3)
—————
289 lbs. total

then subtract 289 lbs. from 900 lbs. (the remaining total weight as shown in step 3), and this leaves 611 lbs., the weight of the serum.
Lb. m.s.n.f. in 1 lb. sweetened condensed skim milk = 0.30, obtained by multiplying 1 lb. sweetened condensed skim milk by 30% (its m.n.s.f. test).
Lb. serum in 1 lb. sweetened condensed milk = 0.58 lb., obtained as follows:
1 lb. sweetened condensed skim milk $\times$ 42% sugar = 0.42 lb. sugar, then,
1 lb. sweetened condensed skim milk containing 0.42 lb. sugar = 0.58 lb. serum

These figures are substituted in formula No. II thus:

$$\frac{81.00 \text{ lbs.} - (611.00 \times 0.09)}{0.30 - (0.58 \times 0.09)} = \text{lbs. sweetened condensed skim milk needed}$$

As the computations are made this formula becomes:

$$\frac{81.00 - 54.99}{0.300 - 0.052} = \frac{26.01}{0.248} =$$

104.88 lbs. sweetened condensed skim milk needed

This figure is entered in the weight column of the proof sheet. Also enter in their respective columns of the proof sheet, the lbs. milk solids-not-fat, lbs. sugar, and lbs. total solids which the 104.88 lbs. sweetened condensed skim milk contain. These are obtained by multiplication as follows:

$$104.88 \text{ lbs.} \times 30\% \text{ m.s.n.f.} = 31.46 \text{ lbs. m.s.n.f.}$$

$$104.88 \text{ lbs.} \times 42\% \text{ sugar} = 44.05 \text{ lbs. sugar}$$

$$104.88 \text{ lbs.} \times 72\% \text{ t.s.} = 75.51 \text{ lbs. t.s.}$$

Step 5.—To calculate the amount of sugar needed, first subtract the 44.05 lbs. sugar supplied by sweetened condensed skim milk (see step 4) from the 126 lbs. sugar needed (see step 3). This leaves 81.95 lbs. sugar to be obtained from cane sugar which is 100% sugar. This means that 81.95 lbs. of cane sugar is needed and that figure can be entered in the proof sheet under weight, sugar, and total solids.

Step 6.—The amount of cream needed is calculated with the aid of formula No. III. The figures to substitute in the formula are obtained as follows:

Lbs. fat needed = 162 (see step 3).
Lbs. milk and cream needed = 712.17 lbs., obtained by calculations as follows:
first find the sum of:
    1.0 lb. stabilizer
    104.88 lbs. sweetened condensed skim milk
    81.95 lbs. cane sugar

    187.83 lbs total
then subtract 187.83 from 900 lbs. (the remaining total weight as shown in step 3), this leaves 712.17 lbs., the weight of milk and cream needed.
Lb. fat in 1 lb. cream = 0.40 lb., obtained by multiplying 1 lb. cream × 40% fat.
Lb. fat in 1 lb. milk = 0.04 lb., obtained by a similar multiplication.

These figures are substituted in formula No. III thus:

$$\frac{162.00 \text{ lbs.} - (712.17 \text{ lbs.} \times 4\%)}{0.40 - 0.04} = \text{lbs. } 40\% \text{ cream needed}$$

As the computations are made, this formula becomes

$$\frac{162 - 28.49}{0.36} = \frac{133.51}{0.36} = 370.86 \text{ lbs. } 40\% \text{ cream needed}$$

This figure (370.86 lbs.) is entered in the weight column of the proof sheet. Also enter in their respective columns of the proof sheet the lbs. fat, lbs. m.s.n.f., and lbs. total solids which are contained in the cream, thus:

$$370.86 \text{ lbs.} \times 40\% = 148.34 \text{ lbs. fat}$$

$$370.86 \text{ lbs.} \times 5.35\% \text{ m.s.n.f.} = 19.84 \text{ lbs. m.s.n.f.}$$

$$370.86 \times 45.35\% \text{ t.s.} = 168.19 \text{ lbs. t.s.}$$

Step 7.—The lbs. of milk needed are obtained by subtraction, thus:

less: 712.17 lbs. milk and cream (see step 6)
               370.86 lbs. cream (see step 6)

leaves: 341.31 lbs. milk needed

This figure (341.31) is entered in the weight column of the proof sheet. Also enter in their respective columns of the proof sheet the lbs. fat, lbs. milk solids-not-fat and lbs. total solids which are contained in the milk. These are obtained by the following multiplications:

$$341.31 \text{ lbs.} \times 4\% \text{ fat} = 13.65 \text{ lbs. fat}$$

$$341.31 \text{ lbs.} \times 8.79\% \text{ m.s.n.f.} = 30.00 \text{ lbs. m.s.n.f.}$$

$$341.31 \text{ lbs.} \times 12.79\% \text{ t.s.} = 43.65 \text{ lbs. t.s.}$$

Step 8.—Each column of the proof sheet is now totaled, and these totals should agree with the corresponding figure of the desired mix. See explanation, problem 4. Step 8.

The total solids test is computed by division, thus:

$$\frac{689.80 \text{ lbs. t.s.}}{1800 \text{ lbs. mix}} = 0.3832 = 38.32\% \text{ t.s.}$$

Likewise compute the "calculated %" for each of the constituents, thus:

$$\frac{180.30 \text{ lbs. m.s.n.f.}}{1800 \text{ lbs. mix}} = 0.1001 = 10.01\% \text{ m.s.n.f.}$$

Step 9.—The correctness of the calculations may be determined by comparing the calculated per cent for each constituent with the corresponding test of the desired mix. For example, in this problem, the "calculated per cent" milk solids-not-fat is 10.01 per cent (see step 8) which is compared with the 10 per cent milk solids-not-fat of the desired mix. Since the difference between these two percentages is less than 0.1 it is not significant. Similar comparisons for each constituent show no significant differences, and therefore the calculations are correct.

Step 10.—Calculate the actual cost if desired and enter in proof sheet.

The completed proof sheet for Problem 5 appears as follows:

Ingredients Used	Weight	Fat	M.s.n.f.	Sugar	Stab.	T.s.	Cost
	lbs.	*lbs.*	*lbs.*	*lbs.*	*lbs.*	*lbs.*	$
Incorrect mix	900.00	90.00	99.00	126.00	4.50	319.50	
Stabilizer	1.00	...	...	...	0.90	0.90	
Sweetened condensed skim milk	104.88	...	31.46	44.05	...	75.51	
Cane sugar	81.95	...	...	81.95	...	81.95	
Cream, 40%	370.86	148.35	19.84	...	...	168.19	
Milk, 4%	341.31	13.65	30.00	...	...	43.65	
Total, lbs.	1800.00	252.00	180.30	252.00	5.40	689.80	
Calculated, %		14.00	10.01	14.00	0.30	38.32	
Check with desired wt.	1800.00[1]	252.00	180.00	252.00	5.40	689.40	
and %		14.0	10.0	14.0	0.3	38.3	

Header spanning Fat through T.s.: *Calculated Constituents*

[1] Includes the lbs. total solids and water which sometimes can be accurately stated only after calculating the mix.

UNUSUAL COMPLEX MIXES

Sometimes, on rare occasions, an unusual combination of ingredients for an ice cream mix will be selected for reasons of economy. These unusual combinations make the calculations somewhat longer and slightly more complicated. They can be grouped in two general types, illustrated by problems 6 and 7.

A. When no dry source of sucrose is available and there are three sources of milk solids-not-fat, one of which is a sweetened condensed milk product.

Problem 6:

Calculate the amount of ingredients needed to make 900 lbs. mix testing 12 per cent fat, 10 per cent milk solids-not-fat, 14 per cent sugar, and 0.4 per cent stabilizer. The available ingredients are: 40 per cent cream, 4 per cent milk, Dri-Sweet 47 per cent sucrose equivalent, 64.68 per cent total solids to supply $1/4$ of the sugar, sweetened condensed whole milk (8 per cent fat, 42 per cent sugar, 23 per cent milk solids-not-fat), liquid sugar (67 per cent sugar, 67 per cent total solids) and stabilizer.

SOLUTION:

This complex mix has three sources of sugar, three sources of milk solids-not-fat, and three sources of fat. Therefore the calculations will be made using formulas No. II and No. III.

Steps 1 through 3.—These steps completed as in problem 3 will yield a proof sheet as follows:

Ingredients Used	Weight	Calculated Constituents					Cost
		Fat	M.s.n.f.	Sugar	Stab.	T.s.	
	lbs.	lbs.	lb .	lbs.	lbs.	lbs.	$
Stabilizer	4.0	. . .	. . .	. . .	3.6	3.6	
Dri-Sweet	67.02	. . .	. . .	31.5	. . .	64.68	
Sweetened condensed whole milk							
Liquid sugar							
Cream, 40%							
Milk, 4%							
Total, lbs.							
Calculated, %							
Check with desired wt.	900.00[1]	108.00	90.00	126.00	3.60	327.60	
and %		12.00	10.0	14.0	0.4	36.4	

[1] Includes the lbs. total solids and water which sometimes can be accurately stated only after calculating the mix.

Step 4.—To find the amount of sweetened condensed whole milk needed, use formula No. II. The figures to substitute in the formula are obtained as follows:

Lbs. m.s.n.f. needed = 90 (from step 2)

Lbs. serum of mix = 605 lbs., obtained by calculation as follows:

First add:

108.00 lbs. fat

4.00 lbs. stabilizer

67.02 lbs. Dri-Sweet

94.50 lbs. sugar (from liquid sugar and sweetened condensed whole milk)

21.48 lbs. estimated water in the liquid sugar used

295.00 lbs. totaled, that are not serum

then: 900 lbs. mix — 295 lbs. = 605 lbs. serum of the mix

Notice that in formula No. II, it is necessary to use the lbs. of sugar **source** and in this problem part of the sugar **source** is liquid sugar. Therefore part of the 94.50 lbs. sugar will come from liquid sugar and the lbs. of sugar **source** will be greater than 94.50 lbs. It is impossible at this time to tell how much greater it will be, so an estimate is made and the figure 21.48 lbs. is used. Any other estimate will be equally satisfactory.

Lbs. m.s.n.f. in 1.0 lb. sweetened condensed whole milk:

 1.0 lb. sweetened condensed whole milk contains 23% m.s.n.f. or 0.23 lb. m.s.n.f.

Lb. serum in 1.0 lb. sweetened condensed whole milk:

 1.0 lb. sweetened condensed whole milk contains 42% sugar or 0.42 lb. sugar

 1.0 lb. sweetened condensed whole milk also contains 8% fat or 0.08 lb. fat

Then 1.0 lb. sweetened condensed whole milk — (0.42 lb. sugar + 0.08 lb. fat) = 1.0 — 0.50 = 0.50 lb. serum in 1.0 lb. sweetened condensed whole milk.

Now substitute these figures in formula No. II and complete the calculations, thus:

$$\frac{90 - (605 \times 0.09)}{0.23 - (0.50 \times 0.09)} = \frac{90 - 54.45}{0.23 - 0.045} = \frac{35.55}{0.185} =$$

$$192.16 \text{ lbs. sweetened condensed whole milk}$$

Since the calculation involved an estimate, this figure 192.16 lbs. is probably incorrect and therefore it must be tested for accuracy before proceeding with other calculations.

Step 4a.—The correctness of the lbs. of sweetened condensed whole milk is tested as follows:

 192.16 lbs. sweetened condensed whole milk × 42% sugar = 80.707 lbs. sugar it will supply

 94.50 lbs. sugar (from liquid sugar and sweetened condensed whole milk) — 80.707 = 13.793 lbs. sugar to obtain from liquid sugar

It follows that

$$\frac{13.793 \text{ lbs.}}{0.67} = 20.59 \text{ lbs. liquid sugar needed}$$

Now add

 20.59 lbs. liquid sugar

 80.71 lbs. sugar supplied by the 192.16 lbs. sweetened condensed whole milk

 ———
 101.30 lbs.

Also add

 94.50 lbs. sugar (supplied by sweetened condensed whole milk and liquid sugar)

 21.48 lbs. estimated water (part of liquid sugar used)

 ———
 115.98 lbs.

Compare the 101.30 lbs. with the 115.98 lbs. Since the difference between these figures is more than 1 lb., it proves that the figure 192.16 lbs. sweetened condensed whole milk is wrong because the estimated 21.48 lbs. was wrong.

Therefore steps 4 and 4a must be repeated using a revised estimate in place of the figure 21.48 lbs. The revised estimate must be such as to make the total (94.50 plus the new estimate), somewhere between 101.30 lbs. and 115.98 lbs. This time assume the estimated water to be 8.0 lbs. which will give a total (94.50 + 8.0) of 102.50 lbs.

Now repeat step 4, using this revised estimate.

Lbs. serum of mix = 618.48 lbs., obtained by calculation as follows:
first add:

> 108.00 lbs. fat
> 4.00 lbs. stabilizer
> 67.02 lbs. Dri-Sweet
> 94.50 lbs. sugar (from liquid sugar and sweetened condensed whole milk)
> 8.00 lbs. estimated water in liquid sugar used
> _____
> 281.52 lbs. total, that are not serum

then:

$$900 \text{ lbs. mix} - 281.52 \text{ lbs.} = 618.48 \text{ lbs. serum of mix}$$

Then substituting in the formula:

$$\frac{90 - (618.48 \times 0.09)}{0.23 - (0.50 \times 0.09)} = \frac{34.34}{0.185} =$$

185.60 lbs. sweetened condensed whole milk needed

Repeating step 4a to test the correctness of this new answer:

$$185.60 \text{ lbs.} \times 0.42 = 77.95 \text{ lbs. sugar from } 185.60 \text{ lbs. sweetened condensed whole milk}$$

$$\frac{94.50 - 77.952}{0.67} = \frac{16.548}{0.67} = 24.70 \text{ lbs. liquid sugar needed}$$

Adding 77.95 lbs. and 24.70 = 102.65 lbs. Compare with 94.50 + 8 lbs. = 102.50 lbs.

The comparison shows that the difference is less than 1.0 lb., and therefore the figure 185.60 lbs. sweetened condensed whole milk is correct.

Sometimes it is necessary to make a second or third revision of the estimate, each time repeating steps 4 and 4a.

When the correct figure for sweetened condensed whole milk has been found, the proof sheet can be filled in with values found by multiplication:

$$185.60 \text{ lbs.} \times 42\% = 77.954 \text{ lbs. sugar}$$

$$185.60 \text{ lbs.} \times 8\% = 14.848 \text{ lbs. fat}$$

$$185.60 \text{ lbs.} \times 23\% = 42.689 \text{ lbs. m.s.n.f.}$$

$$185.60 \text{ lbs.} \times 73\% = 135.491 \text{ lbs. t.s.}$$

Step 5.—The amount of liquid sugar needed as determined in step 4a is 24.70 lbs.

These 24.70 lbs. contain 67% sugar or $24.70 \times 0.67 = 16.55$ lbs. sugar. This figure (16.55) can be entered in the sugar and the total solids column of the proof sheet.

Step 6.—To find the amount of cream needed, use formula No. III.

Lbs. fat needed = 93.15 lbs., obtained as follows:

	108.00 lbs. total fat desired
less:	14.85 lbs. supplied from the 185.60 lbs. sweetened condensed whole milk
leaves:	93.15 lbs. fat needed from milk and cream

Lbs. milk and cream needed = 618.68 lbs., obtained as follows:

first add:

4.00 lbs. stabilizer
67.02 lbs. Dri-Sweet
185.60 lbs. sweetened condensed whole milk
24.70 lbs. liquid sugar

281.32 lbs. total

then

900 lbs. mix − 281.32 lbs. = 618.68 lbs. milk and cream needed

Substituting in formula No. III:

$$\frac{93.15 - (618.68 \times 0.04)}{0.40 - 0.04} = \frac{68.405}{0.36} = 190.01 \text{ lbs. } 40\% \text{ cream}$$

This 190.01 lbs. cream supplies 76.00 lbs. fat, 10.165 lbs. m.n.s.f. and 86.165 lbs. total solids which can be entered in their respective columns in the proof sheet.

Each column of the proof sheet is totaled and these totals should agree with the corresponding of the desired mix. The total pounds of each constituent divided by 900 lbs. gives the percentage of each constituent of the mix.

Steps 7 through 10 are similar to the same steps in problem 3. When completed they yield a proof sheet for problem 6 as follows:

| Ingredients Used | Weight | Calculated Constituents | | | | | |
		Fat	M.s.n.f.	Sugar	Stab.	T.s.	Cost
	lbs.	lbs.	lbs.	lbs.	lbs.	lbs.	$
Stabilizer	4.00	...	...	...	3.60	3.60	
Dri-Sweet	67.02	...	...	31.50	...	64.68	
Sweetened condensed whole milk	185.60	14.85	42.69	77.95	...	135.49	
Liquid sugar, 67%	24.70	...	...	16.55	...	16.55	
Cream, 40%	190.01	76.00	10.17	...	...	86.17	
Milk, 4%	428.67	17.15	37.68	...	...	54.83	
Total, lbs.	900.00	108.00	90.54	126.00	3.60	361.32	
Calculated, %		12.0	10.06	14.0	0.4	40.15	
Check with desired wt.	900.00	108.00	90.00	126.00	3.60	327.60	
and %		12.0	10.0	14.0	0.4	36.4	

B. The second type of unusual combination of ingredients occurs when sweet cream and a condensed whole milk product are used as the only sources of milk solids. This includes the use of sweet cream with such products as sweetened condensed whole milk, whole milk powder, and sweet cream buttermilk powder.

This type problem may involve many ingredients and there may be four or more sources of fat or milk solids-not-fat. Such problems are usually made to the desired volume by the use of water. It is also necessary to use specified amounts of certain products. The calculation procedure involves determining the amounts of constituents supplied by products of which amounts are specified. The amounts of products supplying the remaining required stabilizer, fats, milk solids-not-fat, sugar and the amount of water needed are calculated in order.

Problem 7:

A 700 lbs. mix testing 14 per cent fat, 9 per cent milk solids-not-fat, 15 per cent sugar, and 0.3 per cent stabilizer is desired. The following materials are "left-overs" to be used up to avoid loss: 50 lbs. cream (30 per cent fat, 6.24 per cent milk solids-not-fat), and 100 lbs. milk (3 per cent fat, 8.33 per cent milk solids-not-fat). The following ingredients are also available: stabilizer, cane sugar, 40 per cent cream, and sweetened condensed whole milk (testing 8 per cent fat, 23 per cent milk solids-not-fat, 42 per cent sugar), and water.

SOLUTION:

Steps 1 through 3 completed as in problem 4 will produce the partially completed proof sheet that follows:

Ingredients Used	Weight	Calculated Constituents					Cost
		Fat	M.s.n.f.	Sugar	Slab.	T.s.	
	lbs.	lbs.	lbs.	lbs.	lbs.	lbs.	$
Cream, 30%	50.00	15.00	3.12	. . .	. . .	18.12	
Milk, 3%	100.00	3.00	8.33	. . .	. . .	11.33	
Gelatin	2.33	. . .	. . .	. . .	2.10	2.10	
Cane sugar							
Sweetened condensed whole milk							
Cream, 40%							
Water							
Total, lbs.							
Calculated, %							
Check with desired wt.	700.00	98.00	63.00	105.00	2.10	268.10	
and %		14	9	15	0.3	38.3	

It now appears that 547.67 lbs. total weight containing 80 lbs. fat, 51.55 lbs. milk solids-not-fat, and 105 lbs. sugar remains to be prepared by mixing cream, sugar, sweetened condensed whole milk, and water.

Step 4.—The combined weight of cream and condensed product is calculated as follows:

51.55 lbs. m.s.n.f. desired $\times$ (40.0 — 8.0) difference in the fat tests of the two products = 1649.60

80 lbs. fat desired $\times$ (23.0 — 5.35) difference in the m.s.n.f. tests of the two products = 1412.00

Then:

$$1649.60 + 1412.00 = 3061.60$$

40.0 (fat test of the cream) $\times$ 23.0 (milk solids-not-fat test of sweetened condensed whole milk) $= 920.00$

8.0 (fat test of sweetened condensed whole milk) $\times$ 5.35 (milk solids-not-fat test of the cream) $= 42.80$

Then:

$$920.00 - 42.80 = 877.20$$

Finally:

$$\frac{3061.60}{877.20} \times 100 = 349.02 \text{ lbs. cream and sweetened condensed whole milk}$$

Step 5.—To find the amount of cream needed: Substitute in formula No. III.

$$\frac{80 - (349.02 \times 0.08)}{0.40 - 0.08} = \frac{52.08}{0.32} = 162.75 \text{ lbs. } 40\% \text{ cream needed}$$

Enter in their respective columns of the proof sheet, the weight, lbs. fat, lbs. milk solids-not-fat, and lbs. total solids supplied by the cream.

Step 6.—The amount of sweetened condensed whole milk needed is calculated as follows:

349.02 lbs. (wt. of cream and condensed) — 162.75 lbs. cream = 186.27 lbs. sweetened condensed whole milk needed

Enter in their respective columns of the proof sheet, the weight, lbs. fat, lbs. milk solids-not-fat, lbs. sugar, and lbs. total solids supplied by the sweetened condensed whole milk.

Step 7.—The amount of sugar needed is calculated as follows:

105 lbs. sugar desired — 78.23 lbs. sugar supplied by sweet condensed whole milk = 26.77 lbs. sugar to be supplied by the sugar.

Therefore:

$$\frac{26.77}{100\%} = 26.77 \text{ lbs. sugar needed}$$

Enter this in the respective columns of the proof sheet.

Step 8.—To find the amount of water needed:

700 lbs. — total wt. of all other ingredients = 171.88 lbs. water needed

Completed proof sheet for Problem 7 appears as follows:

Ingredients Used	Weight	Fat	M.s.n.f.	Sugar	Stab.	T.s.	Cost
			Calculated Constituents				
	lbs.	lbs.	lbs.	lbs.	lbs.	lbs.	$
Cream, 30%	50.00	15.00	3.12	...	...	18.12	
Milk, 3%	100.00	3.00	8.33	...	...	11.33	
Stabilizer	2.33	...	...	...	2.10	2.10	
Cane sugar	26.77	...	...	26.77	...	26.77	
Sweetened condensed whole milk	186.27	14.90	42.84	78.23	...	135.97	
Cream, 40%	162.75	65.10	8.71	...	...	73.81	
Water	171.88	...	...	...	...	...	
Total, lbs.	700.00	98.00	63.00	105.00	2.10	268.10	
Calculated, %		14.00	9.00	15.00	0.30	38.30	
Check with desired wt.	700.00	98.00	63.00	105.00	2.10	268.10	
and %		14.0	9.0	15.0	0.3	38.3	

If preferred, this type of problem (Problem 7) may be calculated by the use of formulas No. IV and No. V to find the pounds of condensed product and the pounds of cream needed.

FORMULA NO. IV (SEE PROBLEM 7)

$$\cfrac{\text{cream, \% fat} \times \text{lbs. m.s.n.f. desired} - \cfrac{\text{cream \% m.s.n.f.} \times \text{lbs. fat desired}}{\text{cond. \% fat} \times \text{cream \% m.s.n.f.}}}{\text{cream, \% fat} \times \text{cond. \% m.s.n.f.} -}$$

$$\times 100 = \text{lbs. condensed product needed}$$

Substitute the figures given in the problem, thus:

$$\frac{40 \times 51.55 - 5.35 \times 80}{40 \times 23 - 8 \times 5.35} \times 100 = \frac{2062 - 428}{920 - 42.80} \times 100 =$$

$$\frac{1634}{877.20} \times 100 = 186.27 \text{ lbs. condensed product needed}$$

FORMULA NO. V (SEE PROBLEM 7)

$$\cfrac{\text{cond. \% m.s.n.f.} \times \text{lbs. fat desired} - \cfrac{\text{cond. \% fat} \times \text{lbs. m.s.n.f. desired}}{\text{cond. \% fat} \times \text{cream \% m.s.n.f.}}}{\text{cond. \% m.s.n.f.} \times \text{cream \% fat} -}$$

$$\times 100 = \text{lbs. cream needed}$$

Substitute the figures given in the problem, thus:

$$\frac{(23 \times 80) - (8 \times 51.55)}{(23 \times 40) - (8 \times 5.35)} \times 100 =$$

$$\frac{(1840 - 412.40)}{(920 - 42.80)} \times 100 =$$

$$\frac{1427.60}{877.20} \times 100 = 162.75 \text{ lbs. cream needed}$$

CALCULATING A MIX TO BE MADE IN THE VACUUM PAN

Some dairy plants manufacture condensed whole milk which they later use in making ice cream mix. Nearly half of the time and labor required for these two operations can be eliminated by mixing the ingredients before condensing in the vacuum pan. This process of making the mix in a vacuum pan may be desirable whenever there is available the necessary equipment, a sufficient supply of milk, and a large outlet for the mix.

These vacuum pan mixes are readily calculated by using formulas Nos. VI and VII as in the following steps:

1. List the available ingredients and the number of pounds of each constituent of the desired mix.

2. Make a proof sheet as on page 126, and enter in it the information obtained in step 1.

3. Compute the needed amount of each non-milk product, such as egg, stabilizer, etc., and enter it in the proof sheet.

4. Calculate the needed total pounds of milk and cream by using formula No. VI.

5. Calculate the pounds of cream needed by using formula No. VII, and enter it in the proof sheet.

6. Subtract the pounds of cream needed from the total pounds of milk and cream to obtain the pounds of milk needed. This is entered in the proof sheet.

7. Total each column in the proof sheet and check for accuracy. The total weight of all ingredients will be greater than the desired weight of

the mix, and this excess is the amount of water to remove in the condensing process. The total of each of the other columns in the proof sheet should agree with the corresponding figure of the desired mix.

FORMULA NO. VI

$$\frac{\text{lbs. of mix} \times [\text{m.s.n.f. test of mix} + (0.09 \times \text{fat test of mix})]}{9.0^{1}} =$$

total lbs. milk and cream needed

FORMULA NO. VII

$$\frac{\text{lbs. fat needed} - (\text{lbs. milk and cream needed}^{2} \times \% \text{ fat in milk})}{\text{lbs. fat in 1.0 lb. cream} - \text{lbs. fat in 1.0 lb. milk}} =$$

lb. cream needed

Problem 8:

A vacuum pan will be used in making a 5,400 lbs. mix testing 12 per cent fat, 11 per cent milk solids-not-fat, 14 per cent sugar, 0.5 per cent egg solids and 0.3 per cent stabilizer. The available ingredients are: stabilizer, fresh eggs, Sweetose (43° Baumé) to furnish one-fourth of the total sugar, liquid sugar (67° Brix), cream (35 per cent fat), and milk (3 per cent fat). How much of each ingredient is needed?

SOLUTION:

This mix is smaller and contains a larger variety of ingredients than most mixes which are made in a vacuum pan. Therefore it will not only illustrate the procedure of calculating simple vacuum pan mixes, but will also serve as a guide in calculating the most complex ones.

Step 1.—

Available Ingredients	Desired Mix
Stabilizer, 90% t.s.	Fat, 12% of 5,400 lbs. = 648 lbs.
Fresh eggs, 10.5% fat, 21.6% egg solids, 26.3% t.s.	M.s.n.f., 11% of 5,400 lbs. = 594 lbs.
Sweetose, 67% sugar, 83% t.s.	Sugar, 14% of 5,400 lbs. = 756 lbs.
Liquid sugar, 67% sugar, 67% t.s.	Egg solids, 0.5% of 5,400 lbs. = 27 lbs.
Cream, 35% fat, 5.69% m.s.n.f.	Stabilizer, 0.3% of 5,400 lbs. = 16.20 lbs.
Milk, 3% fat, 8.33% m.s.n.f.	

---

[1] This is assuming that skim milk tests 9% milk solids-not-fat. However skim milk obtained from 3% (fat) milk contains only 8.6% milk solids-not-fat, therefore, in this problem, substitute 0.086 and 8.6 respectively for 0.09 and 9.0.

[2] Obtained by formula No. VI.

Step 2.—Proof Sheet Form:

Ingredients Used	Weight	Calculated Constituents						
		Fat	M.s.n.f.	Sugar	Egg Solids	Stab.	T.s.	Cost
	lbs.	lbs.	lbs.	lbs.	lbs.	lbs.	lbs.	$
Stabilizer								
Fresh eggs								
Sweetose								
Liquid sugar, 67%								
Cream, 35%								
Milk, 3%								
Total, lbs.								
Calculated, %								
Check with desired wt.	5400.00[1]	648.00	594.00	756.00	27.00	16.20	2041.20	
and %		12.0	11.0	14.0	0.5	0.3	37.8	

[1] Includes the lbs. total solids and water which sometimes can be accurately stated only after calculating the mix.

Step 3.—To compute the amount of non-milk products: There is only one source of stabilizer, and it contains 90% total solids. Therefore the 16.2 lbs. of needed stabilizer will require 18.00 lbs. of stabilizer product, 16.2 lbs./0.90 = 18.00 lbs. This figure (18) is entered in the weight column of the proof sheet, also enter 16.2 lbs. in stabilizer column and in total solids column of the proof sheet.

The fresh eggs are the only source of egg solids, and they contain 21.6 per cent egg solids. Therefore 21.6 per cent of the number of lbs. needed must equal 27 lbs., the desired amount of egg solids. It follows that

$$\frac{27 \text{ lbs.}}{0.216} = 125 \text{ lbs. fresh eggs needed}$$

Since the edible portion of a dozen eggs weighs 1.17 lbs. (see Table 20, p. 59) it follows that

$$\frac{125 \text{ lbs.}}{1.17 \text{ lbs.}} = \text{approximately 107 dozen eggs } (107 \times 1.17 = 125.19 \text{ lbs.})$$

Enter the figure (125.19) in the weight column of the proof sheet. Also enter in their respective columns of the proof sheet, the lbs. fat, lbs. egg solids, and lbs. total solids contained in the eggs. These figures are obtained by the following multiplication:

125.19 lbs. $\times$ 10.5% fat $=$ 13.14 lbs. fat

125.19 lbs. $\times$ 21.6% egg solids $=$ 27.04 lbs. egg solids

125.19 lbs. $\times$ 26.3% t.s. $=$ 32.92 lbs. t.s.

The amount of Sweetose needed can now be calculated. Since one-fourth of the total desired sugar equals 756 lbs./4, or 189 lbs., and since Sweetose contains 67 per cent sugar equivalent, it follows that 189 lbs./0.67 $=$ 282.09 lbs. Sweetose needed. This number (282.09) is entered in the weight column of the proof sheet. Also enter in their respective columns of the proof sheet the lbs. sugar, and the lbs. t.s. contained in the Sweetose, and obtained by the following multiplications:

282.09 $\times$ 67% sugar $=$ 189.00 lbs. sugar

282.09 lbs. $\times$ 83% t.s. $=$ 234.13 lbs. t.s.

To find the remaining amount of sugar needed, subtract the 189 lbs. sugar which is supplied by the Sweetose from the 756 lbs. sugar, desired in the mix. This leaves 567 lbs. sugar to be obtained from liquid sugar. The liquid sugar contains 67 per cent sugar and therefore

$$\frac{567 \text{ lbs.}}{0.67} = 846.27 \text{ lbs., liquid sugar needed}$$

This number (846.27) is entered in the weight column of the proof sheet. Also enter 567 lbs. sugar in the sugar column and in the total solids column of the proof sheet.

Step 4.—To calculate the amount of milk and cream needed, use formula No. VI substituting the figures obtained as follows:

Lbs. of mix $=$ 5,400 (from Step 1).

M.s.n.f. test of mix $=$ 11.0 (from Step 1. Note that the decimal point is **not** moved to the left).

Fat test of mix $=$ 12.0 (from Step 1. Note that the decimal point is **not** moved to the left).

In this problem, the milk tests 3.0 per cent fat, and skim milk obtained from it will contain 8.6 per cent milk solids-not-fat. Therefore, use 0.086 and 8.6 in place of 0.09 and 9.0 respectively, substituting these figures in the formula gives:

$$\frac{5400 \times [11.0 + 0.086 \times 12.0]}{8.6} = \text{lbs. milk and cream needed}$$

As the computations are made the formula becomes:

$$\frac{5400 \times (11.0 + 1.03)}{8.6} \text{ or } \frac{5400 \times 12.03}{8.6} = 7553.72$$

Therefore, 7553.72 equals the number of pounds of milk and cream needed.

Step 5.—To find the lbs. of cream needed, use formula No. VII, substituting the figures obtained as follows:

Lbs. fat needed is obtained by subtracting, thus:

648.00 lbs. fat in mix (see Step 1).

less: 13.14 lbs. fat obtained from fresh eggs (see Step 3).

leaves: 634.86 lbs. fat to come from the milk and cream.

Lbs. milk and cream = 7553.72 (see Step 4).
Lb. fat in 1.0 lb. 35% cream = 0.35 lb. fat.
Lb. fat in 1.0 lb. 3% milk = 0.03 lb. fat.

Substituting these figures in the formula gives:

$$\frac{634.86 \text{ lbs.} - (7553.72 \text{ lbs.} \times 3\%)}{0.35 - 0.03} = \text{lbs. } 35\% \text{ cream needed}$$

As the computations are made the formula becomes:

$$\frac{634.86 - 226.61}{0.35 - 0.03} = \frac{408.25}{0.32} = 1275.75 \text{ lbs. } 35\% \text{ cream needed}$$

Therefore 1275.75 lbs. is entered in the weight column of the proof sheet. Also enter in their respective columns of the proof sheet, the lbs. fat, lbs. milk solids-not-fat, and lbs. total solids, contained in the cream. These figures are obtained by the following multiplications:

1275.75 × 35% fat = 446.51 lbs. fat

1275.75 × 5.69% m.s.n.f. = 72.59 lbs. m.s.n.f.

1275.75 × 40.69% t.s. = 519.10 lbs. t.s.

Step 6.—To find the lbs. of 3 per cent milk needed:

Since, in step 4, it was found that 7553.72 lbs. of milk and cream are needed, and in step 5 it was found that 1275.75 lbs. of cream are needed; therefore, subtracting the 1275.75 lbs., from the 7553.72 lbs. leaves 6277.97 lbs., 3 per cent milk needed.

This 6277.97 is entered in the weight column of the proof sheet. Also enter in their respective columns of the proof sheet, the lbs. fat, lbs. milk solids-not-fat, and lbs. total solids contained in the milk. These figures are obtained by multiplication, thus:

6277.97 lbs. × 3% fat = 188.34 lbs. fat

6277.97 lbs. × 8.33% m.s.n.f. = 522.95 lbs. m.s.n.f.

6277.97 lbs. × 11.33% t.s. = 711.29 lbs. t.s.

Step 7.—Each column of the proof sheet is totaled and checked for correctness. It is apparent that the lbs. of fat contained in all of the ingredients is equal to the lbs. of fat desired in the mix. The same is true for the sugar, egg solids and stabilizer. The total milk solids-not-fat (595.54 lbs.) is larger than the desired 594 lbs. of milk solids-not-fat. Therefore compute the milk solids-not-fat test of the calculated mix thus:

$$\frac{595.54 \text{ lbs. total m.s.n.f.}}{5400 \text{ wt. of desired mix}} = 11.03\%$$

This calculated milk solids-not-fat test (11.03 per cent) is slightly higher than the desired 11.00 per cent, but the difference is less than 0.1. It follows that the error is not significant and that the mix is accurately calculated.

The total solids test of the mix is computed by dividing 2080.66 lbs. total solids by the 5,400 lbs. the weight of the finished mix. Thus 2080.66/5400 = 38.53% t.s.

The amount of water to be removed in the vacuum pan is obtained by subtraction thus:

8825.27 lbs., the total weight of all ingredients.

less:

5400.00 lbs., the weight of the finished mix.

leaves:

3425.27 lbs., the weight of water to remove.

The completed proof sheet for Problem 8 appears, thus:

Ingredients Used	Weight	Fat	M.s.n.f.	Sugar	Egg Solids	Stab.	T.s.	Cost
	lbs.	lbs.	lbs.	lbs.	lbs.	lbs.	lbs.	$
Stabilizer	18.00	...	...	...	...	16.20	16.20	
Fresh eggs	125.19	13.14	...	...	27.04	...	32.92	
Sweetose	282.09	...	...	189.00	...	...	234.13	
Liquid sugar	846.27	...	...	567.00	...	...	567.00	
Cream, 35%	1275.75	446.51	72.59	...	...	...	519.06	
Milk, 3%	6277.97	188.34	522.95	...	...	...	711.29	
Total, lbs.	8825.27	648.00	595.54	756.00	27.04	16.20	2080.66	
Calculated, %		12.00	11.03	14.00	0.50	0.30	38.53	
Check with desired wt. and %	5400.00[1]	648.00	594.00	756.00	27.00	16.20	2041.2	
		12.0	11.0	14.0	0.5	0.3	37.8	

Calculated Constituents

[1] Includes the lbs. total solids and water which sometimes can be accurately stated only after calculating the mix.

CHAPTER 10

Calculating Cost of Mixes; Per Cent Overrun

CALCULATING THE COST OF THE MIX

The cost of the ingredients in a mix is best determined after the mix has been calculated. A simple procedure is first to find the cost of one pound of each of the ingredients, then multiply the price per pound by the amount of that ingredient used (i.e., the amount entered in the weight column of the proof sheet); and enter the result in the cost column of the proof sheet. When the cost of each ingredient has been entered in the proof sheet, the column is added to obtain the total cost of all ingredients in the entire batch of mix. When comparing costs one should, of course, be careful to compare the costs of equal amounts of mix.

The cost per pound of mix is a good basis for comparing costs of different mixes and is obtained by dividing total cost by total pounds of mix.

Problem 9 demonstrates how to calculate the cost of ingredients used in problems 1 and 2. Cost in problems 3, 4 and 5 can be calculated in the same manner. The prices of the ingredients are fictitious and any resemblance to actual market value is purely coincidental.

Problem 9 and Solution:

The purchase price of the ingredients used in problems 1 and 2 is assumed to be:

Ingredient	Cost per Lb.
Stabilizer	$0.70
Dried egg yolk	1.00
Cane sugar	0.08
Non-fat dry milk solids	0.15
Cream (30% fat) is $25.00 per 40 qt. can which weighs 84 lbs. (Table 15) $= \dfrac{25.00}{84}$	$= 0.298$
Cream (40% fat) is $33.00 per 40 qt. can which weighs 83 lbs. (Table 15) $= \dfrac{33.00}{83}$	$= 0.3976$
Condensed skim milk (27% total solids) is $5.00 per 40 qt. can which weighs 94 lbs. (Table 15) $= \dfrac{5.00}{94}$	$= 0.0532$
Milk (4% fat) is $5.25 per 100 lbs. $= \dfrac{5.25}{100}$	$= 0.0525$
Water	$= 0.001$

Now that the price per pound of all ingredients has been calculated, the total cost of the ingredients used in Problem 1 (see proof sheet) can be calculated by multiplication as follows:

Ingredient	Amount		Cost per Lb.		Total Cost
Stabilizer	2.50 lbs.	×	0.70	=	$ 1.75
Dried egg yolk	2.39 lbs.	×	1.00	=	2.39
Cane sugar	63.00 lbs.	×	0.08	=	5.04
Cream (30% fat)	145.02 lbs.	×	0.298	=	43.22
Non-fat dry milk solids	41.70 lbs.	×	0.15	=	6.26
Water	195.38 lbs.	×	0.001	=	0.20
Total weight	450.00 lbs.		Total cost of mix		$58.86

Cost per lb. mix in Problem 1 is 58.86/450 = $0.1308. If desired, enter the cost of each ingredient in cost column of Problem 1 proof sheet.

To repeat the procedure, using the ingredients in Problem 2:

Ingredient	Amount		Cost per Lb.		Total Cost
Stabilizer	1.11 lbs.	×	0.70	=	$ 0.78
Cane sugar	26.00 lbs.	×	0.08	=	2.08
Condensed skim milk (27% t.s.)	27.56 lbs.	×	0.0532	=	1.47
Cream (40% fat)	61.63 lbs.	×	0.3976	=	24.50
Milk (4% fat)	83.70 lbs.	×	0.0525	=	4.39
Total weight	200.00 lbs.		Total cost of mix		$33.22

Cost per lb. of mix in Problem 2 is $33.22/200 = $0.1661. If desired enter the cost of each ingredient in cost column of Problem 2 proof sheet.

This shows that mix in Problem 2 costs 0.0353 cents more per pound than the mix in Problem 1.

COMPARE FOR COSTS AND QUALITY

The comparison of the cost of either ingredients or mixes should receive careful consideration because many factors are closely related to cost. The use of less expensive ingredients is often good business in that it lowers the cost of the mix. However, substitutions must be made wisely or sometimes they may result in increasing the tendency of certain defects to appear. For example, the mix in Problem 1 is less expensive than the mix in Problem 2, but it would probably have a more pronounced "condensed" or "serum solids" flavor. Sometimes these defects can be avoided by properly balancing the mix. However, care must be taken so as not to throw the mix out of balance when the ingredients are changed.

For example, in the more expensive mix of Problem 2 the condensed skim milk and whole milk cannot be replaced by non-fat dry milk solids and water unless egg yolk solids are added as in Problem 1.

Since any change of ingredients will frequently throw a mix out of balance, it seems better to balance a mix properly for each group of ingredients before it is calculated and costs are considered. However, it is well for each factory operator to check carefully on the cost of the ingredients of his standard mixes and so far as possible purchase the ingredients from the most economical source, provided that this will not lower the quality, palatability and other desired characteristics of the finished ice cream.

From a practical point of view, it should be kept in mind that butter-fat is nearly always one of the principal items as well as the most expensive one that enters into the ice cream. So in a general way it may be said that the cheapest source of good quality butterfat should be selected.

Other factors that are closely related to cost include the cost of processing, yield, convenience, etc. These factors are not considered here since this chapter deals mainly with the procedure of calculation.

A COMPARISON OF CALCULATING METHODS

Other methods of calculating mixes are available, most of them being either too tedious, too technical and complicated, or unsatisfactory for calculating the more complex mixes. The Pearson square method is successful when the calculation is limited to the proportion of milk and cream needed, but will not readily calculate the needed amount of concentrated milk solids-not-fat. The algebraic method is equally accurate and applicable to the most complex problems, but it involves rather lengthy calculations and a thorough knowledge of setting up and solving simultaneous equations. It is definitely cumbersome and slow. The so-called "serum point method" and various arithmetic methods are basically identical with the formulas presented in these chapters. However, the use of the formulas simplifies the procedure and thus makes it easier to learn.

The use of recipe tables or tabulations which indicate the amount of each ingredient has the advantage of eliminating errors in calculation and saving valuable time. However, a new table must be prepared for every slight change in the desired composition of the mix, and for changes in the source of the constituents. For example, if the mix is prepared using sugar and sweetened condensed skim milk, the table must allow for all variations in the test of the sweetened condensed skim milk both in regard to sugar composition and milk solids-not-fat test. Such a table would be practically useless when liquid sugar is substituted for sugar in making the same mix. This indicates the large number of tables necessary to provide for all possible variations in composition and ingredients. Such a compilation in one volume would be too cumbersome for convenient reference. A final advantage of the formulas given in these chapters is that they make possible the calculation of all the tables required by the particular conditions of any manufacturer whenever the tables justify the effort of preparation.

STANDARDIZING MILK AND CREAM

Sometimes it is desirable to use a simple and easy method for standardizing milk and cream so that stocks on hand are always of the same tests, a convenience in calculating mixes.

There are several methods of standardizing which are very satisfactory. To find the proportions of milk and cream to use, either of the following methods may be employed.

1. Draw a rectangle with two diagonals. At the upper left hand corner place the test of the cream to be standardized. At the lower left-hand corner place the test of the milk to be used in standardizing. In the center of the rectangle, place the desired test. At the right hand corners place the differences between the numbers at the left hand corner and the number in the center. The number at the upper right-hand corner represents the number of pounds of cream of the richness indicated by the number at the upper left hand corner. The number at the lower right hand corner indicates the number of pounds of milk of the richness indicated by the number at the lower left-hand corner. By mixing milk and cream in these proportions the desired test will be obtained. For example, if 35 per cent cream is to be standardized to 20 per cent using 4 per cent milk, proceed as shown in Fig. 12A:

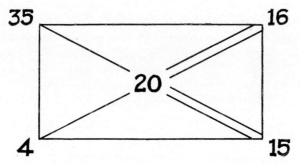

FIG. 12A.   GRAPHIC METHOD OF STANDARDIZING CREAM WITH WHOLE MILK

Sixteen, which is the difference between 4 and 20, represents the pounds of 35 per cent cream that must be mixed with 15 pounds of 4 per cent milk to make 31 pounds of 20 per cent cream. When the proportions of milk and cream have been found any amount of 35 per cent cream may be standardized to 20 per cent by mixing with 4 per cent milk in the proportions of 16/31 of cream to 15/31 of milk. For example: if 310 lbs. of 20% cream is wanted, then 16/31 × 310 = 160 lbs., the amount of 35% cream needed, and 15/31 × 310 = 150 lbs., the amount of 4% milk needed.

If skim milk is used instead of whole milk the figures would be:

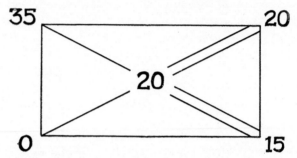

FIG. 12B.   GRAPHIC METHOD OF STANDARDIZING CREAM WITH
SKIM MILK

In this case a mixture composed of 20/35 cream and 15/35 skim milk will test 20 per cent.

2. Another method of standardizing that is quite simple and accurate and involves but little figuring is as follows: Multiply the amount of cream by the difference between its test and the required test, and divide the product by the difference between the required test and the test of the milk to be added.

Example: Standardize 120 lbs. of 30 per cent cream to 20 per cent, using 4.2 per cent milk.   30 − 20 = 10, which is the difference between the test of the cream and the required test.   20 − 4.2 = 15.8, which is the difference between the required test and the test of the milk.

Using these figures we have 120 × 10 ÷ 15.8 or 120 × 10/15.8 = 75.95 lbs.   Therefore, 75.95 lbs. of 4.2 per cent milk are required to reduce the test of 120 lbs. of 30 per cent cream to 20 per cent.   The accuracy of this method is shown by the following figures:

75.95 lbs. 4.2% milk contain	3.1899 lbs. fat
120 lbs. 30% cream contain	36.0000 lbs. fat
Total 195.95 lbs.	Total 39.1899 lbs.

Therefore 195.95 lbs. 20% cream contain 39.19 lbs. fat.

Either of these methods will be found valuable as aids in regulating the quality of the ice cream produced.

CALCULATING THE PER CENT OVERRUN

There are two basic or fundamental methods of calculating percentage overrun: one is by volume, and the other by weight. Each of these has three modifications. The first is the simplest and perhaps the most widely used, while the second modification is more nearly correct and especially useful in evaluating "plant overrun" for cost studies. The third modification is used for determining the overrun obtained on the plain mix used in making composite ice creams. It recognizes the fact that very little overrun is obtained on the coloring and flavoring material. For example, it is usually desirable to take a lower overrun on composite ice creams than is taken on plain ice creams.

MODIFICATIONS WHEN CALCULATING PER CENT OVERRUN BY VOLUME

1. Useful for plain ice cream.

$$\frac{\text{vol. of ice cream} - \text{vol. of mix}}{\text{volume of mix}} \times 100 = \% \text{ overrun}$$

For example: when 5 gals. of mix are frozen to make 9.5 gals. ice cream, then

$$\frac{9.5 - 5.0}{5} \times 100 = 90\% \text{ overrun.}$$

2. More nearly correct and useful in evaluating "plant overrun" for cost studies.

$$\frac{\text{vol. of ice cream} - (\text{vol. of mix} + \text{vol. of flavor})}{\text{vol. of mix} + \text{vol. of flavor}} \times 100 = \% \text{ overrun}$$

For example: when 40 gals. of unflavored mix is colored and flavored with 1.0 gal. of coffee extract and frozen to 77.9 gals. ice cream, then

$$\frac{77.9 - (40 + 1.0)}{40 + 1} \times 100 = 90\% \text{ overrun}$$

3. Useful in determining the overrun on the plain mix used in making composite ice creams.

$$\frac{\text{vol. of ice cream} - (\text{vol. of mix} + \text{vol. of flavor})}{\text{vol. of plain mix}} \times 100 = \% \text{ overrun}$$

For example: when 17.0 gals. of unflavored (plain) mix is colored and flavored with 3.0 gals. of maple nut and frozen to 40.0 gal. ice cream, then

$$\frac{40 - (17 + 3)}{17} \times 100 = 117.6\% \text{ overrun}$$

MODIFICATIONS WHEN CALCULATING PER CENT OVERRUN BY WEIGHT[1]

1. Useful for plain ice cream.

$$\frac{\text{wt. of 1 gal. of mix} - \text{wt. of 1 gal. ice cream}}{\text{wt. of 1 gal. ice cream}} \times 100 = \% \text{ overrun}$$

2. More precise and useful in evaluating "plant overrun"

$$\frac{\text{wt. of 1 gal. of flavored mix}[2] - \text{wt. of 1 gal. ice cream}}{\text{wt. of 1 gal. ice cream}} \times 100 = \% \text{ overrun}$$

For example: when the flavored and colored mix weighing 8.85 lbs. per gal. is frozen into ice cream that weighs 5.06 lbs. per gal., then

$$\frac{8.85 - 5.06}{5.06} \times 100 = 74.9\% \text{ overrun}$$

3. Useful in determining the overrun on the plain mix used in making composite ice cream.

$$\frac{\text{wt./gal. flav. mix} - \text{wt./gal. ice cream}}{\text{wt./gal. ice cream}} \times$$
$$\frac{\text{vol. plain mix} + \text{vol. flavor}}{\text{vol. plain mix}} \times 100 = \% \text{ overrun}$$

For example: 17.0 gals. of plain mix is flavored and colored with 3.0 gals. of maple nut to give a flavored mix weighing 8.85 lbs. per gal.   When this is frozen into ice cream weighing 5.06 lbs. per gal., then

$$\frac{8.85 - 5.06}{5.06} \times \frac{17 + 3}{17} \times 100 = 0.749 \times 1.176 \times 100 = 88.1\% \text{ overrun}$$

---

[1] While these examples mention the weight per gallon, it is equally satisfactory to substitute the weight of any more convenient volume provided the same volume is used throughout the formula.   This emphasizes the fact that these calculations are based on density measurements.

[2] The resulting blend of plain mix with coloring and flavoring material.

CALCULATING THE DESIRED OVERRUN FOR COMPOSITE ICE CREAM

The overrun at which to draw ice cream is discussed in Chapter 12, The Freezing Process. That discussion aids in establishing the correct overrun at which to draw plain ice cream and emphasizes the importance of the right amount of incorporated air in proportion to the amount of plain mix and the solids in the mix. When the most desirable overrun, or ratio of incorporated air to plain mix, has been established for plain ice cream, then the correct or corresponding overrun for composite ice cream can be calculated.

Composite ice cream drawn with too much overrun generally has body and texture defects described as "weak" and "fluffy," a common criticism of fruit and nut ice cream. This can be corrected by drawing a sufficiently lower overrun to obtain the same ratio of incorporated air to plain mix as is obtained in plain ice cream. This desired overrun is calculated as follows:

$$\% \text{ overrun used for plain ice cream} \times \frac{\text{gal. of plain mix}}{\text{gal. of flavored mix}} \times 100$$
$$= \% \text{ overrun for comp. ice cream}$$

Problem 10:

What is the correct overrun at which to draw a composite ice cream containing 3.0 gals. of coloring and flavoring material added to 17.0 gals. of plain mix, if 90% is the desired overrun for plain vanilla ice cream?

SOLUTION:

$$17 \text{ gals.} + 3 \text{ gals.} = 20 \text{ gals. of flavored mix}$$

Substitute in formula:

$$(0.90) \times \frac{17}{20} \times 100 = 76.5\% \text{ overrun at which to draw the composite ice cream}$$

CALCULATING THE WEIGHT PER GALLON OF A MIX

When ten or preferably more cans are carefully filled with mix and weighed, the approximate weight per gallon can be obtained. However, a more accurate value can be calculated from the composition of the mix as illustrated by Problem 12. Although temperature greatly influences the accuracy of this calculation, the following formula is considered sufficiently accurate at ordinary mix storage temperatures.

FORMULA NO. VIII

$$\frac{8.33585}{\% \text{ fat } (1.07527) + (\% \text{ t.s.} - \% \text{ fat.}) \times (0.6329) + \% \text{ water}}$$

$$= \text{lbs. per gal. of mix}$$

Problem 11:

Calculate the weight per gallon of a mix containing: 12.0 per cent fat, 11.0 per cent milk solids-not-fat, 15.0 per cent sugar, 0.30 per cent stabilizer, and 38.3 per cent total solids.

SOLUTION:

Substitute in the formula:

$$\frac{8.33585}{0.12 \times 1.07527 + (0.383 - 0.12) \times (0.6329) + 0.617} = \text{lbs. per gal. of mix}$$

$$\frac{8.33585}{0.12903 + 0.263 \times 0.6329 + 0.617} = \frac{8.33585}{0.12903 + 0.16645 + 0.617} =$$

$$\frac{8.33585}{0.91248} = 9.135 \text{ lbs. per gal. of mix}$$

CALCULATING WEIGHT PER PACKAGE

Calculating the Weight per Package of Plain Ice Cream. Frequently it is important to know the correct weight of a package of ice cream when the ice cream contains the desired amount of overrun. This is readily obtained by adding the weight of the empty package to the calculated weight of ice cream per package. The formula assumes a one-gallon package but any other size of package may be substituted.

FORMULA NO. IX

$$\frac{(\text{wt. of 1.0 gal. of mix})}{1.0 + \text{desired } \% \text{ overrun}} = \text{wt. of ice cream per gal.}$$

Problem 12:

The mix weighs 9.135 lbs. per gal. and the desired overrun is 90 per cent. Calculate the weight of a gallon package which weighs 0.5 lb. when empty.

SOLUTION:

Substitute in the formula:

$$\frac{(9.135)}{1.0 + 0.90} = \frac{9.135}{1.90} = 4.808 \text{ lbs. ice cream per gal.}$$

4.808 lbs. ice cream
+ 0.50 lb. empty package

= 5.308 lbs. = gross weight of the full package

Calculating the Weight per Package of Composite Ice Cream. When making composite ice cream, such as fruit and nut, it is desirable to take a lower overrun, which will insure the same proportion of air to plain mix as is used in the vanilla or plain ice creams. The desired weight of composite ice cream necessary to maintain this same proportion of air to plain mix can be calculated as follows:

FORMULA NO. X

$$\frac{\text{weight of 1 gallon of flavored mix}}{1.0 + (\% \text{ desired overrun}) \times \dfrac{\text{vol. of plain mix}}{\text{vol. of flavored mix}}} =$$

wt. per gal. of ice cream

Problem 13:

The overrun used on plain (vanilla) ice cream is 90 per cent. Maple nut ice cream is to be made using 3.0 gals. (24 lbs.) of coloring and flavoring material to every 17.0 gals. of plain mix (9.0 lbs. per gal.). What should be the weight of a one gal. package of the finished maple nut ice cream if the empty package weighs 0.526 lb.?

SOLUTION:

(a) to find the wt. of 1 gal. of flavored mix:
  3 gals. flavor = 24.0 lbs.
  17 gals. plain mix = 17 × 9 = 153.0 lbs.

  20 gals. flavored mix = 24.0 lbs. + 153.0 lbs. = 177.0 lbs.
    wt. of 1 gal. flavored mix = 177 lbs. ÷ 20 = 8.85 lbs.

(b) $$\frac{\text{vol. of plain mix}}{\text{vol. of flavored mix}} = \frac{17 \text{ gals.}}{20 \text{ gals.}}$$

Substituting in the formula above:

$$\frac{(8.85)}{1.0 + (.90) \times (17/20)} = \frac{8.85}{1.765} = 5.014 \text{ lbs.} = \text{wt. of 1.0 gal. of ice cream}$$

then:

the empty 1 gal. package $= 0.526$ lb.
1.0 gal. finished ice cream $= 5.014$ lbs.

total wt. of package $= 5.540$ lbs.

CHAPTER 11

Mix Processing

In order to make good ice cream, the milk products and other ingredients must first be selected and combined so as to produce the desired body and a delicately blended flavor. Then they must be skillfully processed. Obviously the selection of good wholesome ingredients and calculation of a satisfactory composition, as discussed in previous chapters, precede the mixing of the ingredients in a vat where they can be heated to facilitate dissolving, blending and pasteurizing.

The first step of processing is composing the mix. This procedure may range in scope from the small batch operation, where each ingredient is weighed or measured into a pasteurizing vat, to the large automatic continuous operation where many of the ingredients are metered into the batch. Continuous mix-making procedures may be quite variable and some such operations may actually be modifications of the batch operation. Liquid stabilizers and product blending equipment have been developed to facilitate the continuous operation. In the continuous mix-making procedure, the products are blended into the mix in approximately the same order as for batch processing.

ORDER OF ADDING INGREDIENTS

All liquid ingredients (cream, milk, condensed milk, syrup, etc.) are placed in the vat, and the agitation and heating started at once. The dry ingredients, including skim milk powder, dried eggs, cocoa, sugar and stabilizer (with a few exceptions), are added while the liquid material is agitated and before the temperature reaches 120°F. Proper suspension to avoid lumpiness of the dry ingredients may be obtained by (1) mixing the dry material thoroughly with part of the sugar before slowly adding it to the liquid, or (2) sifting or otherwise slowly adding these substances to the liquid. Skim milk powder, cocoa and similar products should be sifted on top of the liquid (in case a coil vat is used) at the place where the coils go down into the liquid, and always while the agitated liquid is still cool (under 80°F.). If gelatin is the stabilizer used, it is best to add it after it is thoroughly mixed with an equal volume of sugar and before the liquid reaches 120°F. Or it can be sprinkled on the surface of the cold liquid and allowed to soak before the mixture is heated. Another method is to soak the gelatin in water and then heat the mixture to completely dissolve the gelatin. This gelatin suspension is

141

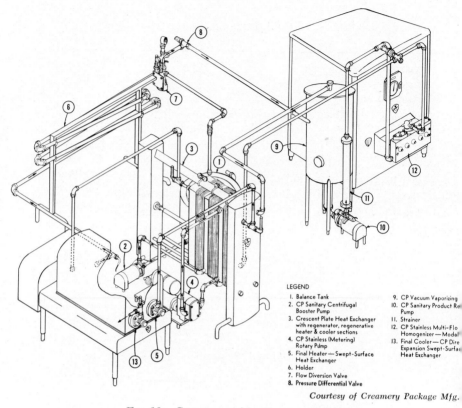

LEGEND

1. Balance Tank
2. CP Sanitary Centrifugal Booster Pump
3. Crescent Plate Heat Exchanger with regenerator, regenerative heater & cooler sections
4. CP Stainless (Metering) Rotary Pump
5. Final Heater — Swept-Surface Heat Exchanger
6. Holder
7. Flow Diversion Valve
8. Pressure Differential Valve
9. CP Vacuum Vaporizing
10. CP Sanitary Product Re Pump
11. Strainer
12. CP Stainless Multi-Flo Homogenizer — Model
13. Final Cooler — CP Dire Expansion Swept-Surfa Heat Exchanger

Courtesy of Creamery Package Mfg.

Fig. 13. Continuous Mix Processing System

Regeneration preheating, pasteurization, vacuum treatment, homogenization and cooling.

usually added to warm (100° to 120°F.) mix. Many other stabilizers such as Krageleen and C.M.C. can be added in a similar manner. However, sodium alginate, such as Dariloid, should not be added until the temperature of the liquid material has reached at least 150°F. The dry Dariloid is not allowed to soak but is stirred up with cold water and immediately dumped into the hot mix. When butter, plastic cream, frozen cream or other frozen products are used, they should be cut into fairly small pieces and added in time to allow complete melting before the pasteurizing temperature is reached. With a few exceptions, coloring and flavoring materials are added at the time the mix is frozen.

PASTEURIZATION OF THE MIX

Proper pasteurization of all mixes should be compulsory because this process destroys all pathogenic or disease-producing bacteria, thereby

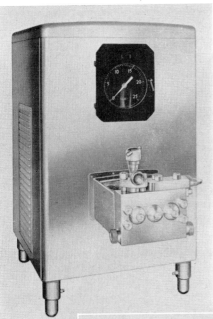

*Courtesy of
Creamery Package Mfg. Co.*

FIG. 14. STAINLESS STEEL MULTI-FLO HOMOGENIZER

Details of the head assembly are shown below:

A—suction or discharge valve
B—suction valve spring
C—suction valve spring retainer
D—hex nut (interchangeable)
E—cylinder locking cover
F—cylinder locking key
G—cylinder
H—plunger seal adjusting nut
J—plunger seal follower
K—plunger seal ring
L—plunger seal seat
M—homogenizing valve assembly
N—pressure gauge stem
O—valve port covers
P—perma-mount sanitary head block

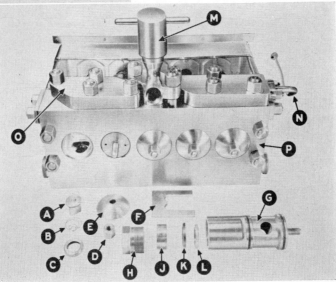

safeguarding the health of the consumer. Pasteurization has come to be considered highly desirable and requires only slight additional expense, since the mix is usually heated to facilitate solution, and since the homogenization process can be best accomplished at the pasteurization temperature level.

Most states and many cities specify certain definite temperature regulations when pasteurization is required, but these generally apply only to the dairy products used. Usually it is permissible to use higher temperatures for pasteurization than are required for market milk, and in many instances it is legal to re-pasteurize products which have already been pasteurized once. Every manufacturer should acquaint himself with the legal regulations which apply in his market area and make special note of the following:

1. What dairy products, if any, may be used without being pasteurized.

2. The maximum bacterial count of ingredients used even when followed by pasteurization.

3. The pasteurization time and temperature requirements.

4. The maximum permitted bacterial count of the finished product. (Usually it is different for ices, ice cream, etc., as well as for products which are not pasteurized, than for those which are pasteurized.)

5. Must the product be frozen on the premises where it is pasteurized?

Proper pasteurization consists in rapidly heating to a definite temperature, holding at that temperature for a definite minimum of time, and then rapidly cooling to below 40°F. Mix pasteurization is required by law in most states and cities and may be accomplished by the batch method, high temperature-short time or other approved procedures as shown in Table 30. (Recommended by U.S. Public Health Service.)

TABLE 30

PASTEURIZATION TEMPERATURES AND TIMES FOR ICE CREAM MIXES

Batch Method	155°F. for not less than 30 minutes
High Temperature-Short Time	175°F. for not less than 25 seconds
Vacreation	194°F. for no apparent holding time (1 to 3 seconds)
Ultra High Temperature	210° to 265°F. for instant to 40 seconds

Pasteurization (a) renders the mix substantially free of pathogenic bacteria, (b) brings into solution and aids in blending the ingredients of the mix, (c) improves flavor, (d) improves keeping quality, and (e) produces a more uniform product. There is a trend toward the higher temperature processes. The introduction of high temperature pasteurization equipment suitable for processing ice cream mix and the establishment of the additional pasteurization standards of 175°F. for 25 seconds for ice cream mix has created considerable interest in the potentials of this method of pasteurization in the ice cream industry during recent years.

Pasteurization equipment is available and is being used which is capable of heating the mix to a temperature much higher than is required for pasteurization standards.

Reasons for high temperature pasteurization of ice cream mix include:

1. Greater bacterial kill resulting in lower bacterial count in ice cream.
2. Suitable temperature and time of pasteurization result in (a) better body and texture, (b) better flavor, and (c) protection against oxidation.
3. Saving of stabilizer.
4. Saving of time, labor, and space.
5. Increased capacity.

Some studies indicate that cooked flavors result above 250°F. This naturally may depend on the type of equipment, but for maximum benefits the mix should probably be processed at 210° to 220°F.

The reduction in stabilizer needed may be 25 to 35 per cent, as compared with that used in batch pasteurization. Stabilizers suitable for high temperature processing usually contain CMC (sodium carboxymethylcellulose) and Irish moss, or algins with additional materials.

Continuous and automatically controlled high temperature units are almost always more economical than batch methods. Factors of difference between high temperature pasteurizing systems may be as follows:

1. Incorporation of regenerative heating and cooling.
2. Amount of regeneration utilized.
3. Ability to maintain long continuous operation without loss in efficiency.
4. Adaptability to circulation cleaning.
5. Pressures maintained in equipment which affect pumping efficiencies.
6. Effectiveness of control—affects properties of finished products.
7. Adaptability to small batches.

Continuous mix making may be quite variable in its meaning. When the continuous mix making operation was first initiated there were almost as many different arrangements of equipment as there were plants using the process. This is not so much the case at present but there is still no standard arrangement of equipment for the continuous operation. The process is considered continuous if the blended raw mix is available during the entire run. Blending should be at a temperature of 50°F. or below.

High temperature mix pasteurization systems vary considerably. Some so-called continuous operations may actually be modified batch operations. Liquid stabilizers or product blending equipment have been suggested to facilitate the continuous operation. Pressure or vacuum control valves, metering pumps, and vacuum vaporizing cyclinders may occur in the system. Heat regeneration may approach 85 per cent. Greater standardization of the typical system featuring more accurate controls may be expected in continuous high temperature pasteurization installation of the future. (See Fig. 15.)

In the batch system, the mix is usually heated and held before going to the homogenizer and from there passes over a cooler. The heating and

FIG. 15. TAYLOR HIGH TEMPERATURE SHORT TIME CONTROLLER
FOR PASTEURIZATION

This instrument controls continuous pasteurization and diverts milk
or mix flow within two seconds if temperature falls below legal
limit.

holding may be accomplished in the vat used for mixing the ingredients.
Many large factories make use of continuous pasteurizers and profitably
incorporate the regeneration principle. This principle employs the use of
the cool mix, which is being heated, as a cooling medium for the hot mix
coming from the homogenizer.

HOMOGENIZING THE MIX

Homogenization is accomplished by passing the mix through a very
small opening under a high velocity and usually a high pressure. The
machines known as "viscolizers" and "homogenizers" employ positive piston pumps to force the mix at high pressure through a minute valve opening. The principal difference between these machines is not in the effect
produced but in the size of the aperture through which the mix passes.
A pressure of 2000 lbs. on the viscolizer is equal to approximately 3000 on
the homogenizer; at these pressures the size of the aperture is 0.003 and
0.007 in., respectively. Typical homogenizers are shown in Figs. 16 to 18.

The main purpose of homogenization is to make a permanent and uniform suspension of the fat by reducing the size of the fat droplets to a
very small diameter, preferably not more than 2 microns. This means that
when a mix is properly homogenized, the fat will not rise and form a
cream layer. Other advantages are also obtained, such as a more uniform

ice cream with a smoother texture, improved whipping ability, a shorter aging period, less opportunity for churning to occur in the freezer, and the use of slightly less stabilizer. Butter, butter oil, plastic cream, and frozen cream can be used in the mix only when the mix is homogenized.

Physical Effects of Homogenization. The process of homogenization is assumed to affect the mix only physically. The fat globules are reduced to about $1/10$ the normal size which increases the total surface of the globules about 100 times. Therefore, it is easy to see why homogenization

Courtesy of Manton-Gaulin Mfg. Co.

FIG. 16. MANTON GAULIN HOMOGENIZER

produces effects which differ considerably with varying composition, acidity, temperature, pressure, etc. The substances in colloidal and true solution tend to be concentrated on the fat globule surfaces. Varying conditions will have different effects on the films forming at these surfaces. There is a tendency for fat globules to form in groups as the mix passes away from the homogenizing valve. This is particularly true of the butter and frozen cream types of mixes, of cold mixes or of acid mixes. This clumping of the fat globules, if marked, causes excessive viscosity and slow whipping. For this reason some homogenizers are equipped with a second valve which breaks up the clumps; in other words, the mix passes through one valve (called the first stage) under a high pressure (above 1000 lbs.) where clumping may occur and then through another valve (called the second stage) under a low pressure (500 to 1000 lbs. is sufficient) where the clumps are broken up, and then the mix passes out of the homogenizer toward the cooler.

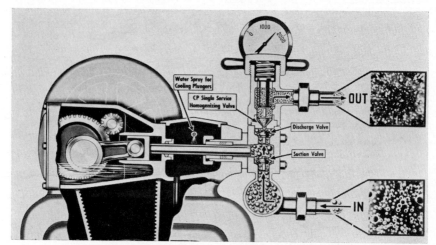

Courtesy of Creamery Package Mfg. Co.

Fig. 17. Diagrammatic Illustration of Multi-Flo Homogenizer

Homogenizing Temperatures. The mix is usually homogenized at temperatures from 145° to 170°F. because at low temperatures (120° to 130°F.) homogenization increases the formation of clumps of fat globules, increases the viscosity, and increases the freezing time in batch freezers. When using a high pasteurizing temperature (170°F.) with the batch system, the mix may be cooled to 150°F. for homogenization, a desirable practice, to reduce the intensity of the cooked flavor and the length of time the mix has to be held at the high temperature especially when homogenization is not completed in 30 minutes. However, within certain limits, better homogenization is obtained with each increase in the temperature used, and sometimes the mix is pasteurized at 145°F. and then heated to 160° to 170°F. for homogenization. The use of these high temperatures results in less clumping of the fat globules, a lower viscosity, and a shorter freezing time in batch freezers.

Pressures for Homogenization. The pressure to use for homogenization depends upon several factors: desired viscosity, composition of the mix, stability of the mix, temperature used, and construction of the homogenizing machine. Because of the influence of each of these factors, one can recommend only a range of pressures, realizing that a specific case may require pressure above or below the range. A pressure of 2000 to 2500 lbs. with one valve or 2500 to 3000 lbs. on the first stage and 500 lbs. on the second stage will usually give good results for an average mix.

Courtesy of Cherry-Burrell Corp.

Fig. 18.   Two-Stage Homogenizer Block

Two-stage valve used.

Chocolate mixes and other high solids mixes usually have sufficient viscosity if the pressure is reduced about 500 lbs. (i.e., 1500 to 2000 lbs. for single stage and 1500–2000 lbs. on the first valve with 500 lbs. on the second valve in two-stage homogenization). The same is true for mixes using butter, plastic cream, etc., as the only source of fat; or concentrated products as the only source of milk solids-not-fat. The pressures in Table 31 are suggested only as an approximation for mixes containing different percentages of fat.

TABLE 31

APPROXIMATE HOMOGENIZATION PRESSURES FOR MIXES OF DIFFERENT FAT CONTENTS

	Single stage	Double stage	
		First valve	Second valve
8–12% fat	2500–3000 lbs.	2500–3000 lbs.	500 lbs.
12–14% fat	2000–2500 lbs.	2000–2500 lbs.	500 lbs.
15–17% fat	1500–2000 lbs.	1500–2000 lbs.	500 lbs.
18% fat	1200–1800 lbs.	1200–1800 lbs.	500 lbs.
Above 18% fat	800–1200 lbs.	800–1200 lbs.	500 lbs.

Causes of Fluctuating Pressures. When operating a homogenizer the needle of the pressure gauge should be steady and should not oscillate, should not change markedly unless the valve is opened or closed, and should change whenever the valve is adjusted. Failure of the pressure gauge to respond to the adjustment of the wheel on the homogenizer valve may be caused by a plugged line to the gauge, by slipping of the belt, by packing or similar material being caught under the homogenizing valve, or by a worn valve. When the gauge pressure changes without the turning of the valve, one should look for a slipping belt, material such as packing under the homogenizer valve, or a loose spring under the valve. Sometimes the change in gauge pressure may be caused by heat expanding the metal and producing a change in the space between the valve and valve seat. Oscillation of the gauge pressure may be due (1) to an uneven amount being pumped by each valve because of the strainer being clogged or air leaks in the suction line, or (2) to anything that allows mix to pass back by the valves into the machine head (such as slipping belt, pumping valves opening too wide and not closing promptly, or valve surfaces damaged by wear or scores). Air leaks in the suction line may be caused by scratches on the surface of the joints in the pipe lines, and therefore the pipes should be carefully handled. Moving parts such as pump pistons passing through packing may be slightly grooved or the packing may become old and cause small pieces of packing to break off into the mix eventually sticking in the small valve openings. Thus the need of extreme care in handling equipment is emphasized.

Factors which favor high viscosity and the clumping of the fat globules are: (1) high pressures with a single valve, (2) low temperature of mix when homogenized, (3) low stability of the mix due to high acidity or improper salt balance and (4) a high ratio of fat content to milk solids-not-fat content. The easiest and most convenient way to reduce the viscosity produced by homogenization is to use lower pressures, especially when homogenizing mixes of low stability. The use of higher temperature during homogenization will also reduce the viscosity and fat clumping. Standardizing the acidity is effective especially when the viscosity is due to high acidity in the mix. The use of a second valve is especially effective in reducing the clumping of the fat globules and reducing the excessive viscosity produced by this phenomenon.

Detection of defective or improper homogenization can be accomplished by examining a sample of the mix with a microscope. This enables an experienced technician to measure the size of the fat globules and detect clumping. Another method such as that used for homogenized milk is simpler but less accurate, and requires less experience on the part of the operator. In this method a quart milk bottle is filled with mix and stored at 40° F. for 48 hours. Then without agitation the top 80 to 100 ml. are quickly poured off into a graduated cylinder. Each portion (the portion poured off and the portion remaining in the milk bottle) is separately mixed and tested for fat content. The difference between the tests of the two portions should be less than 0.7 per cent if the mix has been properly homogenized.

Care of Working Parts of the Machine. Since the working parts of the homogenizer are enclosed, special care of the machine is necessary to prevent bacterial contamination by the homogenizer. It should be taken down frequently, preferably after each use, and left apart until reassembled for immediate use. In this way the parts remain dry. The machine should be flushed out thoroughly with hot water before it is used. The valves should be ground occasionally and kept free from scores.

MAKING THE MIX IN A VACUUM PAN

A vacuum pan is sometimes used in making extremely large quantities of ice cream mixes, and is also used in making condensed and powdered ice cream mix. These procedures require large investments and present a few special problems. Discussion of these problems is omitted here because of the relatively small amount of product handled in this manner.

COOLING THE MIX

Cooling the mix immediately after homogenization to 32° to 40°F. is essential, after which it should be held in aging tanks until used. Unless the mix is cooled to a temperature of 40°F. or lower, it will become very viscous and the ice cream will not melt down smoothly. Also, temperatures below 40°F. retard the growth of bacteria.

Coolers of the surface or cabinet types are generally used for ice cream mix, as the product is too viscous to be cooled effectively in the internal tubular cooler. The surface cooler should be so constructed that moisture condensation forming on the ends of the tubes cannot flow into the mix or

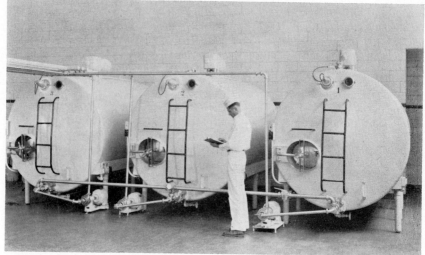

Courtesy of Mojonnier Bros. Co.

FIG. 19. ICE CREAM MIX STORAGE TANKS AT BOWMAN DAIRY, CHICAGO, ILL.

drop into the lower trough. The cabinet cooler, which is essentially a battery of small surface coolers, works very satisfactorily with ice cream mix. In some factories which handle mixes of lower viscosity the modern plate coolers are being used successfully.

AGING THE MIX

Aging the mix before freezing has been practiced since the inception of the ice cream industry.

The changes which undoubtedly occur during aging are:

1. The fat is solidified.
2. If gelatin has been used as a stabilizer it swells and combines with water.
3. The proteins of the mix may change slightly.
4. The viscosity is increased, largely due to the previously mentioned changes.

There is no question but that smoothness of body and texture, resistance to melting and ease of whipping are improved by aging. How much time is necessary for the realization of these advantages is the question. Until recently, the generally accepted time for aging the mix was about 24 hr. Recent experimental work seems to prove that under the average commercial conditions 3 or 4 hr. of aging is all that is essential unless batch-type freezers with limited whipping mechanisms are used. Then a longer aging period seems to give better results. With high fat mixes which have been homogenized at very low pressures, 24 hr. of aging produce good results.

The aging temperature should not exceed 40°F. Many plants age the mix around 36°F. or a little lower. At these temperatures, the bacteria count will not increase during aging. Aging temperatures as low as 28° to 30°F. are sometimes used. There seems to be no advantage in this; in fact, there is the danger that the first of the mix to enter the freezer might freeze fast to the cold walls of the freezer and tend to damage the dasher.

When the mix has been properly aged it is ready for the freezing process which generally follows immediately. Holding the mix for more than about five days is likely to cause at least some deterioration in both flavor and quality.

CHAPTER 12

The Freezing Process

Freezing the mix is one of the most important operations in the making of ice cream for upon it depend the quality, palatability and yield of the finished product.

The freezing process may for convenience be divided into two parts: (1) The mix, with the proper amount of color and flavoring materials generally added at the freezer, is quickly frozen while being agitated to incorporate air in such a way as to produce and control the formation of small ice crystals so necessary to give smoothness in body and texture, palatability and satisfactory overrun in the finished ice cream. (2) When the ice cream is partially frozen to a certain consistency it is drawn from the freezer into packages and quickly transferred to cold storage rooms where the freezing and hardening process is completed without agitation. Changes that take place in the hardening room are discussed in Chapter 13.

The general procedure of the freezing process is easily learned since it involves only accurate measurement of the ingredients into the freezer where they are agitated and frozen only to a certain consistency and then removed from the freezer. However, the correct handling of the details to produce a uniform product requires expert judgment and almost split-second timing—technique acquired only through experience guided by continual, careful study. In fact it is very seldom that any two people will execute the details in exactly the same manner and therefore they obtain different ice creams even when using the same ingredients, formulas and equipment. The effect of slight variations in the amount of coloring and flavoring materials which are usually added at the freezer is readily observed, but equally important are the variations in details of operation.

CLASSIFICATIONS OF FREEZERS

1. Batch freezers
   a. Salt and ice type (obsolete)
   b. Brine freezers (obsolete)
   c. Direct expansion (ammonia or Freon refrigerant)
      1. Vertical—used mainly in some counter freezers
      2. Horizontal—mostly replaced by continuous freezers.
2. Continuous freezers
   Horizontal, direct expansion; used by commercial plants
3. Soft serve freezers
   Batch and automatic continuous freezers of direct expansion-type.

IMPORTANCE OF THE FREEZER

Fast freezing is essential for a smooth product because ice crystals that are formed quickly are smaller than those formed slowly. Therefore, it is desirable to freeze and draw from the freezer in as short a time as possible. A continuous freezer accomplishes this in a few seconds while batch freezers take 6 to 10 minutes depending on factors mentioned later. Also, since freezing continues after the ice cream is placed in the hardening rooms, the ice crystals formed during the hardening period are larger because they form more slowly than in the freezer. For this reason it is desirable to freeze the ice cream as stiff as possible and yet have it liquid enough to draw out of the freezer.

The freezing time and temperature are affected by the type of freezer used. See Table 32.

TABLE 32

FREEZING TIMES AND DRAWING TEMPERATURES

Kind of Freezer	Freezing Time to 90% Overrun Approximate	Drawing Temperature, °F.
Batch freezer	7 min.	24 to 26
Continuous freezer	24 sec.	21 to 22
Counter-freezer	10 min.	26
Soft serve freezer	3 min.	18 to 20

Factors influencing the freezing time (time the mixture is in the freezing chamber of the freezer) are of two types. Some are mechanical while others are inherent in the mix itself. Some **mechanical factors** which influence the freezing time include:

1. Type and make of freezer.
2. Condition of freezer wall and blades.
3. Speed of dasher.
4. Temperature of refrigerant.
5. Velocity of refrigerant passing around freezing chamber.
6. Overrun desired.
7. Temperature at which ice cream is drawn.
8. Rate of unloading freezer.

Character of the mix also influences freezing time. Some of the main considerations here are:

1. Composition of the mix.
2. Freezing point of the mix.
3. Acidity content of ingredients.
4. Kind of ingredients, particularly those carrying fat.
5. Methods of processing the mix.
6. Kind and amount of flavoring materials added.

CHANGES WHICH TAKE PLACE DURING THE FREEZING PROCESS

The function of the freezing process is to freeze a portion of the water of the mix and to incorporate air into the mix. This involves the lowering of the temperature of the mix from aging temperature to the freezing point, freezing a portion of the water of the mix, incorporating air into the mix and cooling the ice cream from the temperature it is drawn from the freezer to hardening room temperature. The temperature of the mix which is put into the freezer drops very rapidly while the sensible heat (which thermometers measure) is being removed and before any ice crystals are formed. This process should take less than a minute or two. Meanwhile, the rapid agitation reduces the viscosity by partly destroying the gel structure and by breaking up the fat globule clusters. The gel structure may partially re-form during the hardening process in the hardening room. Also, the rapid agitation hastens incorporation of air into the mix.

When the freezing point is reached, the liquid water changes to ice crystals which appear in the mix. The ice crystals are practically pure water in a solid form, and thus the sugar, as well as other solutes, becomes more concentrated in the remaining liquid water. Increasing the concentration of these solutes causes the freezing point of the liquid portion to be slightly lower so that the temperature (or sensible heat as it is called) must be lowered before more ice crystals will form. However, the heat called **latent heat of fusion** that must be removed to change liquid water into solid ice crystals is not measured by the thermometer, so that the temperature of the mix would not change noticeably while ice crystals are forming. This actually happens when pure water is frozen, but in freezing ice cream the freezing point is continually being lowered by the formation of the ice crystals, so that the temperature continues to drop but at a slower rate than during the first minute or two while approaching the initial freezing point. While the temperature drops, more ice crystals are formed, increasing the concentration of sugar and other solutes in the remaining liquid water until the concentration is so great that freezing will not occur, thus all of the water is not frozen even after long periods in the hardening room.

During the period in the freezer while ice crystals are forming, more air is incorporated into the mix, and such ingredients as acid fruit juices, fruits, or nuts may be added without any danger of coagulating the mix. Also, at this time the refrigerant may be shut off from the batch freezers. Agitation, in hand or home freezers, is usually stopped when the product has reached a certain consistency or stiffness. This point depends upon the amount of water already changed into ice crystals, and the amount of

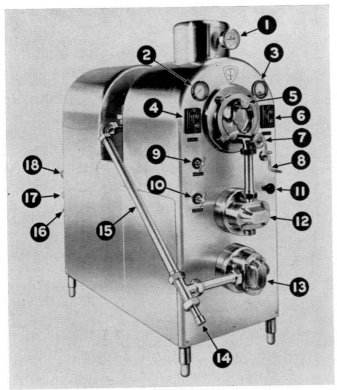

Courtesy of Creamery Package Mfg. Co.

FIG. 20.   THE CONTINUOUS FREEZER

1—*ammonia gauge*
2—*air pressure gauge*
3—*ammeter*
4—*start-stop push button station for pump operation*
5—*mix level inspection port*
6—*start-stop push button station for dasher operation*
7—*ice cream discharge valve*
8—*ice cream pump speed control handle and indicator*

9—*air pressure regulator*
10—*ammonia pressure regulator*
11—*ammonia shut-off control*
12—*ice cream pump*
13—*mix pump*
14—*mix relief valve*
15—*mix inlet line to freezer cylinder*
16—*ammonia liquid line*
17—*ammonia suction line*
18—*air intake filter*

air incorporated into the mix. In commercial freezers, when this point is reached the ice cream is drawn out of the freezers into packages to be placed in the hardening room. At this time, the ice cream contains the desired amount of air, but not all of the desired amount of ice crystals.

The results of the freezing process can best be explained by examining the internal structure of the frozen product. The texture of ice cream is

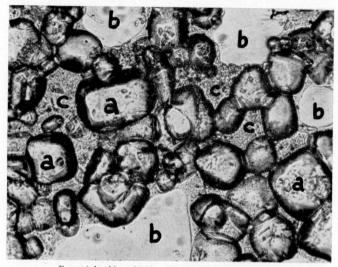

From Arbuckle. 1940. Missouri Research Bull. No. 320, 25–32

FIG. 21. THE INTERNAL STRUCTURE OF ICE CREAM

(a) Ice crystals—average size, 45 to 55 microns. (b) Air cells—
average size, 110 to 185 microns. (c) Unfrozen material—average
distance between ice crystals or ice crystals and air cells, 6 to 8
microns. Average distance between air cells—100 to 150 microns.

known to be affected by many factors but depends principally upon the
presence of ice crystals, air cells and unfrozen material.

The physical structure of ice cream represents a complicated physico-
chemical system. Air cells are dispersed in a continuous liquid phase
with embedded ice crystals. The liquid phase also contains solidified fat
particles, milk proteins, insoluble salts, lactose crystals in some cases, stabilizers of colloidal dimension, and sucrose, lactose, other sugars and soluble salts in true solution. Such a material consisting of liquid, air and
solid is a three-phase system.

THE CONTINUOUS FREEZER

The principle of the continuous freezer process was first patented in
1913 but did not become widely used until 1930 to 1935. Briefly described, the process consists of continually feeding into one end of the
freezing chamber a metered amount of ice cream mix and air. As the mixture passes through the freezing chamber it is agitated and partially frozen
and then discharged in a continuous stream of about the same consistency
usually obtained from a batch freezer. This partially frozen stream is delivered into packages which are then placed in the hardening room to

Courtesy of Cherry-Burrell Corp.

FIG. 22A.   VOGT INSTANT FREEZER

complete the freezing process. The modern machines for this purpose are known as "continuous" or "instant" freezers. (See Figs. 20, 22A–26 and 29.)

Some important advantages of the continuous method are:

1. Less stabilizer is needed, because a larger amount of the ice crystals can be formed in the freezer instead of in the hardening room where slow freezing gives larger crystals, and because less viscosity is needed in the mix. (See Fig. 21.)

2. A shorter aging time is possible because less viscosity is needed and the incorporation of air is less dependent upon the character of the mixture.

3. Less flavoring material is needed because the smaller ice crystals melt more rapidly in the mouth and make the flavor slightly more pronounced.

4. Smoother ice cream is obtained because the ice crystals are much smaller and more uniformly small, and fewer larger crystals are formed in the hardening room.

5. There is less tendency toward sandiness because rapid freezing favors small lactose crystals.

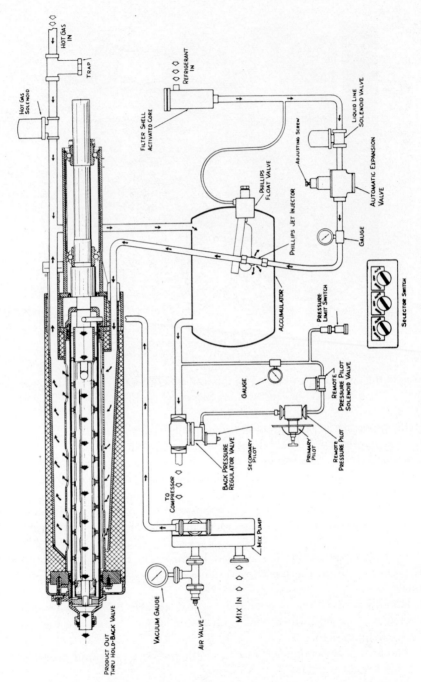

FIG. 22B.   DIAGRAM OF MODEL NO. 603 FREEZER

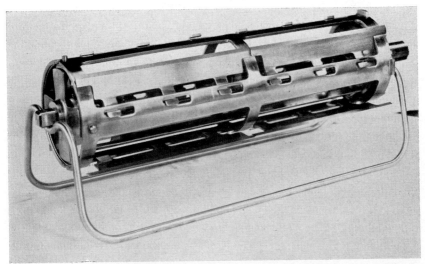

Courtesy of Creamery Package Mfg. Co.

FIG. 23. A CONTINUOUS FREEZER DASHER

The action of this dasher is two-fold: first, it provides a means of mounting and rotating the freezer blades so that the inner wall of the freezing cylinder is properly scraped clean of frozen ice cream and, second, it provides a means of whipping air into the finished ice cream so that the desired overrun and texture can be obtained. The thin film of ice cream mix that freezes on the cylinder wall must be constantly and completely removed by the freezer blades, otherwise the insulating effect of the built-up mix film will reduce the heat transfer of the cylinder by as much as 50%. Proper maintenance of freezer blades can contribute more to freezer performance than and other single factor.

6. A more uniform yield is obtained with less variation between packages, especially when small packages are filled.

7. Continuous freezing facilitates the making of specialties such as center molds, special shapes, combinations of different flavors or colors in one package, variegated ice creams, individual serving-sized package, etc.

8. The volume of ice cream frozen per man-hour of labor is increased. This is most pronounced in packages of the one-pint or one-quart size.

9. There is less opportunity for contamination when filling packages and specialties.

Some disadvantages of the continuous method are inherent in the process while others may eventually be eliminated by better engineering:

1. Great care must be taken in handling the parts of the machine which fit with very small clearances.

2. Operator and mechanics must have special experience and training in order to avoid operational difficulties and possible damage to equipment.

3. It is too easy to obtain excessive overrun.

4. There is a greater tendency for ice cream to shrink in volume after hardening. However, research on this problem may indicate that changing the composition of the mix will correct this difficulty.

5. More help is needed to supply containers and carry packages.

6. Initial cost of the more elaborate equipment is high.

Courtesy of Creamery Package Mfg. Co.

Fig. 24.   Modern Freezer Installation

Three M-10 continuous freezers with Anderson Extru-Wrap Machine at Abbotts Dairies, Inc., Philadelphia.

OPERATING THE CONTINUOUS FREEZER

Use of Continuous Freezer. In the continuous or instant freezers, the mix is continually pumped into the machine and the frozen product is continually discharged from the machine. The operator's principal work is (1) to regulate the amount of air being introduced into the mix to give the desired overrun, and (2) to regulate the temperature of the refrigerant on the freezing chamber. Once the machine is started, the refrigerant is shut off from the freezing chamber only when the machine is to be stopped. Usually the refrigerant is shut off a few minutes before the last mix enters the machine, so that the rinse water (100°F.) which follows the mix will pass through the freezing chamber without being frozen. The temperature of the refrigerant on the freezing chamber is adjusted to give the desired consistency when the product leaves the machine. While these two variables require frequent checks, changes in adjustments are not frequent and thus a large quantity of ice cream can be made with comparatively slight variations in quality.

Courtesy of Delvale Dairies, Inc.

FIG. 25. MODERN FREEZER INSTALLATION

Vogt freezers and Anderson automatic packaging machine at Delvale Dairies Inc., Baltimore, Maryland.

The operation of the continuous freezer demands care and management on the part of the operator. The following are the chief requisites for keeping the freezer operating properly.

1. Keep the ammonia jacket clean and free from oil, water and nonvolatile ammonia fractions. (Check oil trap for oil, water, etc.) Drain as needed.

2. Keep the scraper blades sharp and straight. (Be careful in handling and cleaning. Do not drop this piece of equipment and never bend any parts to better clean it.)

3. Keep the mix pumps in proper working condition. (Check pump motor for proper lubrication and tightness of pulley belts.)

4. Make certain that there is always a plentiful supply of ammonia at the freezer. (Proper ammonia supply insures proper freezing.)

Courtesy of Creamery Package Mfg. Co.

FIG. 26.   MODERN FREEZER INSTALLATION

3M-30 triple-continuous freezer.

5. Provide a steady suction pressure at all times, a pound or so lower than that at which the freezer must operate to give ice cream of the proper temperature. (The continuous freezer makes a continual drain on the liquid ammonia line and refrigeration system. Any lack of liquid or great rise in the suction pressure will soon make itself evident by softness of the ice cream on being discharged.)

The proper method for cleaning the continuous freezer is the same as for most of the dairy equipment.

1. Remove all conveyor pipes which carry ice cream mix to the freezer.

2. Remove the front of the freezer unit, and pull out the freezer dasher. Rinse all parts of machine which come in contact with ice cream mix, with a warm wash water about 90 to 110°F. Flush the freezing tube with cold water, followed with warm and then hot. Thoroughly wash and clean all parts of the freezer and sanitary piping.

3. Rinse parts with warm water and check for cleanliness.

4. Rinse with scalding hot water and allow to dry. Wipe outside surfaces of freezer with chamois cloth.

5. Do not assemble unless directed to do so.

Precautions to be remembered when handling the continuous freezer.

1. Have all mix line connections tight to prevent mix leaking out and air leaking in.

2. Check controls frequently to insure proper operation.

3. Drain oil trap frequently to insure that all oil, water, etc., has been removed from the system.

4. Never bend scraper blades. Never drop the freezer dasher. Be careful when removing from the freezing cylinder.

5. Allow freezing chamber to warm up prior to rinsing with hot or warm water.

6. Check the pump motor to insure proper lubrication and proper tightness of pulley belts.

7. Use extreme care in handling mutator (dasher) in assembling or in dismantling the freezer in order to prevent personal injury.

Fruit and nut flavors can be frozen in the continuous freezers by finely grinding or chopping the fruit or nuts and adding to and mixing thoroughly in the ice cream mix before freezing. The mix with fruit and nuts added may be thoroughly mixed in the flavor tank of the freezer. This procedure is convenient for small batches of five or ten gallons. If larger batches are to be made, the most convenient method is to mix and prepare the fruit or nut mixes in a 50 or 100-gal. flavor vat with the outlet connection piped to the pump inlet at the freezer.

When fruit or nut ice cream is desired with large particles of fruit showing, the fruit juice flavoring and color is added to the mix prior to freezing, and a fruit feeder for the large particles must be used connected to the *outlet* of the freezer.

Changing Flavors

Darker flavors should follow lighter ones without shutting down.

In case strawberry or any other flavor containing seeds, particles of fruit or nuts have been frozen, it is necessary to stop the freezer, open the pumps and wash pumps, lines, freezing tube and tank, in order that fruits, seeds, etc., will be removed, before freezing the next flavor. Practically all the mix, of which there will be only a small quantity, can be saved by draining before washing out the equipment.

Preparing Fruits and Nuts

The juice should be drained from fruit and the fruit placed into the hopper as dry as possible. This prevents undesirable ice formation in the ice cream from the introduction of unfrozen fruit juice. The fruit juices and flavoring materials must be added to the mix before the mix is frozen.

The nuts are usually dry and can be put into the hopper without further preparation.

Specially prepared fruits and nuts should be drained if they come packed in syrup or juice and the syrup or juice added to the mix. It may be found desirable with canned nuts packed in heavy syrup to dissolve the syrup with a small amount of mix before draining the nuts.

Mixtures of fruit and nuts should be mixed together in the fruit hopper and not before. Do not fill the hopper full of a mixture as the fruits and nuts will then mix slowly and may not mix as completely as desired. It is better to fill the hopper about half full and add the fruit and nuts to the hopper a little more frequently.

Candy must be well broken up into pieces which are to show in the ice cream and should not be larger than $3/8$ in. square. Large pieces of candy are liable to cause jamming in the equipment. The candy should be screened to take out large pieces. The hopper should not be filled full, only small portions should be added at frequent intervals since, if large amounts are put in, the candy is likely to stick together and form balls. It is very desirable, where possible, to put any nuts together with candy as would be the case with walnut and pecan crunch. The higher the percentage of nuts in the mixture, the better the operation, since some of the moisture in the candy is absorbed by the nuts and the tendency of the candy to stick together is minimized. An alternative method of using candy, which gives good results, is to add just enough mix to it to give it a slight flow. This helps prevent the candy from sticking and aids materially in feeding it into the ice cream.

Any product to be fed into the ice cream, particularly nuts and firm bodied fruits, in large pieces should not be fed into the freezer or fruit feeder. Break or cut the pieces to some extent, but they should remain large enough to show well in the finished ice cream.

AUTOMATION IN ICE CREAM PROCESSING

The processing procedures in the manufacture of ice cream have become fully mechanized and various degrees of automation of these processes are now taking place. Automation is the bringing of mechanized systems under automatic control. This means several pieces of equipment are unified and work together. Some applications may include any one or more of the automatically controlled procedures: batch operations, mix processing, packaging, equipment cleaning, inventory, and mix computing. The goal of automation is increased labor productivity. The potentials for automation adaption are great but careful planning is always important and the extent of efficient adaption may vary considerably among different operations.

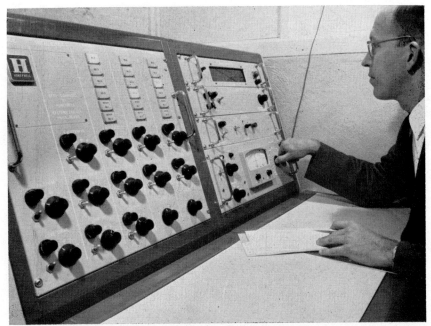

FIG. 27. AUTOMATIC RECIPE MAKER

This analog computer at H. P. Hood & Sons of Boston, one of the nation's leading processors of dairy products, solves ice cream mix formulae. Developed by Minneapolis-Honeywell's Brown Instruments Division, computer complements a fully automatic ice cream batching operation, the first such installation of its kind. Ice cream mix recipes change daily due to variations in butterfat and other contents of dairy ingredients, but computer comes up with right answer in matter of minutes. Recipe, digitally coded on punch card, is then "read" by other electronic devices that open valves and measure flow of ingredients to blending tanks.

The following is a description of an automated plant recently installed in Boston (H. P. Hood and Sons and Minneapolis-Honeywell Regulator Co., 1960.) (See Figs. 27 and 28.)

Ice cream is automation's latest conquest.

Recipes for bulk production of America's favorite dessert are calculated by a computer far more quickly and accurately than possible by any human.

Electronic equipment "masterminded" by coded punch cards opens valves sending basic ice cream ingredients from storage to blending tanks, measures their flow with electrical impulses from metering devices, and then closes the valves when the pre-determined amount is reached.

Instruments watch over the pasteurization, homogenization and cooling processes to see that nothing goes wrong. Even the cleaning of lines, valves and tanks, once a time-consuming chore, is pushbutton programmed from a

Courtesy of H. P. Hood & Sons and Minneapolis-Honeywell Regulator Co.

FIG. 28.   ELECTRONIC MONITOR

At H. P. Hood & Sons Boston ice cream plant this Electronic Monitor indicates, records and controls flow of mix ingredients from storage to blending tanks based on computer-calculated formulae coded on punch cards.   Flow instrumentation, developed by Pottermeter Company, is incorporated in automatic batching system, application engineered by Brown Instruments Division of Minneapolis-Honeywell Regulator Company, that includes an analog computer for resolving mix recipes and pushbutton CIP programming.   Pottermeter equipment is used in conjunction with turbine-type flow meter which produces a frequency for measuring flow and drives totalizers and other controls.

master control panel that portrays the entire ice cream-making process.

H. P. Hood & Sons, one of the nation's leading independent processors of dairy products, took the wraps off the automated system at its Boston ice cream plant today for a press audience.   The system, described as "the world's first fully automatic batching process for ice cream mix," was conceived by the dairy company and application engineered by Brown Instruments Division of Minneapolis-Honeywell Regulator Company.

Advanced Control Concepts

"To the best of our knowledge, this is the only system of its kind," said Carl A. Blanchard, Jr., Hood Director of Engineering. "It incorporates automatic control concepts believed to be the most advanced in the ice cream industry, and the improvement in mix batching over conventional methods borders on the miraculous. It takes the guesswork out of making ice cream and assures a product of uniformly high quality."

Blanchard credited the automatic equipment with eliminating much of the heavy manual labor normally involved in batching—the combining of dairy and other products to make fluid ice cream mix.

In addition, he said, integration of the automatic system with new equipment has enabled the company to increase production capacity at this plant approximately 70 per cent.

"In an industry noted for low profit margins, and in which there is a continuing trend toward a larger number and variety of items to meet consumer demands, it is essential to attain maximum productivity of labor and facilities," Blanchard said.

He pointed out that the installation of the automatic equipment was accomplished without any decrease in the work force, which was, he said, in line with company policy.

Mix a Complex Problem

Mix proportioning of the dairy ingredients, he continued, is highly complex. Butterfat and non-fat content, called serum solids, fluctuate daily, requiring changes in basic recipes. Seasonal availability and raw materials costs, as well as maintenance of quality of the finished ice cream, also are important considerations. Furthermore, different types of mix vary widely in combinations and proportions of dairy ingredients.

The computer, separate from the control system, selects the two or three dairy ingredients required for a mix from among a number available and decides how much of each is needed for a specific mix.

In a fraction of a second—a computation speed more than 20,000 times faster than it takes a human to solve a formula, and without any chance for error—the analog-type computer has the answer. If it's impractical, it says so.

"Recipe" Coded on Punch Card

The recipe is digitally coded on a punch card that also may be used for production control and accounting purposes. It is "read" by instrumentation that opens and shuts valves and measures and controls the simultaneous flow of all liquid ingredients from storage to blending tanks. All the operator need do is to set switches which will determine the flow sequence of ingredients for batching called for by the punch card.

Key to the measuring process, Blanchard explained, is a flow-sensing device known as a Pottermeter. It records the flow rate of ingredients with a turbine-type rotor imbedded with a powerful magnet. As liquids pass through the meters, the rotor generates a pulse train proportional to the rate of flow. These automatically drive totalizers, recorders and other controls in the control room.

The overall system includes a graphic programming console from which the entire mix operation, including automatic cleaning of batching equipment, can

Courtesy of Delvale Dairies, Inc.

FIG. 29.   MODERN FREEZER INSTALLATION

Cherry-Burrell 403 Freezers—at Delvale Dairies, Inc., in Baltimore, Maryland, completely automatic with instant stop and start to eliminate necessity for rerun operation.

be controlled by a single person.   The console, with more than three miles of hidden wiring, includes pushbuttons for starting and stopping pumps, indicators showing tank liquid levels and integrators that total the amount of ingredients used in batching operations.

A pushbotton programmed clean-in-place system with built-in cost savings refinements is an integral part of the automated mix operation at the Boston ice cream plant of H. P. Hood & Sons.

The automatic CIP system—actually five systems in one, each operating independently—is incorporated in a console which graphically represents the entire mix process, including tank levels, flow totals of ingredients, valve positions and pump operations.

A unique feature of the system, developed by Brown Instruments Division of Minneapolis-Honeywell Regulator Company in collaboration with this leading New England dairy products processor, is the recycling, in sequential cleaning of tanks, of the final rinse for use as the pre-rinse for the next tank to be cleaned.

Sequential Cleaning

All individual CIP circuits have high and low level tank probes, temperature controllers, adjustable cam timers for governing sequence and length of cleaning operations, and cycle circuit steppers.   The cam timer is equipped with a Micro Switch whose on-off action causes valves to pulsate.   This agitation dislodges hard-to-remove solids from the valves.

Another system feature is a series of interlocks which prevent start-up if improper manual field connections are made.

All mix process equipment at the ice cream plant is cleaned-in-place in five steps: (1) raw product pipelines, (2) HTST[1] (3) pasteurization lines, (4) raw product tanks and (5) mix storage tanks. Two solution tanks permit simultaneous cleaning of any two steps.

Normally, pipelines and HTST CIP is performed at the end of each day's batching operations while tank cleaning may be done during batching.

Six basic three-way valves—three for each solution tank—control cleaning cycles. Automatic regulation of the valves permits these functions to be performed:

1. Filling of solution tanks with water. For example, in using Solution Tank No. 1, valves CV-11, CV-12 and CV-13 (see diagram) are in the C to B position with pump CP-1 off. Water valve (CVWS1) is then energized to admit water which is shut off when probe control signals proper level has been reached.

2. Pre-rinse. With valve CV-11 in the C to A position, pump CP-1 circulates water through the piping system. Water is returned to valve CV-12, which is in the C to A position, then to CV-13 in the C to B position, from where it is returned to the tank and recirculated for a timed period. Next, CV-12 is energized to the C to B position for disposal of solution tank water.

3. Wash and final rinse. These follow the necessary pattern until all lines are cleaned. Timing is pre-set to adequately clean the system.

4. Control of process valves from graphic console.

The Hood CIP system is equipped with a selector switch for periodic cleaning of tank with an acid wash instead of a detergent wash.

THE BATCH FREEZER

The dasher, which fits into the freezing chamber and can be easily removed for cleaning, is an important part of every batch freezer. In the batch freezer it consists of two parts, the scraper blades and the beater, to perform the following functions:

1. Aids in transmission of refrigeration by keeping the mix in continuous contact with freezer walls.
2. Scrapes freezer walls free from ice crystals.
3. Beats in air.
4. Pushes mix continually forward which is essential in unloading the freezer.

It is important to have the dasher in proper alignment and the blades must be sharp.

The temperature of the refrigerant is very important and should be from —10° to —20°F. in order to get a rapid formation of ice crystals. This rapid formation favors the development of small crystals and results in a smoother ice cream. However, the freezing should be slow enough

---

[1] High temperature—short time pasteurization.

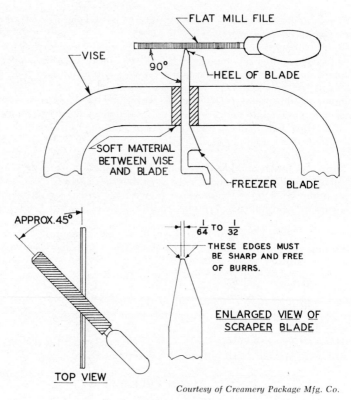

FIG. 30.   THE CORRECT METHOD FOR SHARPENING HARDENED
STAINLESS STEEL SCRAPER BLADES

This blade is used on continuous ice cream freezers.

to permit incorporating the desired amount of air, since this also affects
the body and texture of the ice cream.   The most desirable refrigerant
temperature to use depends upon:

1. The efficiency of the freezer, i.e. the heat transfer rate of the walls.
2. The freezing point of the mix (dependent upon the amount of milk solids-
   not-fat, sugar and flavoring material present).
3. The sharpness of the scraper blades.
4. The amount of refrigerant available.

In the direct expansion freezers, the freezing chamber is surrounded by
liquid ammonia or other refrigerant.   Ammonia is the most common refrigerant.   This type of freezing medium has now nearly replaced other
types for both the batch and continuous freezers in ice cream factories

because it is cheaper due to saving in power and equipment, as well as increasing refrigeration capacity.

THE FREEZING PROCEDURE FOR BATCH FREEZERS

The first step in the freezing procedure is to prepare the freezer. Its parts should be inspected to be sure they are clean and dry, and then assembled in accordance with instructions from the manufacturer. The operator's hands should be clean to avoid contamination of the product which later contacts these parts. When the freezer is assembled, some operators sanitize the machine by running hot water or a cold solution of a chemical sanitizing agent through the machine. In addition to sanitizing, this may also serve to test for leaks and faulty operating condition. While sanitizing, do not turn the dasher more than a few revolutions thus avoiding excessive wear. If hot water is used, it must be at least 180°F. to obtain any sanitizing effect, and must be followed by a cold water rinse to cool the freezer. When a chemical sanitizing agent is used, complete draining is essential.

The second step in the freezing procedure is adding the mix. When the freezer has been properly prepared, it is ready for the measured amount of mix, flavoring and coloring. It is always desirable to have the temperature of the mix below 40°F. when it goes into the freezer. Color and flavorings should be accurately measured, and poured into the mix rather than carelessly poured on the sides of the vat or freezer. Uniform drainage of the measuring cups is essential to accurate measurement. The total volume of the mix, flavor, and color should be about half the total capacity of the freezing chamber. Thus in vanilla and similar ice creams flavored with a pint or less of extract and color, it is customary to use 20 quarts of mix in a 40-qt. freezer; while in fruit or nut ice creams 18 quarts of mix with about 2 quarts of fruit or nuts make up the 20 quarts of mixture for a batch.

The flavoring and coloring materials must be added so as to become uniformly distributed, but the actual moment or order of adding them may be varied. Special precautions apply when adding acid fruits, nuts, etc.; these should be added only after some ice crystals have formed. Acid fruits will coagulate the milk in the mix if they are added before the ice crystals start to form. Nuts, candy and cookies will be less likely to dissolve if added late, and fruits will remain in larger pieces. Therefore, such materials should be added as late as possible and still give time enough to have them uniformly distributed; it is best to determine the exact time for each machine, since some machines are more efficient in carrying the nuts back into the freezer, but generally it is safe to accept the manufacturer's directions as a basis. When using a continuous freezer, the solid materials (nuts, fruit, etc.) must be added as the ice cream is being discharged from the freezing chamber and all liquid material including fruit juices must be added to the mix before it passes into the freezing chamber.

Finally, the freezer should be operated uniformly as to speed, refrigerant, temperature, etc. The refrigerant temperature should be well below 0°F.

The mix is run into the freezer, the dasher started, and then the refrigerant is turned onto the freezing chamber. This sequence must be preserved to avoid damage to the machine. To avoid rapid dulling and wearing of the scraper blades, the dasher must never be operated when there is no mix in the freezer. The refrigerant must never be turned on unless the dasher is in motion because even a drop of water may freeze the dasher to the wall of the freezer and cause the dasher to be bent or twisted when attempting to start the machine. This order of operation and these precautions apply to all freezers regardless of size, type, or installation.

OPERATING THE BATCH FREEZER

The use of "batch" freezers makes it difficult to prevent undesirable variations and burdens the operator with many more details to get uniform quality. Each batch of mix must be measured, colored, and flavored separately, requiring the measurement of smaller quantities which presents many more chances for errors with resulting lack of uniform quality of finished ice cream. A carefully prepared work-plan will avoid many errors such as forgetting to add color, etc.

Using the sequence previously described, the machine is started, and then the operator must determine largely by observation, through the peep-hole, the correct time to shut off the refrigerant. At this correct time, only a small part of the water in the mix is frozen giving it a certain lustre and consistency which he must learn to recognize.

Shutting off the refrigerant too soon results in (1) longer time to obtain overrun, (2) possible failure to obtain the desired overrun as the softer condition will repel overrun, (3) too high temperature when drawn from the freezer, (4) soft ice cream and (5) a tendency for coarse ice cream since the ice crystals formed slowly in the hardening room will be larger. When the refrigerant is not shut off soon enough, the mixture is too hard and results in (1) difficulty in obtaining overrun, (2) longer time in the freezer, as stiff ice cream repels whipping (even if it is allowed to soften in an effort to incorporate air), (3) usually a lower temperature when drawn from the freezer and (4) a smoother ice cream provided it does not become soft in obtaining overrun.

After the refrigerant is shut off, the machine within certain limits continues to operate, incorporating air and freezing more of the mixture until the product attains both the desired overrun and the desired consistency. Then the operator allows the product to be drawn from the freezer. Since the air is incorporated during the freezing process and by the whipping action of the dasher, the operator must adjust the refrigerant to allow the right amount of time for whipping. This time will vary with the composition of the mix, the construction of the freezer, the rate of cooling or freezing, and the consistency, temperature, etc., in the freezer. These latter conditions change so rapidly in the freezer that they can only be estimated by the operator's observation and this requires study as well as considerable experience. While there is some loss of air, in general it can be said, that up to a certain point air is being continually whipped into the ice cream mix. However, after that point is reached it loses air faster than it gains it, if the whipping is carried on too long. Therefore the operator must adjust the refrigerant so that the ice cream can be drawn at the moment when he has obtained the desired overrun and the desired consistency of the ice cream. When the ice cream is drawn from the freezer it should be stiff enough to "ribbon" or almost hold its shape, and yet soft enough to "settle" or lose its shape within a minute or two.

Filling the Containers. The container or package into which the ice cream is drawn should be cooled sufficiently to prevent melting the ice cream. When such melting around the edges does occur, it will be frozen again later in the hardening room and the ice crystals formed will be large, giving a coarse and icy condition at the edge of the package. Furthermore, this melting will cause a loss of overrun. Another precaution to take is against the formation of air-pockets which leave the container partly filled. This can be avoided easily if the ice cream is not too stiff when drawn. Precaution should also be taken to see that chocolate ice cream, acid-fruit flavored ice cream, sherbets and ices are placed either in well-tinned containers or more safely in paper or paper-lined containers, since the acid in these products will react with the iron to cause undesirable defects.

The freezer should be emptied as rapidly as possible to prevent wide fluctuations in overrun in the packages. Therefore, avoid filling small packages directly from the batch freezer. When a 40-qt. freezer is emptied into $2^1/_2$-gal. containers, the first one may have 90 per cent overrun, the second 100 per cent, the third 80 per cent and the fourth 70 per cent overrun. The variation will follow this general up and down trend, the extent of variation depending on the length of time required for filling each container.

If metal containers are filled it is usually desirable to put a parchment paper over the top under the cover. This paper protects from the metal cover and may also be used to designate the flavor of the ice cream, date made and possibly a key number to identify the operator, the batch of mix and freezer batch—information which aids in handling inventories, records and tracing the cause of defects.

While the ice cream is being drawn from the freezer it gradually becomes softer and should not be "drained" out when it gets too soft. A possible exception to this rule is to drain the freezer completely when the freezer is to be taken apart and cleaned. At other times the small amount left in the freezer goes into the next batch, which can follow immediately without stopping the dasher. However, if the next batch is of a different flavor or color, i.e., one which will not cover up or blend with the previous batch, it is necessary to take out the dasher and clean the freezer. This is especially true of nut and fruit ice creams, since pieces of nuts and fruit cannot be removed from the dasher without taking the freezer apart, but if left in the freezer they will appear in the next batch of ice cream.

CLEANING THE FREEZER

When the freezer is not going to be used for two hours or more, it should be taken apart, cleaned and sanitized. This is most easily and efficiently done immediately after the last ice cream is drawn. The rinse water should not be over 100°F. to rinse out the ice cream, and the dasher during this process should be turned only a few revolutions. The dasher and other removable parts should be removed to a sink and thoroughly scrubbed with a hot (120°F.) washing solution, rinsed, sanitized and stored where they may dry. The freezing chamber and other parts which cannot be placed in a sink must be scrubbed with a hotter (130°F.) washing solution using special care to remove the greasy film left on the surface and in the corners (all places difficult to reach) especially at the rear of the chamber. These parts should also be thoroughly rinsed and left open to dry. The freezer should not be assembled until it is to be used.

HOW TO OBTAIN AND CONTROL OVERRUN

Overrun is usually defined as the volume of ice cream obtained in excess of the volume of the mix. It is usually expressed as "per cent overrun." This increased volume is composed mainly of air incorporated during the freezing process. The amount of air which should be incorporated depends upon the composition of the mix and the way it is processed, and is regulated so as to give that per cent overrun or yield which will give the proper body, texture and palatability necessary to good quality ice cream. Too much air will produce a snowy, fluffy, unpalatable ice cream; too little air, a soggy, heavy product. Generally, mixes which have a high total solids content justify the incorporation of a higher per cent air—a higher overrun—than mixes lower in total solids. Although no definite per cent can be stated, some authorities indicate as most desirable a per cent overrun between two and three times the per cent total solids content of the mix. For example: a mix with a total solids content of 40 per cent might justify an overrun of as high as 100 per cent. Formulas for determining the overrun and solving problems in overrun are discussed in Chapter 10.

Five factors which are usually considered when determining the amount of overrun are:

1. Legal regulations enforced in the market area.

2. Total solids content of the ice cream. Higher total solids may permit use of a higher overrun.

3. Composite ice creams (such as fruit and nut) require a lower overrun than plain ice cream in order to obtain an equally desirable body and texture. The correct overrun to take may be estimated as described in Chapter 10.

4. Selling price of ice cream.

5. Type of package. So-called "bulk" packages which are sold for "dipping" usually contain 90 to 100 per cent overrun, while packages of the carry-home type (not dipped before reaching the consumer) usually are most satisfactory if they contain 70 to 80 per cent overrun.

The ability to obtain overrun at the freezer depends partly on the concentration and type of ingredients in the mix (see previous discussion in Chapter 11 on influence of sugars, total solids, etc.) and on the freezing process itself. Sharpness of scraper blades, speed of dasher, volume of refrigerant passing over freezing chamber and temperature of refrigerant are important, as described previously, to produce rapid freezing and favor overrun. The stiffness of the product at the time refrigerant is shut off and the fullness of the freezer are two of the most important factors and perhaps the two most likely to fluctate under careless operation.

To secure uniform overrun and yield, the following points should receive attention:

1. Uniformity in refrigerant temperature and rate of flow of refrigerant.

2. The use of overrun testers, Draw-Rite or Willman controls.

3. Uniform make, etc., of freezers for the freezer man.

4. Not too many freezers per man.

5. Hopper systems for filling containers if batch freezers are used. This allows freezers to be emptied rapidly into a hopper where there is

less agitation while filling packages. Higher overrun at the freezer is necessary to compensate for some loss in overrun in the hopper.

6. The use of a system of checking the weight of packages or containers as they enter the hardening room.

The control of overrun is very important and should be maintained as nearly constant as possible from batch to batch and from day to day. A variation of 10 per cent in overrun represents a sizable difference in profit to the manufacturer. Lack of uniformity is also frowned upon by the retailer and the consumer. The experienced, intelligent operator, with the aid of an overrun tester or laboratory checks, should not have much trouble with the control of overrun.

The correct overrun percentage depends upon the kind and composition of product and freezing equipment. The overrun on different products may normally range as shown in Table 33:

TABLE 33

PERCENTAGE OVERRUN FOR DIFFERENT PRODUCTS

Product	Overrun, Per cent
Ice cream, packaged	70 to 80
Ice cream, bulk	90 to 100
Sherbet	30 to 40
Ice	25 to 30
Soft ice cream	30 to 50
Ice milk	50 to 80
Milk shake	10 to 15

CHAPTER 13

Packaging, Hardening and Shipping

PACKAGING

When the ice cream is drawn from the freezer it usually is collected in containers which give it the desired shape and size for convenient handling during the hardening and marketing processes.

The multi-service package. This type of container is seldom used in modern operation. Originally, heavily tinned steel cans were used, and even now these are practically the only type of multi-service package in use. They are cleaned, sanitized and used repeatedly.

The single-service type of package has met with increasing favor, especially during recent years. The rapid improvement of roads, delivery trucks and mechanically refrigerated cabinets, as well as the wide use of continuous freezers and automatic packaging machines, have hastened the increasing use of single-service containers. Also, the consumer's demands and purchasing habits have encouraged a definite change in favor of this type of package. In general, these packages are constructed of paper or cardboard which has been treated to make it impervious to moisture. The larger sizes have the minimum of very light-weight metal necessary to give correct shape to the package. As yet their use in special molds has been restricted to the simplest forms, such as replacing the metal 8-qt. brick pan or slab.

Some **advantages** of the single-service type of package are:

1. Less space required for storing a given volume of ice cream.

2. Less time required to harden a given volume of ice cream in the hardening room.

3. Elimination of the time, labor and materials used to salvage, recondition and properly clean the container, not only for regular customers but especially for the occasional orders like picnic gatherings.

4. Less rapid deterioration of delivery trucks and dispensing cabinets, because these cans are lighter in weight and have no sharp edges.

5. Less wear and tear on shipping bags.

6. Usually neater and cleaner in appearance.

7. Less danger of injuring the flavor of the ice cream.

Some **disadvantages** of the single-service type of package are:

1. The initial cost is high and cannot always be matched by the savings indicated under advantages.

179

2. When made of poorly processed paper, they increase the tendency toward the defect known as shrinkage.

3. They foster the habit of discarding property in contrast to the habit of thrift which endeavors to obtain the maximum usefulness of property.

4. They may be uneconomical even under conditions of mass production and high-cost, low-skilled labor.

The bulk package, so-called, has always been used in selling the hardened ice cream to retailers who repackaged it by dipping it into servings such as cones or into small containers generally of a quart or less. Either single-service or multi-service containers may be used for bulk packages. When metal containers were widely used, these bulk packages included sizes of 1, 2, 3, and 5 gallons. During recent years, along with the advent of the single-service type of package, there has been a tendency to standardize on bulk packages of only the 2.5-, 3-, and 5-gallon, the one-gallon size being listed among the "carry-out" packages. The bulk packages are always factory-filled, usually directly from the freezer (freezer filled) or sometimes from a hopper which collects the ice cream from the freezer. The hopper is insulated or refrigerated and is generally installed so that a number of batch freezers can be emptied into it without interrupting the freezer-emptying process, and so that the ice cream can flow by gravity to a lower level where it is packaged. When filling bulk packages many manufacturers use ice cream having 90 to 100 per cent overrun, which is slightly higher than for ice cream placed in "carry-out" packages.

The "carry-out" or "take-home" package represents the most important development in the packaging of ice cream. This change has paralleled the adoption of the continuous freezer, the automatic packaging machine, and the development of the single-service type of package, as well as the emphasis by the consumer on the "ready" packaging of all food products. The carry-out package for ice cream has practically always been the single-service type and made of paper or cardboard in sizes of one-half gallon or less. When packages of such sizes are filled directly from the batch freezer, consecutive packages will contain ice cream having widely different overruns. A possible exception to this is the brick ice cream that is molded in 8-qt. slabs and then cut into individual bricks which are wrapped and cartoned by hand.

PACKAGING MACHINES

Packaging machines or fillers are used to fill the small carry-out packages. These machines are either insulated or refrigerated and are so constructed that the contents of the freezer can be emptied into them quickly. There is only gentle agitation of the ice cream in these machines, which prevents wide variation of overrun in the packages. The major **disadvantages** of fillers are:

1. The ice cream has to be too soft to give an ideal smoothness of texture in the finished prduct.

2. Some overrun (3 to 10 per cent) is necessarily lost, and the loss is not easily controlled.

3. It is difficult to maintain the temperature of the ice cream so as to avoid either partial melting or continued freezing.

However, these machines are still the most economical and satisfactory method of factory-filling packages containing less than one pint regardless of the type of freezer being used. The continuous freezer has already made it possible to fill packages containing one pint or more directly from the freezer economically and satisfactorily, and new equipment now in use in several ice cream plants seems to indicate that eventually much if not most ice cream will be pre-packed in individual serving-sized portions.

Some **advantages of the factory-filled** carry-out package are:

1. Greater convenience in handling.

2. Retailing at much lower temperature, thus reaching consumer in better condition.

3. Less danger of the retailer damaging the quality of the product.

4. Less chance of bacteriological contamination, especially during retailing.

5. Less variation in quantity as well as quality from one package to another.

6. Faster and more convenient serving of customers.

7. Less difficulty in estimating profits and keeping records.

8. Neater appearance of package.

The ice cream put into the factory-filled carry-out package should usually have a lower overrun than the same product put into bulk packages. This should encourage the consumer to switch to factory-filled packages. The difference in overrun is commonly from 15 to 20 per cent and partially compensates for the greater weight obtained when the retailer "dips" a similar package from the retail cabinet.

THE HARDENING PROCESS

When ice cream is drawn from the freezer and put into the container to be placed in the hardening room it has a semi-fluid consistency not stiff enough to hold its shape. Therefore the freezing process is continued without agitation until the temperature of the ice cream reaches 0°F. or lower, preferably —15°F. Here, as in the freezer, it is desirable to get quick freezing or quick hardening, since slow hardening favors large ice crystals and coarseness.

The time required for hardening has been assumed to be the time necessary for the temperature at the center of the package to drop to $0°F$. This hardening time for a still air operation may be as short as 30 minutes for quarter-pint packages or as long as 24 hours for a still air operation for five-gallon packages, and the shorter time always gives a smoother ice cream. A hardening time of 6 to 8 hours for five-gallon packages is usually considered excellent operation, but most operators allow at least 12 hours. When hardening tunnels are used the rate of hardening is several times faster.

Factors Affecting the Hardening Time. Some of the more important of these factors are:

1. Size and shape of package. Doubling the size of the package increases the hardening time by about 50 per cent; when $2^1/_2$-gallon packages require 14 hours, the 5 gallon packages will require about 22 hours. The shape is important in determining the amount of surface area per gallon of ice cream and also the speed of air-flow around the package. Light-colored packages and those having good reflecting surfaces are slower to cool.

2. Air-circulation. With forced circulation like an air blast, hardening requires only about 60 per cent of the time required in still air. Of course the speed of the air blast is also important. This emphasizes the need of properly stacking the packages to facilitate rapid air movement, and also suggests the desirability of hardening each package rather than making bundles of packages.

3. Temperature of the air. Temperatures above $-10°F$. and colder than $-25°F$. are less desirable from the standpoint of quality of product and economical operation.

4. Section of the room. In the "still air" type of room the ice cream hardens about as quickly near the ceiling as on the floor, while directly on the ammonia coils it requires only two-thirds as much time. The center aisle requires twice as long.

5. Temperature of ice cream drawn from the freezer. Drawing the ice cream at one degree higher temperature will increase the hardening time by about 10 to 15 per cent.

6. Composition of the mix. There is a tendency for shorter hardening time as the fat content decreases and as the freezing point of the mix rises.

7. Per cent overrun. There is a slight tendency for the hardening time to increase as the percentage overrun increases.

Hardening Rooms (see Figs. 31 to 33) where the packaged ice cream is placed in dry air maintained at a temperature between $-10°$ and

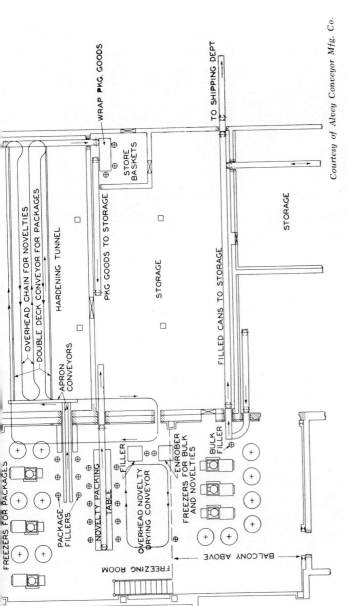

FIG. 31. CONVEYOR EQUIPMENT FOR HARDENING TUNNEL QUICK FREEZING

Courtesy of Alvey Conveyor Mfg. Co.

The drawing shows a typical freezing plant for producing and finishing bulk and package ice cream novelties, either coated or uncoated. In a plant of this general size there is, conservatively estimated, a producing capacity for freezing as much as 450 gallons in pint cartons per hour and 200 trays of frozen novelties, with facilities for enrobing if desired. The preparation of the mix is usually accomplished in another location in the plant and the finished mix is delivered to the storage tanks in the freezing department for processing. Conveyors propel the packages of novelties through the hardening tunnels and into the storage room and are also arranged to speed delivery to the shipping department.

FIG. 32. CONVEYING CARTONS OF ICE CREAM ON MOJONNIER CONVEYOR CHAIN IN PROCESSING ROOM

H. P. Hood and Sons, Portland, Maine.

—50°F. are used by modern manufacturers. Most factories employ ammonia as the refrigerant to maintain a temperature of —20° or —25°F. For economical operation, the hardening room should be entered through an ante-room which may be large enough to permit storage of some ingredients at about 30°F. The hardening rooms may be classified as follows according to the arrangement of the ammonia coils used for cooling.

1. Ceiling Coils. When the coils are located along the ceiling there may be a metal baffle plate immediately beneath them to facilitate air circulation by gravity. This type allows great freedom in the use of floor space for conveyors, arrangement of ice cream, etc. The major **disadvantages** are:

(a) The lack of uniform temperature unless fans are used to aid air circulation.
(b) The temptation to pile packages too close together, causing slow hardening.
(c) Difficulties in taking inventories.
(d) Difficulties in defrosting the ammonia coils.

2. Horizontal Shelf Coils. The most common arrangement of the ammonia coils is in horizontal shelves as well as along the ceiling. These

Courtesy of Mojonnier Bros. Co.

Fig. 33. Hardening Room Arrangement and Conveyor Equipment

Grocer's Dairy Co., Grand Rapids, Mich.

are the so-called "still air" type and seldom gain much efficiency by the use of fans. The major **disadvantages** of this type are:

(a) Much valuable space is made useless by the mass of coils.
(b) The coil shelves interfere with the use of conveyors.
(c) There are difficulties in defrosting the ammonia coils.

3. Vertical Coils. A third type of hardening room arranges the coils in a vertical position like a fence dividing the room into sections or bins. The main **disadvantages** of this type are:

a. The temptation to pile packages too closely.
b. Less convenient use of conveyors.
c. Difficulties in defrosting, although these coils are more easily kept in good condition than are those in the two previously mentioned types.

4. Forced Air Cabinet. A fourth type of hardening room is now approved and widely accepted by modern manufacturers. In this type the ammonia coils are arranged in a cabinet through which the air is circulated by fans. Air ducts with openings at various parts of the room aid in obtaining the rapid air movement necessary for uniform temperatures and rapid freezing. The cabinets containing the ammonia coils may be located outside of the hardening room—an aid to defrosting. The main **disadvantages** of this type are: (1) The temptation to pile packages too closely; (2) difficulties in taking inventory.

Hardening Tunnels. Some manufacturers of larger volumes use hardening tunnels containing an air blast at —30° to —50°F. for fast hardening. These may or may not contain a conveyor belt, and have their greatest advantages when hardening the smaller packages which can be hardened in an hour.

Hardening Cabinets resemble the retail ice cream cabinet, and are refrigerated by mechanical refrigeration. The ice cream package is placed in the dry, watertight compartments, each of which will hold one or two 5-gallon containers. These are usually operated at a temperature between —10° and —15°F., are most economical for a limited volume of business, and avoid exposure of the operator to sudden chilling temperatures.

Summing up, modern manufacturers place the packaged ice cream in a dry-air hardening room maintained at a temperature between —10°F. and —50°F. Small manufacturers now use the cabinet type which has individual water-tight compartments each of which will hold one or two 5-gallon containers, and is refrigerated by mechanical refrigeration. These are usually operated at a temperature between —10°F. and —15°F., and are most economical for a limited volume of business, and avoid exposure of the operator to sudden chills.

Precautions to observe in the operation of hardening rooms:

1. Provide facilities for calling aid should operator accidentally be trapped inside the hardening room. Sometimes the latch on the door fails to operate properly, making it impossible to open the door from the inside. At such times, a telephone or alarm system for calling for help is necessary and should be installed in such a manner as to attract help from outside when regular workers in the plant are absent.

2. Keep both an ax and a sledge hammer in a definite place just inside the door. These might be needed for breaking through the door as a last resort in case assistance cannot be obtained.

3. Keep wooden doors, etc., well painted, since the moist wood tends to give off odors which are absorbed by unprotected ice cream.

4. Keep floors, walls, etc., clean. Specialties decorated with whipped cream acquire off-flavors from odors in the air due to dirty floors, etc.

5. Do not store non-dairy products, wooden boxes or crates in the hardening room.

6. Avoid placing ice cream packages close together until hardened.

7. Avoid placing newly frozen ice cream close to packages that are already hardened.

8. Have the packages plainly dated and remove the older packages first.

9. Avoid fluctuations in temperature.

10. Remove frost from the ammonia coils frequently. Frost $1/4$ inch thick or more greatly decreases the efficiency of the coils. For methods of defrosting see page 284.

11. Whenever feasible avoid keeping the same ice cream in the hardening room for more than five days.

12. Take inventory at regular intervals, preferably daily.

FAST HARDENING SYSTEMS FOR ICE CREAM

The problems of the fast hardening of ice cream and fast hardening systems for ice cream have been capably discussed and illustrated and include some of the following suggestions (Anderson, 1958):

The ice cream manufacturer may act in three ways to fast-harden ice cream. These are: (1) improve hardening room design, (2) install fast hardening system for contact or blast hardening and (3) install fast hardening systems with controlled handling in a portion of the hardening room.

Hardening Room. In a good hardening room, fast hardening can be accomplished by following these suggested rules: (1) have plenty of refrigeration to maintain temperatures at —20°F. or colder, (2) maintain good air turbulence around products, (3) provide sufficient space for a 5 or 6 day inventory based on 14 gal. per sq. ft. and 8 to 10 gal. per sq. ft. for a few large items, (4) recognize the limitations of the hardening room.

Unit Hardening Systems. Numerous types of fast hardening units are in use for pints, half gallons, single units or wrapped gallon units. The plate or contact hardeners and blast tunnel hardeners are in general use. Contact hardeners include: the plate hardener on the elevating platform, the stationary plate and rotary plate types.

Blast tunnel hardeners have been in use for several years. The conveying systems have been expanded more recently to include the wide flat belt, fixed tray, suspended free tray and multi-shelf carrier types of conveyors. The zone hardening tunnel and the ceiling conveyor systems are other types of hardeners. Both of these systems occupy areas within the hardening room. Large volumes of air are discharged in these areas to accomplish fast hardening.

STORAGE

After the ice cream is hardened it may be immediately marketed, or it may be stored for a week or two at the most. Manufacturers plan on a maximum of five days between freezing and marketing, with an average of a 3-day turnover. At least 12 hours of this time is required for hardening the ice cream which frequently remains in the hardening room until marketed, thus using the same room for both hardening and storage. Since the hardened ice cream can be stored satisfactorily at slightly higher temperatures than are required for hardening, it is sometimes more economical to use special storage rooms. This is particularly true of retailers who may use one cabinet for storage in addition to the dispensing cabinets.

The operation of storage rooms is the same as for hardening rooms with two exceptions:

1. The temperature should be maintained uniformly at a point between $-10°$ and $0°F$.

2. The packages should be piled very closely to delay changes in the temperature of the ice cream.

SHIPPING

When the ice cream is marketed, the manufacturer usually ships it to the retailer under refrigeration at the same temperature as is maintained in the retailer's cabinets.

Dry ice is used extensively for package deliveries. This ice is sawed into pieces of appropriate size, which are wrapped in paper to delay the rapid evaporation, and then placed around the package of the ice cream inside an insulated packer, or in the single-service type packer. The latter are usually cardboard boxes insulated with corrugated cardboard and are used especially for the carry-out packages. There are several distinct **advantages** of this type of refrigeration:

1. Free from moisture and messiness.
2. Requires no salt.
3. Package is neat in appearance.
4. Does not water-log the insulation.
5. Is very light weight.
6. Is especially good for "specialties" sold direct to the consumer where no return trip to pick up packers is required.

The main disadvantages of dry ice are:

1. Present high cost and limited availability.

2. Loss during handling and storage, amounting to 10 to 15 per cent in many cases, due to the impracticability of providing sufficient insulation in storage boxes.

3. Danger of "burns" to handlers. The very low melting point makes it easy to freeze fingers without the sensation of cold, causing severe damage. Therefore care must be taken by those who handle it.

4. Necessity for unpacking or removing the ice cream. The ice cream must be unpacked or removed from the dry ice sufficiently long to allow it to soften so as to be easily eaten and so that the delicate flavors may be properly appreciated.

5. The greater opportunity for "heat-shock." When ice cream warms up and then freezes harder again, it receives a "heat-shock" which may injure the texture. Dry ice freezes the ice cream to lower temperatures than do the usual hardening rooms. The freezing point of dry ice (carbon dioxide) is about $-109°F$.

Mechanical refrigeration is most commonly used for the refrigeration of ice cream during shipping. This uses a complete refrigeration system with the expansion coils cooling the packer. These packers are similar to storage rooms, and are mainly truck bodies for trucking large volumes and for long hauls as much as 48 hours.

The many problems and the variety of special conditions connected with shipping by truck have made it impossible to standardize the procedure or the truck, and especially difficult to get comparative cost data. For example, costs, efficiency and depreciation are all influenced by such items as road conditions, the driver, frequency of opening the truck for partial unloading, etc. Therefore, definite limitations and advantages cannot be stated.

CHAPTER 14

Soft-Frozen Dairy Products and Special Formulas

There is a marked demand for the form of ice cream which has generally come to be known as "soft" ice cream. This term has been applied largely because these products are marketed in a soft form and are ready for consumption shortly after they are drawn from the freezer. The fact that these products are marketed under these conditions makes it possible to use formulas which are considerably different from the usual formula.

The principal types of mixes used in the production of soft-frozen dairy products are: (1) mixes to be frozen and served in a soft form, (2) mixes to be used in the preparation of milk shakes and (3) products to be frozen on soft-serve freezers drawn into packages and hardened.

The composition of soft frozen products varies according to legal standards and the type of product. Typical compositions are given in Table 34.

TABLE 34

COMPOSITION OF SOFT FROZEN PRODUCTS

Kind of Product	Fat Content	Milk Solids-Not-Fat	Sugar	Stabilizer and Emulsifier
	per cent	per cent	per cent	per cent
Soft Serve Products (usual range)[1]	3 to 6	11 to 14	12 to 15	0.4 to 0.6
Soft Serve Ice Milk	3	14	14	0.4 to 0.5
Soft Serve Ice Milk (better than av.)	6	11.5	13	0.4 to 0.5
Ice Milk (hardened)	6	12 to 13	15	0.4 to 0.5
Ice Cream (av.)	12	11	15	0.3
Ice Cream (better than av.)	16	7 to 8	15	0.25
Milk Shake	4.5	11	8	0.5

The mix composition for soft frozen products[1] may be modified to fulfill local needs and can be processed to meet specifications.

The problems involved in the preparation of soft-serve frozen products are somewhat different from those problems encountered in the manufacture of regular ice cream. Some of these differences include: composition, freezing procedures, stability and whipping properties of the mix, and

---

[1] The term frozen custard is often used erroneously as referring to all soft serve products. In most areas, frozen custards are required to contain egg solids. Generally the requirements range from 2.5 to 5.0 dozen egg yolks per 90 pounds of products. Custards may be served soft or hardened.

190

maintenance of smooth, dry, stiff characteristics of the products as drawn from the freezer.

The fat content of soft frozen products is important. If the fat content is low (less than four per cent) the product tends to be coarse, weak and icy. If the fat is high (above twelve per cent) the product may be too rich and less palatable in addition to presenting freezing difficulties involving possible fat separation during the freezing process.

The milk solids-not-fat content of soft frozen products vary inversely with the fat content and may be as much as 14 per cent for a low fat formula. Milk solids-not-fat serve to provide proper firmness of body. In high milk solids-not-fat content products, the lactose may separate during freezing and result in a sandy defect.

Usually the sugar content of soft frozen products is 13 to 15 per cent which is somewhat lower than for regular ice cream, and the amount of corn sugar used to replace cane sugar is limited to about 25 per cent in order to avoid too low a freezing point.

Stabilizers are used in amounts ranging from 0.2 to 0.4 per cent. Emulsifiers are used in amounts ranging from 0.1 to 0.2 per cent to provide smoothness, desirable whipping properties, melting resistance and firmness. Such products as calcium sulfate used in amounts of 0.12 per cent may be used to produce dryness and stiffness body characteristics.

Soft frozen products are usually drawn from the freezer at 18 to 20°F. Freezer design varies greatly and the automatic cycling of the ice cream in the freezer may cause major problems including: fat separation, occurrence of sandiness (lactose crystallization) or coarse texture.

The overrun of soft serve products may be in the range of 30 to 50 per cent depending on the total solids content. A higher overrun can be obtained on a product with a high total solids content with the maintenance of desired body and texture characteristics.

The following soft frozen product formulas may be expected to give satisfactory results:

LOW FAT MIX

Constituent	Per cent	Per cent
Fat	4.0	6.0
Milk solids-not-fat	14.0	13.0
Sugar (cane)	12.0	12.0
Sugar (corn syrup solids)	4.5	3.5
Stabilizer	0.4	0.4
Emulsifier	0.1	0.1
Total solids	35.0	35.0

HIGH FAT MIX

Constituent	Per cent	Per cent
Fat	10.0	12.0
Milk solids-not-fat	11.0	10.0
Sugar (cane)	12.0	12.0
Sugar (corn syrup solids)	3.0	3.0
Stabilizer	0.3	0.3
Emulsifier	0.1	0.1
Total solids	36.4	37.4

FORMULAS FOR FROZEN CUSTARD

5 Per cent Fat Ingredients for 100-Lb. Mix		Percentage Composition	
Lbs.			Per cent
0.5	stabilizer	Fat	5.0
15.0	sugar	M.s.n.f.	11.0
1.5	egg yolk (dry)	Sugar	15.0
18.0	condensed skim milk (30%)	Egg yolk solids	1.4
7.0	cream (40%)	Stabilizer	0.5
58.0	milk (4%)	Total solids	32.9

10 Per cent Fat Ingredients for 100-Lb. Mix		Percentage Composition	
Lbs.			Per cent
0.4	stabilizer	Fat	10.0
15.0	sugar	M.s.n.f.	11.0
1.5	egg yolk (dry)	Sugar	15.0
20.6	condensed skim milk (30%)	Egg yolk solids	1.4
20.0	cream (40%)	Stabilizer	0.4
42.5	milk (4%)	Total solids	37.8

SOFT FROZEN ICE CREAM—HIGH SOLIDS FORMULA

A good formula for soft ice cream with high solids and high overrun would be as follows:

Ingredients for 100-Lb. Mix		Percentage Composition	
Lbs.			Per cent
0.30	stabilizer	Fat	12.0
13.00	sugar	M.s.n.f.	14.0
8.27	non-fat dry milk solids	Sugar	13.0
24.62	cream (40% fat)	Stabilizer	0.3
53.81	milk (4% fat)	Total solids	39.3

Any desired flavoring can be used.

The mix weight is 9.17 pounds per gallon. A desirable finished product will have approximately 100 per cent overrun and will weight 4.6 pounds per gallon.

Note the differences in milk solids-not-fat in this special formula as compared with that of a good average standard formula such as is suitable for ordinary hard ice cream where one has to guard against lactose crystallization during storage. Proper stabilization and freezing procedures, however, will avoid lactose crystallization in this soft frozen product.

FORMULAS FOR ICE MILK MIX

In recent years ice cream makers have been confronted with steadily mounting production costs. This situation has meant increased costs to consumers or lowered production costs. Those who believe that constantly increasing costs are not the right answer have turned to lower cost formulas for soft ice milk, candy covered bars (sticks) novelties, etc., as a better answer.

Ice milks are frequently used in chocolate or other candy coated and novelty forms. The popular soft ice milks are marketed for immediate consumption, in cones and other kinds of packages. Where ice milks are to be used for hardened products such as the candy coated, various stick products, etc., the following formulas are typical:

FORMULAS FOR HARDENED PRODUCTS

Ingredients for 100-lb. Mix		Percentage Composition	
Lbs.			Per cent
0.50	stabilizer	Fat	4.0
15.00	sugar	M.s.n.f.	11.2
4.26	non-fat dry milk solids	Sugar	15.0
2.24	cream (40% fat)	Stabilizer	0.5
78.00	milk (4% fat)	Total solids	30.7

The mix weight is 9.20 pounds per gallon. A desirable finished product will have approximately 53% overrun, and will weigh 6.0 pounds per gallon.

Ingredients for 100-Lb. Mix		Percentage Composition	
Lbs.			Per cent
0.40	stabilizer	Fat	4.0
10.64	Frodex	M.s.n.f.	11.3
10.00	cane sugar	Sugar solids	20.2
4.84	non-fat dry milk solids	Stabilizer	0.4
2.88	cream (40% fat)	Total solids	35.9
71.24	milk (4% fat)		

The mix weight is 9.40 pounds per gallon. A desirable finished product will have approximately 80% overrun, and will weigh 5.2 pounds per gallon.

Ingredients for 100-Lb. Mix		Percentage Composition	
Lbs.			Per cent
0.50	stabilizer	Fat	6.0
15.00	cane sugar	M.s.n.f.	12.0
5.61	non-fat dry milk solids	Sugar	15.0
8.50	cream (40% fat)	Stabilizer	0.5
70.39	milk (3.7% fat)	Total solids	33.5

The mix weight is 9.22 pounds per gallon. A desirable finished product will have approximately 63% overrun, and will weigh 5.6 pounds per gallon.

For soft ice milk marketed directly from the freezer and for immediate consumption, the following formulas are typical and quite satisfactory.

ICE MILK FORMULAS

Ingredients for 100-Lb. Mix		Per cent Composition	
Lbs.			Per cent
0.4	stabilizer	Fat	3.0
0.1	emulsifier	M.s.n.f.	14.4
14.0	sugar	Sugar	14.0
33.0	condensed skim milk (30%)	Stabilizer	0.4
2.7	cream (40%)	Emulsifier	0.1
49.8	milk (4%)	Total solids	31.9

Ingredients for 100-Lb. Mix		Per cent Composition	
Lbs.			Per cent
0.4	stabilizer	Fat	6.0
0.1	emulsifier	M.s.n.f.	11.8
13.0	sugar	Sugar	13.0
21.5	condensed skim milk (30%)	Stabilizer	0.4
9.5	cream (40%)	Emulsifier	0.1
55.5	milk (4%)	Total solids	31.3

The mix weight is 9.22 pounds per gallon. A desirable finished product and a desirable soft serve product made from these mixes should be drawn at an overrun ranging between 30 and 50 per cent.

FORMULAS FOR SOFT PRODUCTS

Ingredients for 100-Lb. Mix		Percentage Composition	
Lbs.			Per cent
0.30	stabilizer	Fat	4.0
8.00	Frodex	M.s.n.f.	16.4
11.24	cane sugar	Sugar solids	19.0
10.36	non-fat dry milk solids	Stabilizer	0.3
3.33	cream (40% fat)	Total solids	39.7
66.77	milk (4% fat)		

The mix weight is 9.54 pounds per gallon. A desirable finished product will have approximately 98% overrun, and will weigh 4.8 pounds per gallon.

Ingredients for 100-Lb. Mix		Percentage Composition	
Lbs.			Per cent
34.00	plain ice cream mix (12% fat, 10% m.s.n.f., 15% sugar, 0.3% stabilizer)	Fat	4.0
		M.s.n.f.	16.0
		Sugar solids	20.0
0.22	stabilizer	Stabilizer	0.3
10.00	Frodex	Total solids	40.3
5.20	cane sugar		
13.00	non-fat dry milk solids		
37.58	water		

The mix weight is 9.58 pounds per gallon. A desirable finished product will have approximately 100% overrun, and will weigh 4.7 pounds per gallon.

Ingredients for 100-lb. Mix		Percentage Composition	
Lbs.			Per cent
0.40	stabilizer	Fat	6.0
10.00	Dri-Sweet	M.s.n.f.	12.2
10.30	cane sugar	Sugar solids	19.9
6.13	non-fat dry milk solids	Stabilizer	0.4
9.10	cream (40% fat)	Total solids	38.5
64.07	milk (3.7% fat)		

The mix weight is 9.40 pounds per gallon. A desirable finished product will have approximately 90% overrun, and will weigh 4.9 pounds per gallon.

Ingredients for 100 Lb. Mix		Percentage Composition	
Lbs.			Per cent
0.30	stabilizer	Fat	6.0
7.00	Dri-Sweet	M.s.n.f.	14.2
11.71	cane sugar	Sugar solids	18.4
8.24	non-fat dry milk solids	Stabilizer	0.3
9.12	cream (40% fat)	Total solids	38.9
63.63	milk (3.7% fat)		

The mix weight is 9.41 pounds per gallon. A desirable finished product will have approximately 90% overrun, and will weigh 4.9 pounds per gallon.

Ingredients for 100 Lb. Mix		Percentage Composition	
Lbs.			Per cent
0.30	stabilizer	Fat	6.0
10.00	Dri-Sweet	M.s.n.f.	14.2
10.30	cane sugar	Sugar solids	19.9
8.40	non-fat dry milk solids	Stabilizer	0.3
9.30	cream (40% fat)	Total solids	40.4
61.70	milk (3.7% fat)		

The mix weight is 9.48 pounds per gallon. A desirable finished product will have approximately 100% overrun, and will weigh 4.7 pounds per gallon.

MILK SHAKE BASE

Constituent	Per cent	Per cent
Fat	4.0	6.0
Milk solids-not-fat	12.5	12.5
Sugar (cane)	13.0	13.0
Sugar (corn syrup solids)	5.0	4.0
Stabilizer	0.4	0.4
Total Solids	34.9	35.9

HIGH FAT AND HIGH MILK SOLIDS-NOT-FAT ICE CREAM

When ice cream is made and sold under the usual commercial conditions of large scale operation, it contains between 36 and 41 per cent total solids, and is acceptable to the largest group of consumers. Ice cream containing more than 41 per cent total solids is frequently called high-solids ice cream and seems to be preferred in certain limited or special markets. It contains a larger amount of the expensive milk fat solids than is found in the ordinary commercial ice cream. A noticeable characteristic is that it does not melt down to a smooth creamy liquid. The term high-solids ice cream also may be applied to ice cream which contains less than 41 per cent total solids, but has a greater concentration of milk solids-not-fat than the maximum usually prescribed.

CHARACTERISTICS OF HIGH MILK SOLIDS-NOT-FAT ICE CREAM

High milk solids-not-fat ice cream has been made in the western part of the United States for a long time. It is made by using such specially prepared products as soluble casein and low-lactose skim milk powder. These ingredients increase the "chewiness" and the percentage of desirable milk proteins while at the same time avoiding the lactose concentration which so often causes sandiness. It is also one way of avoiding the high fat content or excessive richness. High milk solids-not-fat ice cream always contains a higher concentration of milk solids-not-fat than the maximum as stated on p. 56, but may contain less than 41 per cent total solids provided the fat is less than 14 per cent and no corn syrup solids are used. When balancing a high milk solids-not-fat ice cream mix, it is generally desirable to obtain part of the sugar from dextrose which will slightly lower the freezing point so that the ice cream can be more easily and efficiently dipped from cabinets maintained at the usual temperatures. It is also possible to lower the sugar concentration by as much as two percentage points without sacrificing any sweetness of taste. At the same time the milk solids-not-fat concentration may be raised as much as three or four points. These ice creams need slightly different processing procedures from those used for ordinary commercial ice cream. For example, the homogenizing pressures may need to be lower to avoid a curdy appearance in the melted ice cream; the capacity of the cooler may have to be increased due to the extra viscosity of the mix; and a higher overrun is advisable to avoid sogginess.

HIGH FAT ICE CREAM

High fat ice cream contains more than 16 per cent fat and more than 40 per cent total solids. Such ice cream, rich and smooth in texture, has long been a favorite.

High fat[2] ice cream presents special problems because the influence of the fat on the properties of the ice cream is accentuated. The use of butter, plastic cream or frozen cream tends to produce excessive viscosity which interferes with cooling the mix and obtaining the proper overrun. When these products are the only source of fat they should be emulsified in fresh, sweet skim milk or milk before the other ingredients are added. For this quality of ice cream usually only fresh cream and fresh milk are used to supply the milk solids. No additional sources, such as condensed milk, condensed skim milk or skim milk powder are used. Thus the resulting flavor is that of fresh cream entirely free from any milk solids-not-fat flavor—an important character of this type of ice cream.

Low milk solids-not-fat content is important. The milk solids-not-fat content of these ice creams must be low, decreasing as the fat increases. For example, 7.5 per cent milk solids-not-fat with 18 per cent fat, or 7.0 per cent milk solids-not-fat with 20 per cent fat give good results. The low concentration of milk solids-not-fat in relation to the fat content favors a crumbly body which is a common defect of high fat ice creams. This crumbly body may be avoided by using 16 to 17 per cent sucrose (de-

[2] The late Professor M. J. Mack of the Mass. Expt. Sta. did much research on "high fat" ice cream, and the authors wish to credit him with much of the information given here regarding high fat ice cream. Mack (1934).

pending somewhat on the fat content), or by using dextrose (not corn syrup solids) to supply about one-fourth of the total sugar. High-fat ice cream needs a higher concentration of sugar than lower fat ice cream in order to please the majority of consumers. This higher concentration of sugar and especially the use of dextrose improves the melt down of the ice cream which frequently is very slow and curdy. The stabilizer content must be about the same as for ice cream containing only 14 per cent fat if smoothness is to be secured because lower homogenization pressures are used and the temperature of the ice cream when drawn from the freezer is higher.

Problems in Processing and Freezing. High fat ice cream also presents problems in processing and freezing. *Homogenization* is considered essential to prevent partial churning in the freezer, especially in those freezers constructed to accomplish a drastic whipping action. However, relatively *low homogenization pressures* must be used, decreasing as the fat content is increased. When fresh cream and fresh milk are the only sources of milk solids, either single stage or double stage homogenization can give good results. The range of pressures in Table 35 is recommended as a guide:

TABLE 35

HOMOGENIZATION PRESSURES FOR HIGH-FAT ICE CREAM

18 Per cent Fat Mix		20 Per cent Fat Mix	
Lbs.		Lbs.	
1500 single stage	Minimum	1000 single stage	
2000 single stage		1500 single stage	
or	}Optimum{	or	
1500—500 lb. double		1000—500 lb. double	
2500 single stage	Maximum	2000 single stage	

If three-stage homogenization is practiced, the fat may be obtained from such sources as butter, plastic cream or frozen cream. The three-stage homogenization has been obtained by attaching a reducing valve to the discharge line of a two-stage homogenizer. Pressures of 2000, 500, and 150 pounds are suggested as satisfactory maximum pressures for the first, second and third stages, respectively, for homogenizing an 18 per cent fat mix. Slightly lower pressures of 1500, 500 and 150 pounds are suggested maximum pressures for homogenizing a mix containing 20 per cent fat. In addition to changing the homogenization pressure it is necessary to change the freezing procedure by raising the freezing temperature progressively with each increase in fat content. Drawing temperatures of 25.5°F. for 18 per cent fat and 25.8°F. for 20 per cent fat ice cream allows rapid whipping and ease of emptying the freezer, thus avoiding the excessive stiffness in the freezer which would decrease the rate of whipping and the ease of emptying the freezer. Finally, these high fat ice creams are slow to melt and often are excessively viscous, and therefore relatively high serving temperatures of 16° to 20°F. improve the flavor and the ease and efficiency of dipping.

CHAPTER 15

Sherbets and Ices

An increase in the consumption of sherbets and ices has developed in recent years, as indicated by the annual United States production of over 50 million gallons of these products.

A sherbet is a frozen product made from sugar, water, fruit acid, color, fruit or fruit flavoring, stabilizer and a small amount of milk solids added in the form of skim milk, whole milk, condensed milk or ice cream mix. An ice contains the same ingredients as does a sherbet except an ice contains no milk solids.

Sherbets and ices are differentiated from ice cream by the following characteristics:

(1) A higher fruit acid content, minimum of 0.35 per cent which produces a tart flavor; (2) a much lower overrun, usually 25 to 45 per cent; (3) a higher sugar content, between 25 and 35 per cent which gives a lower melting point; (4) a coarser texture; (5) a greater cooling characteristic while being consumed, due to their coarser texture and lower melting point; (6) an apparent lack of richness due to lower milk solids content.

While sherbets and ices are in greatest demand during the summer months, they are important products throughout the year as condiments, two or three flavor packages in combination with ice cream or in fancy ice cream and specialties.

The following sherbet sales flavor analysis for the United States (Table 36) shows the popular flavors for this product are: orange, pineapple, raspberry, lime and lemon.

THE COMPOSITION OF SHERBETS AND ICES

Important factors in the manufacture of sherbets and ices include: (a) choice of stabilizer; (b) control of kind and amount of sugar; (c) control of acidity and pH for optimum flavor; (d) control of composition for desirable body and texture; (e) maintenance of uniform natural color.

Legal standards for sherbets and ices usually requires a certain minimum acidity (usually 0.35 per cent as lactic acid) and minimum weight per gallon ranging to the same as for ice cream. Standards also often specify a minimum and maximum percentage of milk solids in sherbets (3 to 5 per cent). (See page 24.)

Sherbets contain a low concentration of milk solids, 2 to 5 per cent. Some states have established a minimum for milk solids content and in

TABLE 36

SHERBET SALES FLAVOR ANALYSIS IN THE UNITED STATES[1]

Flavor	United States		North Atlantic		Central Eastern		Middle Western		Southern		Western	
	rank	per cent	rank	per cent	rank	per cent	rank	per cent	rank	per cent	rank	per cent
Orange	1	38.62	1	37.77	1	46.03	1	42.71	2	31.22	1	38.65
Pineapple	2	22.06	3	11.41	2	20.33	2	18.91	1	34.71	2	26.75
Raspberry	3	12.30	2	27.08	5	7.53	4	9.43	5	2.63	4	7.36
Lime	4	11.44	4	9.67	3	12.54	5	7.47	3	26.40	5	4.92
Lemon	5	6.08	5	5.41	4	10.17	3	17.62	7	0.34	6	3.82
Rainbow	6	3.37									3	11.71
Strawberry	7	1.66	8	0.92	10	0.22	9	0.01	6	1.62	7	3.77
Banana	8	0.88	6	3.18								
Orange-Pineapple	9	0.61	13	0.08	7	0.54	8	0.17	4	2.69	15	0.04
Cranberry	10	0.60	14	0.07	9	0.39	6	3.05	8	0.32	10	0.48
Cherry	11	0.50	7	1.58			7	0.50				
Grape	12	0.27	10	0.67	8	0.42					12	0.29
Tangerine	13	0.26	9	0.70	6	1.79					16	0.02
Raspberry Salad	14	0.26										
Lemon-Lime	15	0.21	11	0.62							14	0.14
Boysenberry	16	0.19									8	0.67
Cherry Mint	17	0.17									9	0.59
Hawaiian	18	0.09									11	0.31
Nectarine	19	0.08	12	0.21							13	0.28
Butterscotch	20	0.06										
All Others	..	0.29	..	0.68	..	0.04	..	0.13	..	0.07	..	0.20
Total	..	100.00	..	100.00	..	100.00	..	100.00	..	100.00	..	100.00

[1] Flavor Preference and other Products Sold Analysis—1952 Special Bul. No. 87 IAICM Dec. 1953.

others a maximum is set for the amount of milk solids that may be contained in the sherbet. Requirements range up to 5 per cent as a minimum while some have 5 per cent as a maximum.

Sherbets and ices have lower melting points, coarser texture and apparent lack of richness due to low milk solids content. Best dipping temperature may range from —5°F. to +5°F. Recent practice is to adjust the sugar composition and overrun in order that these products can be dipped at the same temperature as ice cream.

Sugar.—In general the sugar content of these products is about double that of ice cream. The range may be from 25 to 35 per cent. Sources of sugar include: cane or beet sugar, corn sugar, corn syrup solids, invert sugar or liquid sugar. In making good sherbet it is necessary to control the sugar content and overrun. An excess of sugar results in a soft product and a deficiency results in a hard, crumbly product.

The amount of sucrose used should be the least that will give the desired sweetness in the finished ice, thus giving a higher melting point more suitable for dipping at the usual cabinet temperatures of 3° to 8°F.

The amount of corn syrup, invert sugar or corn sugar should be about one-third of the amount of sucrose. This sugar reduces the tendency to form a surface crust which sometimes happens when sucrose is used alone. The use of Frodex, Sweetose, Karo or other source of corn syrup solids tends to keep the melting point nearer to that of ice cream, so that the product will have a firmness most suitable for dipping at the usual cabinet temperature. The amount of sugar present in the fruit added to sherbets and ices should be known. The natural sugar is higher in some fruits than in others, and the amount of sugar added to fruit by processors may vary. By controlling the sugar content the firmness of the product can be controlled. Lack of uniformity of sherbets and ices in the past has been a serious quality defect.

The sugar contained in fruit preparations or ice cream mix, contributing to the sugar content of the sherbet or ice mix, should be given consideration in order to maintain uniform characteristics in the finished product.

Stabilizers.—Most of the basic stabilizers used in ice cream may be used for sherbets and ices. The amount of basic stabilizers needed to stabilize ices and sherbets is approximately as follows: gelatin (200 Bloom) 0.45 per cent, CMC gum 0.20 per cent, pectin 0.18 per cent, algin products 0.20 per cent, locust bean gum 0.25 per cent. Slightly less stabilizer is needed in sherbets than in ices.

Stabilization in sherbets and ices is even more important than for ice cream because of greater danger of sugar separation and body crumbliness.

Stabilizers are more important in ices than in ice cream because of the lower total solids content. In the selection of a stabilizer, consideration should be given to its effect on overrun, syrup drainage and body (crumbliness) as well as its availability, convenience of use and personal preference. Of the various stabilizers—cellulose gum, gum tragacanth, India gum, agar-agar, gelatin and pectin—the last two are most widely used. Best results are obtained by using a combination of two or more of these stabilizers, the ratio of combination depending on the grade and kind of stabilizers being combined. Enough stabilizer should be used to cause a partial gelling at cold room temperatures.

Acidity of Sherbets and Ices.—Citric acid is the most commonly used acid and it is usually added as a 50 per cent solution. The acid content differentiates sherbets and ices from ice cream. The amount of acid depends on the fruit used, the amount of sugar present and the demands of the consumer. The following amounts of acids have been recommended for products with a sugar content, as follows: 25 to 30 per cent sugar—0.36 per cent acid, 30 to 35 per cent sugar—0.40 per cent acid and 35 to 40 per cent sugar—0.50 per cent acid.

Overrun of Sherbets and Ices.—Overrun also controls the firmness and dipping qualities of sherbets and ices. Overrun in sherbets is usually 30 to 40 per cent while for ices it is 25 to 35 per cent.

Preparation of Base Mix.—This base is prepared by slowly adding the dry ingredients to at least part of the water, using care to avoid lumpiness. Heating may be necessary to facilitate solution, especially when stabilizers like gelatin or agar-agar are used. Pasteurization is optional, but homogenization is not practical. The prepared base is cooled before other ingredients are added. Aging is necessary only when gelatin or agar-agar is used in the stabilizer, and then an aging period of 12 to 24 hours is desirable.

This base mix is now ready for the flavor and color material. To each 80 lbs. of the cooled base mix enough flavor, color and water is added to make the total weight 100 lbs.

The flavor and color mixture is made from the following ingredients:

1. *Fruit juices.* Although the amount varies with the intensity of the flavor, it should be from 15 to 20 per cent of the weight of the finished ice. Avoid having too many seeds.

2. *Flavoring.* The amount of fruit needed for flavoring varies from three quarts to two gallons per ten gallons of finished mix depending on the kind of preparation and variety of fruit used. Natural extracts and artificial flavors may not produce as desirable a flavor as the fruit juices, but they are often used to fortify the flavor and thereby produce a more uniform product.

3. *Coloring.* Approved artificial food coloring aids in maintaining a uniform shade of color characteristic for and suggestive of the flavor.

4. *Citric acid solution.* To obtain the desired tart flavor a fruit acid such as citric acid or tartaric acid may be added. When fruit acids are not available, either saccharic acid, phosphoric acid or lactic aid may be used, but these do not impart an equally desirable flavor. It is a common practice to use a 50 per cent solution (i.e., 1 lb. of crystals to 1 lb. of water) of either citric acid or tartaric acid. The amount of this solution generally used varies from 4 oz. to 10 oz., depending on the acidity of the fruit juice. The titratable acidity of the finished ice should not be less than 0.35 per cent nor more than 0.50 per cent when expressed as lactic acid.

5. *Additional water* may be necessary to make the total weight of this mixture up to 20 lbs.

The freezing procedure in the making of ices is similar to that for ice cream. Many manufacturers prefer to use a special batch or continuous freezer since the absence of fat causes the scraper blades to become dull rapidly. The scraper blades must be sharpened more frequently since sharp blades favor more rapid freezing, smaller ice crystals and a smoother product. The refrigerant should be at least $-10°F.$ and should not be turned off as soon as for freezing ice cream. Frequently by using a very cold refrigerant the desired overrun and consistency for drawing can be obtained before the refrigerant is shut off. Ices should have an overrun of between 25 and 30 per cent. Fruit, color, citric acid and flavor should be added at the time of freezing.

Controlling the overrun is very important in ices. A high overrun favors syrup drainage, a lack of firmness and poor body. Therefore stabilizers that improve whipping ability are less desirable than the gum type where it is desired to limit the overrun. Methods for controlling overrun using a batch freezer may be listed in the following order of preference:

1. Operate freezer with colder refrigerant and longer time before refrigerant is shut off (i.e., shorter whipping time).

2. Select the proper stabilizer.

3. Over-load the freezer. Use $5^1/_2$ or 6 gallons of mix in a 40-quart freezer.

4. Under-load the freezer. Use $3^1/_2$ or 4 gallons of mix in a 40-quart freezer.

5. Have the beater on a separate gear so that it can be made to idle while the scrapers turn.

PREPARATION OF SHERBETS

A base or stock mix is often prepared which can be used for any flavor of sherbet. The base or stock mix may be varied in order to produce the finished product with desired body, texture and handling characteristics. The importance and relative volume of sherbets is the same as for ices, but the dairyman should be more interested in selling milk solids than in selling ices. One common procedure employs fresh milk or cream to furnish the total milk solids.

A base or stock mix for sherbets consists of:

1. Between 21 and 25 lbs. of sucrose (cane or beet sugar), the same as for an ice.

2. Between 7 and 9 lbs. of glucose, invert sugar or corn sugar, the same as for an ice and for similar reasons.

3. Between 0.4 and 0.6 lb. of stabilizer, the same stabilizer as used in ices and for the same reasons.

4. At least 35 to 40 lbs. of milk—or enough to supply 5 lbs of total milk solids.

5. Enough water to make a total of 80 lbs. of base or stock mix.

Milk Solids Content.—Milk solids should be supplied in the amount to satisfy regulations. They also enhance the body and texture and flavor of the product and the fat content influences the overrun. The milk solids may come from homogenized milk, condensed milk, non-fat dry milk solids or ice cream mix. The amount of dairy products required to give approximately 5 per cent solids in 100 lbs. of sherbet mix is as follows: skim milk—55 lbs., 4 per cent milk—45 lbs., condensed skim milk—(30 per cent solids) 15.9 lbs., sweetened condensed milk (27 per cent milk solids-not-fat, 42 per cent sugar) 18.5 lbs., ice cream mix (12 per cent fat, 11 per cent milk solids-not-fat) 24 lbs.

This base is prepared by slowly adding the dry ingredients to the milk and heating if necessary to obtain complete solution free from lumps. The mix need not be pasteurized provided the milk products have already been pasteurized. It should be remembered that some gum stabilizers like gum arabic will coagulate milk when heated. Therefore when using this stabilizer the milk should be pasteurized separately. Sherbet mixes are seldom homogenized, but must be cooled; and, if gelatin is used for a stabilizer, the base should be aged for 12 to 24 hours. Then to this 80 lbs. of base is added 20 lbs. of the mixture of fruit juices, flavoring, coloring, citric acid solution and water as described for making ices. Since the citric acid solution may curdle the milk it is sometimes added at the freezer after some ice crystals have started to form.

Another common method employs ice cream mix to furnish the milk solids. In many ice cream factories ice cream mix is more easily available than is fresh milk. Furthermore, it is already pasteurized and homogenized. Since the mix supplies some sugar and stabilizer, the sherbet base must be adjusted accordingly. The following suggestions indicate the necessary changes:

1. Between 18 and 22 lbs. of sucrose (cane or beet sugar).
2. Between 7 and 9 lbs. of corn syrup, invert sugar or corn sugar.
3. Between 0.35 and 0.55 lb. stabilizer.
4. Between 18 and 25 lbs. ice cream mix to furnish approximately the same amount of total milk solids as could be obtained from fresh milk.
5. Enough water to make a total weight of 80 lbs. of base mix.

The preparation of this base is the same as described for the first method, and the fruit mixture is added in the same manner. The freezing of sherbets is identical with the freezing of ices except that a higher overrun (35 to 45 per cent) is taken. The desired body and texture characteristics may vary in different markets ranging from smooth, chewy and heavy to medium resistant and slightly coarse. The following formulas produce finished products of different characteristics.

SHERBET FORMULAS

1. Sherbet (Smooth, Chewy, Heavy, Body and Texture)

Ingredients		Fat	M.s.n.f.	Sugar	T.s.
	lbs.	lbs.	lbs.	lbs.	lbs.
Cane Sugar	9.0	..	..	9.00	9.00
Corn Syrup Solids (42 DE) (Frodex)	22.0	..	..	21.20	21.23
Ice Cream Mix (12% fat, 11% m.s.n.f., 15% sugar	17.5	2.1	1.92	2.62	6.65
Stabilizer	0.4	...	...	...	0.40
Fruit-puree (5 + 1)	15.0	...	...	2.50	4.75
Water- and 10³/₄ oz. of 50% citric acid solution and color	36.1	...	...	...	...
	100.0	2.1	1.92	35.32	42.03

Acidity—0.57%; freezing point 26.4°F.

2. Sherbet (Medium Smooth, Medium Firm Body and Texture)

Ingredients		Fat	M.s.n.f.	Sugar	T.s.
	lbs.	lbs.	lbs.	lbs.	lbs.
Cane Sugar	11.0	...	...	11.00	11.00
Corn Syrup Solids (30 DE)	10.0	...	...	9.65	9.65
Ice Cream Mix (12% fat, 11% m.s.n.f., 15% sugar)	17.5	2.1	1.92	2.62	6.65
Stabilizer	0.4	...	...	...	0.40
Fruit-puree (5 + 1)	15.0	...	...	2.50	4.75
Water- and 10³/₄ oz. of 50% citric acid solution and color	46.1	...	...	...	...
	100.0	2.1	1.92	25.77	32.45

Acidity—0.55%; freezing point 28.4°F.

3. Sherbet (Medium Coarse, Medium Firm Body and Texture)

Ingredients		Fat	M.s.n.f.	Sugar	T.s.
	lbs.	lbs.	lbs.	lbs.	lbs.
Cane Sugar	17.0	. . .	. . .	17.00	17.00
Dextrose	7.0	. . .	. . .	6.44	6.44
Ice Cream Mix (12% fat, 11% m.s.n.f., 15% sugar)	17.5	2.1	1.92	2.62	6.65
Stabilizer	0.4	. . .	. . .	. . .	0.40
Fruit-puree (5 + 1) orange	15.0	. . .	. . .	2.50	4.25
Water- and 10³/₄ oz. of 50% citric acid solution and color	43.1	. . .	. . .	. . .	. . .
	100.0	2.1	1.92	28.56	34.74

Acidity—0.55%; freezing point 26.4°F.

4. Sherbet Using Ice Cream Mix

Ingredients	
lbs.	
11.0	Cane Sugar
10.0	Corn Sugar (Frodex)
17.5	Ice Cream Mix
0.4	Stabilizer
61.1	Fruit juice, color, citric solution and water
100.0	Total

5. Sherbet Using Whole Milk

Ingredients	
lbs.	
16.0	Cane Sugar
10.0	Corn Sugar
32.0	Whole Milk
0.4	Stabilizer
41.6	Fruit juice, color, citric solution and water
100.0	Total

6. Sherbet Using Condensed Skim Milk

Ingredients	
lbs.	
16.0	Cane Sugar
10.0	Corn Sugar
13.0	Condensed Skim Milk (30%)
0.4	Stabilizer
60.6	Fruit juice, color, citric solution and water
100.0	Total

7. Sherbet Using Skim Milk

Ingredients	
lbs.	
16.0	Cane Sugar
10.0	Corn Sugar
45.0	Skim Milk
0.4	Stabilizer
28.6	Fruit juice, color, citric solution and water
100.0	Total

PREPARATION OF ICES

Base or Stock Mix.—Ices are frequently calculated on the basis of hundred pound lots and manufacturers prepare a "base" or "stock" mix as follows:

21 to 25 lbs. sucrose (cane or beet sugar)
7 to 9 lbs. glucose, invert sugar or corn sugar
0.4 to 0.6 lb. stabilizer

Water to make a total weight of 80 lbs. of base or stock mix—balance of the 100 lbs. being flavoring and additional water.

ICE FORMULAS

Ingredients		Ingredients	
lbs.		lbs.	
23.0	Cane Sugar	16.0	Cane Sugar
7.0	Corn Sugar	10.0	Corn Sugar
0.3	Stabilizer	0.4	Stabilizer
69.7	Fruit juice, color, citric acid solution and water	73.6	Fruit juice, color, citric acid solution and water
100.0	Total	100.0	Total

DIFFICULTIES AND DEFECTS

Control of Overrun.—The percentage of overrun should be kept between 25 and 30 per cent for ices and between 35 and 45 per cent for sherbets. This is not easy to do, especially if gelatin is used as the stabilizer, without modifying the ordinary routine of freezing. Agar, gums or commercial stabilizers for ices are recommended largely because they retard the rate of whipping. However, many manufacturers prefer to use gelatin because it is usually on hand.

The refrigerant should be at least −10°F. to freeze ices or sherbets and should be kept on until they are firm enough to draw. Usually a very cold refrigerant makes it possible to draw a low enough overrun. If not, in case of the batch freezer, the freezer must be over-loaded or under-loaded, or the beater must be on a separate gear so that it can be made to idle. Over-loading the freezer is the usual procedure followed to control the overrun.

Firmness at Dipping Temperatures.—Ices and sherbets should be of the same firmness, at ordinary cabinet temperatures as ice cream since they usually are sold from the same cabinets. If the overrun is kept between 30 and 35 per cent and the sugar content at 28 to 32 per cent, the firmness will be suitable for dipping at the usual cabinet temperatures of 3° to 8°F.

Sherbet and ice defects include the following flavor defects: unnatural, not typical of flavor represented, artificial; excessive, caused by addition of too much acid or flavor material; excess sweetness, resulting from high percentage sugar; metallic or oxidized flavor development during storage and lack of sweetness due to the use of the improper amount or kind of sugar.

Body and texture defects include coarse, crumbly, hard, snowy, sticky, surface crustation and bleeding.

Excessive Coarseness.—Undue coarseness may be prevented by keeping the sugar content between 28 and 32 per cent; using about one-fourth of the sugar as corn sugar; using the right amount and kind of stabilizer;

drawing from the freezer in a firm condition; and marketing promptly. The base should be aged for 12 to 24 hours and enough stabilizer should be used to cause a partial gelling at cold room temperatures.

Coarseness may result from insufficient solids, sugar or stabilizer, drawing from freezer at too high temperature, or improper storage and handling. A crumbly body indicates improper stabilizer or insufficient amount of stabilizer or sugar. The hard body characteristic may be caused by low overrun or insufficient sugar content. Snowy body usually results from excess incorporation of air. A sticky body may be caused by use of too much stabilizer or too much sugar.

Surface crust sometimes forms on ices and sherbets. This is due to surface evaporation of moisture and can be prevented by covering with parchment paper and can cover. If about one-fourth of the sugar is corn sugar, a surface crust will not occur. With cane sugar alone as the sweetener, this trouble occurs more often. Surface encrustation sometimes appears on the surface of the ice or sherbet because some of the sucrose crystallizes and liberated water freezes into ice. Use of a greater amount of stabilizer or use of corn sugar to lower the freezing point of the mix will help prevent this defect.

"**Bleeding**" is the term applied to the settling of the sugar syrup to the bottom of the can. The usual causes are: excessive overrun; insufficient stabilizer; too much sugar (over 32 per cent); too high temperatures in the cabinet. Use of more effective stabilizer or more stabilizer, reducing sugar content and avoiding high overruns will aid in preventing this defect.

Color defects include unnatural, due to improper amount or kind of color, and uneven, resulting from improperly distributed color.

Meltdown defects are: melts too fast, does not melt; curdy.

Many of the sherbet and ice products produced by ice cream manufacturers are not of the superior quality of the ice cream produced. Great strides in improving the quality of sherbet can be made by maintaining uniform composition, color, flavor and body and texture characteristics. It is evident that standardization of quality of sherbets and ices is needed.

CHAPTER 16

Fancy Molded Ice Creams, Novelties and Specials

Very early in the history of the ice cream industry, the small manufacturer with imagination often emphasized the possibilities and profits to be gained in making fancy ice creams and novelties. But the larger manufacturer, in many instances, seems to have been a little slow in pushing this class of ice cream, due largely, perhaps, to the high cost of the skilled labor involved. However, recent advances in equipment for making, filling and decorating indicate the possibility of mass production at lower cost which should make the future for this type of business very bright.

FANCY MOLDED ICE CREAM

Ice cream belonging to the class known as fancy molded ice cream differs from plain bulk ice cream chiefly in the form in which it is marketed. In some cases there may be a slight difference in the formula, but the principal difference is in the manner of coloring, and in the size and form of the package.

Difference in formula consists usually of the addition of a little more stabilizer and emulsifier or a little more milk solids in order to obtain a firmer body.

The difference in package is one of the distinguishing features of fancy ice cream. The most common item or form is the decorated slice which is easy to serve. The individual cup mold (enough to serve one person) is also popular. However, much ice cream is molded in the form of animals, statues, flowers, fruits or other objects. The mold may be of individual size or it may contain a number of quarts of ice cream.

Calculated to increase sales and also to reach a different clientele, the fancy molded ice creams are generally made for special occasions—parties, balls, banquets and the like. Here the ice cream maker with imagination and artistic ingenuity can be of great help to the hostess or chef in carrying out a special design or color scheme in the party dessert. Success in this line requires no small amount of originality and artistic taste, which is rewarded by the better price and increased demand for these fancy products. Never forget that the customer is willing to pay a special price for something new and appropriate to the occasion, and the ice cream maker capable of giving these suggestions is sure of increasing the demand for his product if he exercises good taste.

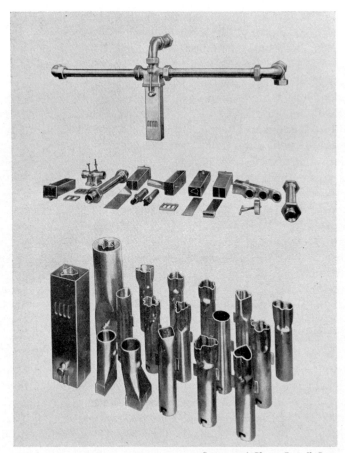

Courtesy of Cherry-Burrell Corp.

FIG. 34.   FILLING ATTACHMENTS FOR NO. 603 FREEZER

Harmony in color and flavor is of great importance in bulk as well as in fancy ice cream.   Colors and flavors should therefore be selected with great care.   That is to say, the color must suggest the flavor and must harmonize with it.   For example, a vanilla ice cream is yellowish (creamy in color), but a strawberry ice cream is pink because that is the color imparted to the cream by the natural fresh strawberry fruit.   Fruits often do not color the mix sufficiently so it is customary to add enough coloring to remind one of the natural color of the fruit.   But it would most certainly be a bad combination of colors and flavors if one were to color vanilla ice cream pink or strawberry ice cream brown.   Not that coloring adds or detracts from the flavor, but unless the two harmonize, there is nothing suggestive in the color.

The color, however, should not be too deep, for that suggests artificiality and cheapness. Light and dainty tints are the most pleasing to the eye. Therefore, color should be used sparingly.

Flavor and Color Combinations.—Most of the fancy ice creams are composed of two or more flavors and colors of ice cream combined in such a manner that each serving will consist of proportionate amounts of each. Examples are: the rainbow or variegated effects produced by carefully marbling or veining several colors of creams as they are drawn from the freezers into the molds or packages; the aufaits, produced by combining a pectinized fruit, in either layered or rippled design, with a plain ice cream; or ice cream combined with sherbets or ices in alternate layers. Ice cream may also be used in combination with bakery products as in the cake rolls, and it may be coated with chocolate or other frostings, as in the well-known chocolate bar. Each or all of this great variety of combinations of colors and flavors may be molded into a variety of shapes and forms, ranging from the well-known two- or three-layer brick to the most intricate flower or geometric designs. These fancy molds or shapes are frequently used in carry-out packages, as individual servings of two ounces or more, or in packages up to two or three quarts.

These carry-out packages may be filled directly from the filling machines or from the continuous freezer by means of special nozzles of the proper size and shape, designed so as to deliver the right proportions of the different color and flavor combinations desired in the mold. (See Fig. 34.) The continuous freezer permits drawing the ice cream at a colder temperature and thereby producing sharper dividing lines between the different flavored creams as they are filled into the molds or packages.

Individual molds such as animals, flowers, etc., are filled by dipping the ice cream from a bulk package, usually, a five-gallon can. Large molds and center molds may also be filled in this manner. The best procedure is to fill the molds immediately after the ice cream is drawn from the freezer, while it is soft and has time neither to melt nor to harden appreciably. When this is not feasible, the already hardened ice cream may be softened to the usual serving temperature (3° to 8°F.) of retail cabinets, and then dipped into the molds. When this hardened ice cream is used, care must be taken to avoid packing the cream too firmly because the solidly packed ice cream will be difficult to cut for eating.

Ice Cream Cake—How Made.—Ice cream cakes are made in much the same way as the brick. (See Fig. 35.) For the form, use any ordinary cake pan. Cut a round hole the size of a dime in the center of the pan. This makes it easier to remove the frozen cake from the pan. Cover the hole with parchment paper before filling the ice cream. Fill about as in making brick ice cream. If the cake is to have several layers, it can still be made in a deep cake pan by letting the first layer harden before filling in the second, and so on for the third, taking care that each layer is hardened before the next one is poured in. Here the ice cream maker can use his ingenuity in stacking the layers so as to have an artistic arrangement of colors and flavors. When the cake has been properly hardened it is ready to be defrosted and decorated.

Courtesy of Zenker School of Cake Decorating, Chicago

Fig. 35.   Ice Cream Cake

Decorated with whipped cream borders, sweet peas and rose, including the lattice work which is made with chocolate whipped cream.

Special molds for making a pre-cut cake are being made. This new, quick method enables the operator to fill segmented molds direct from the freezer or from the hopper. This new development apparently will eliminate or reduce many manufacturing problems and also will provide pre-cut portions that can easily be separated when the cake reaches the consumer.

Ice Cream Pies.—In small quantities ice cream pies are usually made by shaping and hardening a half-inch layer of slightly caramel-colored vanilla ice cream in a common pie plate. The shaping is more naturalistic if a second pie plate is set in the first with the ice cream between them while the hardening is taking place. They may be made as one-crust or as two-crust pies. After the crusts are hardened they may be filled with fruit ice cream or any other specially flavored ice cream, or with preserved fruits which have first been hardened in a pie plate of a size to fit into the crust. If there is to be a top crust this is carefully inverted over the filling layer and the pie is ready for the decorator. The top surface of the pie is usually decorated with meringue or with whipped cream and given an oven-browned appearance by lightly spraying on with an atomizer a suitable coloring material.

Where pies are made in large quantities, rigid paper pie plates are used. When these have been filled they are set in tin plates for easier handling, the filling is piped in right from the continuous freezer, and the top smoothed over with a spatula before the pie is sent to the decorating table.

If a fruit center is to be used the crust of ice cream is shaped in the plate, and the hardened fruit center from the small pie plate, as described above, is fitted into it, a second layer of ice cream is piped on top and smoothed over with a spatula, and the pie is decorated as desired.

These pies and cakes are often successfully worked in as week-end or holiday specials. They lend themselves nicely to many different flavor and color combinations. Vanilla, strawberry, caramel, banana and chocolate seem to be the most popular but this may vary in different localities.

DECORATING

In the past much of the decorating of fancy ice creams was done by hand and by the use of various forms and screens. However, now in general commercial practice the decorating tool is a cone-shaped bag made of parchment paper into the tip of which is inserted the metal points or nozzles through which the cream is extruded and laid down on the cake surface. These points or nozzles, which come in various shapes such as cord, ribbon, leaf, rose, star, can be secured from dairy supply houses. (See Figs. 36–38.)

The cone-shaped bag is made by rolling the paper into a cone; just enough of the tip of the cone is cut off to allow the nozzle point to be inserted from the inside. The top flap of the cone is left to be turned down over the top after the bag has been filled. The bag is filled with the decorating media, whipped cream and grasped in the right hand. Using the left hand as a rest for the right wrist, the bag is squeezed enough to extrude the cream at the same time that the nozzle is moved forward over the cake to lay down the desired design. The actual process is not easy to describe but the art is easily acquired even by the novice, especially if he is gifted with artistic sense. He should, however, seek the opportunity of watching a skilled decorator at work. Plenty of practice is needed before a perfect job can be expected. Mashed potatoes are an excellent substitute for whipped cream in obtaining this needed practice. After the artist has acquired proficiency in handling a one-color job, a two-color job may be attempted. By carefully filling one side of the parchment bag with one color and the other side with a second color of whipped cream, a two-color effect can be produced as the cream is squeezed through the nozzle. In general, the decorator prefers to make up several bags, one for each of the colors he intends to use, or for the various shapes of nozzles he needs for his designs.

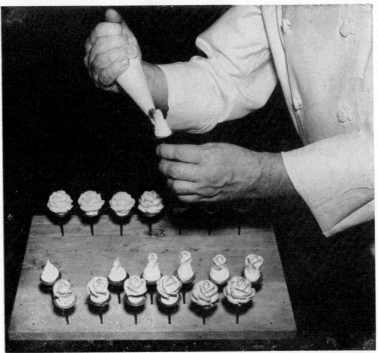

Courtesy of Zenker School of Cake Decorating, Chicago

Fig. 36. Steps in the Making of Roses

Ice cream decorators like a small turntable on which to place the cake or pie or brick to be decorated. This facilitates working all around the cake without disturbing its position. Such a turntable is easily made by using a block of wood 6 to 8 inches high for the pedestal to which is nailed rather loosely a smooth round board for the table top. The cake is placed on the turntable and is first smoothed over with a thin coating of whipped cream applied with an ordinary spatula. A 45 per cent cream which has been aged for at least 48 hours, chilled to 40°F., then whipped to a smooth consistency, not so thick that it becomes grainy or buttery,

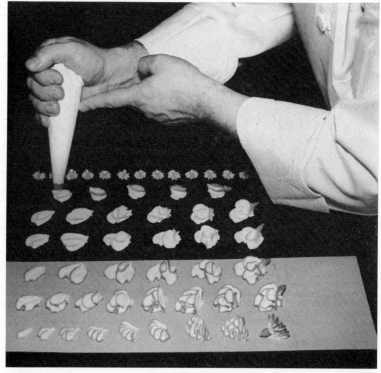

Courtesy of Zenker School of Cake Decorating, Chicago

Fig. 37. Making Forget-Me Nots, Rose-Buds, Sweet Peas and Pinks

Courtesy of Zenker School of Cake Decorating, Chicago

Fig. 38. Other Examples of the Decorator's Art

FIG. 39.   THE BOX OF STRAWBERRIES (MINIATURE NOVELTY)

These delicious strawberry ice creams cleverly resemble nice, ripe natural strawberries. The coating is a nearly perfect counterpart of the natural berry both in color and flavor, and each berry has its green stem decoration.   To complete the illusion they come packed in an ordinary quart-size strawberry box from which they are to be served. A novelty for children's parties and other small at home parties.

nor so thin that it runs off the cake, is most satisfactory for decorating. To make it more palatable 5 per cent of sugar and a little vanilla or other flavoring may be added.   This cream can be tinted in any desired color with flavor to harmonize, and the designs in which it can be shaped are limited only by the skill and artistic ingenuity of the decorator.   (See Figs. 39–42.)

Other frostings may be used for special purposes.   This thin, smooth coating to cover the surface of a mold may be made of cream, coloring, sugar and stabilizer to give a fairly heavy batter, but not whipped.   The cake, or other mold, is quickly dipped in the batter, or the batter poured over it and the excess allowed to drain off.   Butter frosting prepared by mixing butter, sugar, color and flavor is also effectively used.

Special effects are obtained in a variety of ways.   The "fuzzy" coloring effect on peaches may be obtained by chilling the molded cream on dry ice and then spraying it with colored water from an atomizer.   A shiny glazed surface may be obtained by chilling the molded cream on dry ice and then briefly dipping it in water which may or may not be colored. Silhouette effects may be obtained by stencils as described on p. 225.

NOVELTIES

The manufacturer who puts out ice cream novelties generally has an inside track with people and especially with the children of his community, and he receives more per gallon for his frozen product in the form of novelties than in any form of bulk ice cream. Classed as novelties are

Courtesy of Hendler Creamery Co.

Fig. 40. The Ice Bowl of Assorted Fruit (Miniature Novelty)

Bowl of almost crystal clear ice is filled with individual ice creams flavored, molded, colored and decorated to resemble miniature assorted fruits. Served in the ice bowl this is a surprisingly appealing dessert for special occasions.

fancy center brick molds, melon molds, logs, individual molds in endless variety, and all such special products as are hardened and served in paper molds and in paper cups. Also included in this class are chocolate covered ice cream bars, walking sundaes, take-home sundaes, frosted malteds, popsicles, etc., all of which are very popular with many groups and offer a good way of competing successfully with soft drinks and certain confections. While these novelties and fancy ice creams are sometimes classed as something of a nuisance and mean extra work for the

Courtesy of Hendler Creamery Co.

FIG. 41. BOX OF BON-BONS

The transparent semi-plastic box contains an assortment of ice creams of a variety of flavors, cut and molded into various shapes and decorated to resemble a box of fancy assorted candy bon-bons. Very attractive and especially suitable for special gifts for birthdays, for hospital patients and other occasions.

manufacturer, they are very helpful in creating good will for his trade, especially for such events as weddings; anniversary parties; Thanksgiving, Christmas, New Year's, Washington and Lincoln Birthday celebrations; family birthday parties; and many others; and they help stretch the ice cream season well into or through the winter months. Thus they all help to build up sales.

Center Mold Bricks.—Center brick molds are very popular. There are several ways in which these can be made. The first of these is the fancy center mold which is made in two parts—the outside can or shell in brick form and the inside core open at both ends made in the form of the desired design when seen in cross section. This core is attached to one of the lids. In making the brick, one cover lined with parchment paper is securely fastened over the end of the form which is then inverted and filled to within an inch and a half of the top with fairly soft ice cream of the kind desired for the main part of the brick. The center core attached to the other cover is then pressed down into this filled form until the cover comes into place. The cover keeps the center core exactly centered.

The form is then refrigerated. When hardened sufficiently, cool or luke-warm water is poured into the center core to loosen it so that it can easily be pulled out leaving a hole through the center of the brick the shape of the desired fancy center. This hole or space is then filled with the ice cream of the desired color and flavor planned for the center. This must be quite soft (soupy) so as to readily fill all the space left by the removal of the center core. The cover is then put on and the form is again re-frigerated until ready for wrapping and packaging.

Courtesy of Hendler Creamery Co.

Fig. 42.   A Bowl of Walnuts

The walnut ice cream in this novelty is very cleverly shaped and decorated to appear as natural walnuts.   The wooden bowl comes packaged with the ice cream.   A specialty for men's parties.

In another type of center mold the fancy centers are frozen first in a separate mold. They are then removed and imbedded in the lightly frozen ice cream used for the body of the quart brick. If eight-quart molds are used, much care must be taken to see that each piece is properly imbedded so as to appear in exactly the right place in each of the eight bricks.

Still another way is sometimes resorted to for quick work. It makes use of a center design mold something on the order of a cookie cutter. This is punched down through the center of the brick lengthwise and the hollow thus created is then filled with mix of the desired color for the center design.

Fancy Centers with the Continuous Freezer.—The extra stiffness of continuous freezer frozen ice cream opens up many new possibilities as to both speed and economy. These continuous freezers fitted with special shaped discharge tubes now make it possible to deliver the ice cream in layers of one, two or three colors in brick molds. It also makes it possible to put fancy centers in many different types of packages. To deliver three

Courtesy of Waukesha Foundry Co.

Fig. 43. Equipment for Producing Variegated Ice Cream

different colors simultaneously three freezers must of course be hooked up and operated as one battery, delivering the different colored ice cream in the exact proportions wanted in each layer. To get good sharp outlines it is best to have the ice cream flowing through the center stiff enough to retain clear-cut form and outline. Freezer manufacturers will gladly furnish full information and details as to the many specially designed tubes available. Among the more popular designs for center brick molds are: Lodge, club and class emblems; class numerals; spade, heart, diamond and club; Washington and Lincoln busts; Santa Claus; turkey, hatchet, cherries, rose, lily, etc.

NOVELTIES POPULAR IN SOME PARTS OF THE COUNTRY

Rainbow ice cream made by carefully mixing (marble cake fashion) several different colors, as the product is drawn from the freezer.

Rainbow cones made by putting thin spoonings of six or eight different colors of ice cream on top of each other, cone fashion.

Spumoni, a fancy ice cream, is generally made in cup-shaped form in pint or quart size. The outside layer is usually made of vanilla ice cream. In the bottom of this shell is placed macaroon or chocolate mousse and this is topped with tutti-frutti mousse. In serving, it is cut in wedge-shaped pieces like cake.

Courtesy of Delvale Dairies Inc.

FIG. 44. NOVELTY EQUIPMENT

Vita Freeze operation for frozen stick confections at Delvale Dairies, Inc., Baltimore, Maryland.

Ice cream tarts are made from vanilla bricks, cut into eight slices, and again cut in halves trianglewise. A small dent is made in the center of one triangle and the depression filled with some highly colored fruit; the second triangle is fitted over this, the sides are smoothed up, and the top sprinkled lightly with bisque crumbs. The tart thus formed is wrapped in wax paper and placed in the hardening room.

Ice cream waffles are made in waffle shaped molds which generally come in a size to make six or eight to the quart. These molds are filled with vanilla ice cream. When hardened the molds are removed, both sides of the waffle are covered with bisque crumbs and two of these are placed together and wrapped in wax paper until ready to be served.

Many of the novelties quite worth while are controlled by patents held by commercial companies who sell licenses to those interested. To protect these products and to insure uniformity, the licensor insists on standard formulas and standard trade marks. Among these novelties are Eskimo Pie, Popsicle, Fudgsicle, Creamsicle, Drumstick, Chocolate Bar, etc. The licensor generally has special equipment, packages, flavoring, formulas with detailed directions, as well as advertising matter, available to those interested in making this type of product.

SPECIALS

Too many ice cream businesses, like certain animals, hibernate during the winter months. This should not be the case in this business, for ice cream is the universal dessert, one that is good at all seasons of the year. During the cool weather of the winter season, why not put extra stress on the fact that ice cream abounds in fats which carry the vitamins so necessary to build up resistance against the many infections that plague us during the winter?

Selling Ideas.—The ice cream manufacturer should make it his job to sell these ideas regarding the value of ice cream to the consumers in his territory just as the people who grow and handle lettuce, citrus fruits, etc., have spent money in putting their idea across, with the result that copious quantities of these products are now being consumed.

Even though advertising is effective, it is well to remember that people tire of the same diet, and the ice cream maker, like a good chef, should be constantly on the alert for new ways in which to present his wares. He should vary the flavors and the style of his product, for no matter how good a food may be, if it appears on the menu too often in the same form or flavor, it becomes monotonous.

More of an attempt should be made to look at things from the busy housewife's point of view. Encourage her in her desire to have something new both as regards flavor and style of product. Help her develop new ideas, new names, new specials, for different seasons, and even weeks of the year, to keep consumer interest from lagging.

Among progressive ice cream people there is plenty of evidence to indicate that if special flavors are pushed when they are in season, and fancy ice creams and novelties are developed and offered as they synchronize with the various holidays and festive occasions, business is very materially increased. Although catering to this new demand requires some energy and some originality, many ice cream manufacturers can make use of some of these suggestions to help their particular local business.

Any progressive manufacturer can offer the consumer some variety in ice cream specials. Ordinarily it is not considered wise for the small concern to carry too many kinds of ice cream at one time. Rather, it should be good business to carry less variety but to have a definite plan of something new and special at least each week and for the special holidays and festive occasions that are being observed in his locality. There are many ice creams containing certain fruits and nuts that can be featured at the appropriate time of the year.

The large ice cream factories make countless different individual molds varying in shape, of which the following are samples: flowers such as the rose and the lily; Washington and Lincoln busts; dogs and horses; heart, spade, club, and diamond; Masonic, K. of C., Rotary, Kiwanis and numerous other emblems. The dairy supply houses list many more and generally they will make up any design the ice cream maker may wish.

Increase Consumption.—Although in most surveys vanilla ranks first, with strawberry and chocolate as runners-up, the manufacture of new and special products should be considered a good practical way to increase the per capita consumption of ice cream. While certain flavors may be almost unknown in one territory, if properly introduced and advertized they may prove to be quite popular and very materially assist in increasing ice cream consumption and stretching the season, so that the demand for ice cream will be more uniform throughout the year.

Be constantly on the alert for new and popular flavors for ice cream use. Study the reaction of the consuming public to them. If in trying out a score of new flavors one or two real hits are found, the experiments and effort are well repaid. Of course, have enough of the standard flavors on hand to take care of the demands of loyal customers.

Many manufacturers in widely scattered sections of the country have taken advantage of new flavor appeals to increase their local business. Thus, coffee has become a favorite in New England, and maple a good seller in Canada. Prune ice cream is now successful in California, and ginger ice cream is popular among certain nationalities.

Combinations.—Various new combinations of fruits develop appealing flavors for ice cream specials. As examples, pineapple combinations such as grape-pineapple, mint-pineapple, orange-pineapple, pineapple marshmallow prisms, glacé cherry-pecan mix of pineapple, nuts, raisins and cherries. Caramel flavor combinations offer other attractive specials as well as do candies and candy-nut combinations such as buttercrunch, butterscotch, peppermint, lemon drops, butter toffee, maple pecan, pecan crunch and the like.

Here's a suggested list of fancy ice cream specials for gatherings of various kinds:

Weddings and Showers

Decorated cake.

Individual molds such as slipper, bell, dove, bride and groom, tulip, heart, cupid, ring, etc.

Baby Showers

Decorated cake with emblems such as stork and baby.

Individuals of the same design.

Bridge Parties

Decorated cake.

Individual molds of ace of hearts, clubs, spades and diamonds.

Sometimes a stencil with similar designs can be used very satisfactorily on sliced bricks.

Birthdays

Decorated cake, with Happy Birthday and sometimes with numerals.

Many individual molds with the stenciled numerals indicating age, class, etc.

Children's Parties

Individual molds of elephant, engine, horse, butterfly, monkey, boat, cannon, etc., are some of the possibilities.

Athletic Functions

Ice cream cake in the form of a football or basketball.

Individual forms showing an athlete or a football.

Decorated slices.—The decorated slice is perhaps the most popular of the decorated pieces. There are many special designs available as stencils. Special colored whipped cream is spread over the stencil design with a spatula and the stencil is quickly removed before it freezes to either the ice cream or the whipped cream design. When the stencil is removed the sharp colored outline of the pattern will remain. The decorated pieces are hardened in the hardening room and placed in appropriate packages for protection.

Aufait Ice Cream.—Aufait ice cream usually consists of a layer of fruit between two layers of ice cream. The aufait ice cream can be modified by using fruit-flavored gelatin instead of the usual layer of fruit preserves, jams or candied fruit. The fruit-flavored gelatin has the advantage of being less sweet than the fruit layer which is ordinarily used. This fruit-flavored gelatin should be slightly less firm than the gelatin cubes, and is cut in slabs to form layers in the mold. These slabs are alternated in the mold with layers of ice cream.

Ice cream pies can be modified by using fruit-flavored gelatin instead of the filling of preserved fruits or fruit ice cream which is ordinarily used. The fruit gelatin used in ice cream pies is similar to that used in modified aufait ice cream. The pie crusts are about one-half inch in thickness and may be made by hardening vanilla ice cream between two pie plates. Closed or open pies may be made.

The **modified ice cream cake** is made by placing alternate layers of ice cream and fruit-flavored gelatin in cake pans. The gel is the same as that used in modified ice cream pies. It is desirable to have the gel filling for ice cream pies and cakes and modified aufait slightly weaker than that used for gelatin cubes. The pies and cakes may be decorated with whipped cream.

Frosted foods, especially frozen fresh fruits and vegetables, offer the possibility of profitable use of refrigeration space and sales effort throughout the year. According to recent figures the use of frosted foods has increased by leaps and bounds. While this industry is in a state of flux, may it not be possible to include some of this business with the ice cream business in such a way as to help the year-round sales?

Frosted malteds are increasing in popularity during the winter as well as during summer, according to recent reports. In some places the consumption of this product has increased substantially. Frosted malteds are made of a mix similar to malted milk shakes, and frozen in a freezer as is ice cream. The partially frozen mix is held in the freezer and drawn into cones or paper cups when the customer's order is taken. In consistency it resembles soft ice cream ready to be drawn from the freezer.

Soft ice cream is ice cream marketed directly from the freezer by using any desired mix; or previously hardened ice cream may be softened by special process. Proper publicity and attractive advertising of this product should promote further sales along this line, and thus help to bring in additional income to the ice cream manufacturer.

Display Material.—The advantage of a proper display of the product and of the advertising material is well known to the manufacturer and also to the dealer and retailer. The retailer generally makes a special effort in displays during the spring and summer, and obtains the beneficial result of increased sales. A similar effort will greatly stimulate winter sales and there is much display material suitable for this purpose. The retailer, like the manufacturer, should make a special effort to keep tuned to all possibilities for stimulating sales throughout the year.

Florist Educated Public.—Our friends the florists have done many clever things besides educating the public to "Say it with flowers." They have educated the American public to associate poinsettias with Christmas, lilies with Easter, shamrocks with St. Patrick's Day, etc. They have done all this in spite of the difficulty of getting their flowers to bloom at the exact time desired. The ice cream people of course must do some planning but they do not have to begin preparations so far ahead with so many uncertainties to contend with, as is the case with the florists. They must, however, plan and order needed stock at the proper time so that their specials for certain holidays may be timely and attractive.

The right kind of an advertising man can popularize cherry-nut ice cream for Washington's Birthday. Why couldn't a "victory special" ice cream sell well after the home team has won a big victory or when the results have come out just right for the majority at one of our heated elections? Why not make maple special ice creams in the month of March when maple syrup is fresh and when people are in the mood for it? Some additional possibilities are:

New Year's
Decorated cake featuring the baby New Year, or a bell as part of the decoration, or a brick with a bell center.

Lincoln's Birthday
Decorated cake.
Bust of Lincoln, flag and other patriotic decorations in individual molds or sliced brick.

Washington's Birthday
Decorated cake.
Hatchet, flag, cherry tree, Washington bust either in cake or individual form.

St. Valentine's Day
Heart and cupid decorations on cake.
Heart center or cupid center bricks and individual molds of same design.

St. Patrick's Day
Shamrock cake or shamrock center brick and countless individual molds, carrying out the shamrock idea.

Easter
Cake decorated with egg or lily.
Individuals in the shape of lilies, eggs, or rabbits.
Individual chickens or chickens in center of slices.
Two-quart standing rabbit, etc., etc.

Mother's Day
Whipped cream decorations with "Best Wishes to Mother," "Many Happy Returns," etc.
Carnations.
Designs of assorted flowers.

Memorial Day
Special decorated cakes.

Fourth of July
Many individual designs such as flags, shield, cannon, liberty bell, etc.
Red, white and blue bricks.
Special cakes with patriotic decorations.

Hallowe'en

Individual pumpkin, witch, corn cob, black cat, owl designs.
Special decorated cakes with these or combinations for decorations.

Thanksgiving

Special decorated cakes showing turkey, horn of plenty, pumpkin or other decorations suggestive of Thanksgiving scenes.
Individual designs of numerous kinds along this line may be secured.

Christmas

Special decorated cakes with "Merry Christmas" or other designs that appeal to various groups or nationalities may be used.
Individuals may be made up in the form of a bell, stocking, Christmas tree, Santa Claus or Christmas tree centers may be featured.

Fall and winter, when the ice cream business is the most sluggish, should be the best time for putting on special campaigns calling attention to ice cream in connection with the numerous receptions, banquets and parties all the way from bridge to special social functions.

Dealer Suggestions.—First, try some new sundaes with new names and new shapes. For example, why not vary the regular banana split by standing it on its head and by serving it in a tall dish instead of a flat one? Give it a new name that may appeal, say—"Banana Skyscraper."

Second, try new flavors. A survey, conducted some time ago and reported in one of the *Ice Cream Trade Journal* issues indicated that the following flavors proved to be popular among consumers: vanilla, strawberry, chocolate, cherry and variations, orange-pineapple, butter pecan, black walnut, banana and variations, peach, lemon, pineapple, chocolate chip, fruit salad, tutti-frutti, caramel, peppermint stick, butterscotch, butter crunch, pecan crunch, almond, almond toffee and pistachio.

Third, try glass containers of neat, modern design in which to serve ice cream. Modern glassware, in contrast to earthenware or china sauce dishes, shows off to better advantage the fine colors of frozen desserts. It gives them "eye appeal." More persistent effort should be made to present ice cream, like other merchandise, in the most attractive package or container available.

Fourth, make use of the best possible technique in the making of ice cream sodas. By so doing you will please and satisfy the most discriminating customer, who quite likely will object to the icy, cloying or unpalatable concoctions dispensed at some counters.

Fifth, observe careful sanitation. Be proud to have your customers see how clean the ice cream dippers are and how thoroughly all dishes are washed and sanitized in your store. Clean the tops of the fountains and all accessory equipment. There should be plenty of clean towels, sponges and washing powders on hand. The dispensers themselves, their bodies and hands, should be clean, neat and trim. Clean uniforms should be provided and worn at all times. An attractive, clean, shining fountain stimulates business. A sloppy-looking place is liable to drive many patrons from the door.

Ice cream manufacturers and dealers should consider themselves fortunate to be connected with a business whose product is liked by nearly everyone and is recognized by nutrition and health experts as an exceptional food.

In conclusion, if more attention is paid to making use of the best available suggestions regarding products, flavors, style and service, much can be done toward increasing sales and stretching the ice cream season from a few months to all year.

CHAPTER 17

Formulas for Flavors and Mixes

It is desirable that the maker of ice cream be well versed in calculating the amounts of the various ingredients needed in the ice cream mix. However, to those new in the business or to the operator who has not mastered the technique of calculating mixes, the following formulas may prove helpful. For convenience, unless otherwise specified, these formulas have been figured on the basis of 5 gallons of mix, and to yield approximately 10 gallons of finished ice cream. In cases where fruit and syrups are added, adjustment must be made for the excess volume of these flavoring materials so as to comply with the prevailing legal standards, and also avoid overloading the freezer. For plain mixes see pp. 237 to 245.

Vanilla
From 3 to 6 ounces to flavor 5 gallons of plain mix. The amount to use varies with the strength of the vanilla, quality of the mix and personal preference.

Coffee
Five gallons of mix plus one pint of coffee extract. A strong coffee cooked from 1 pound of ground coffee may be used in place of the coffee extract. A suitable amount of burnt sugar color should be added.

Maple
Five gallons of mix plus true or imitation maple flavor to suit the taste. A pure maple extract of concentrate is preferable to the use of maple syrup. If maple syrup is used, a special mix of 10 to 12 per cent sugar must be used.

Caramel
Five gallons of mix and enough caramel flavor to impart a satisfactory caramel taste and color. The color should be a deep tan.

Mint
Five gallons of mix flavored to taste with mint extract. Color light green.

Chocolate
To 4.5 gallons of mix add chocolate syrup made from 1.5 pounds cocoa (or 2 pounds chocolate liquor), 1.5 pounds sugar, add 2 to 3 quarts of water. Mix the cocoa and sugar together and add enough water to make a paste. Heat in a steam jacketed kettle or double boiler. As the syrup thickens, add the water gradually, with constant stirring. Heat to 175°F., draw off the syrup, cool and use. Just enough water to prevent an excessively thick syrup is needed. The syrup can be made up in quantity and stored for a few days in the cold storage room (35° to 40°F.).

Chocolate Malt
One-half the chocolate syrup used for chocolate ice cream, 1 quart of malt syrup and 4.5 gallons mix. If malt syrup is not available, use 1 to 2 pounds of malted milk.

Mocha

Same amount of mix and chocolate syrup as for chocolate malt plus 4 to 6 ounces of coffee syrup, or enough to give a mild coffee flavor.

Strawberry

Use 4.5 gallons mix plus 3 quarts of fresh berries (washed, mixed with one-half their weight of sugar and held overnight in the cold storage room) or the same amount of frozen (cold pack) berries. Fruit to sugar ratios of 2:1 or 3:1 are best for frozen berries. Color to strawberry pink.

Cherry

Two to 3 quarts of cherries added to 4.5 gallons of mix at the freezer. Usually maraschino process cherries are used. If processed cherries are not used, it is necessary to select sour cherries and use cherry extract to strengthen the flavor. Color light red.

Raspberry

Four and one half gallons of mix plus 2 to 3 quarts of raspberries added at the freezer. Since raspberries are very seedy pureed raspberries are frequently used. Addition of true fruit raspberry extract to strengthen the flavor is often practiced. Often a small amount of citric acid is added to bring out the flavor.

Peach

Four gallons of mix flavored with 1 gallon of sweetened (25 per cent sugar by weight) fresh fruit or pie grade canned peaches. Peach extract is frequently used to fortify the mild fruit flavor. Color light egg yellow.

Pineapple

Two to 3 quarts of pie grade shredded or crushed pineapple, plus 4.5 gallons mix. Color light yellow.

Banana

Four pounds of very ripe bananas crushed and mixed with one pound of sugar. Use this with 4.5 gallons of mix. Color light yellow. Often a small amount of lemon juice or citric acid is added to prevent a slightly flat taste.

Orange

Use 2 quarts fresh or canned orange juice or the equivalent of orange concentrate (frozen), plus 1 pint of lemon juice; add 1.5 pounds of sugar to the juice. An orange extract is often substituted for a part or all of the juice. Add to 4.5 gallons of mix. Color light orange.

Orange Pineapple

Usually 2 quarts of a prepared flavor is used which consists of crushed pineapple mixed with orange oil or emulsion. Use 4.5 gallons of mix. Color light orange.

Fig

Add to 4.5 gallons of mix 2 to 3 quarts of canned figs. Color light tan. A good fig-nut ice cream can be made using 2 quarts of canned figs and one pound of chopped nut meats.

Ginger

To 5 gallons mix add 4 pounds preserved, chopped ginger root. Or add a No. 10 can of ginger root flavoring.

Maple Walnut

To maple ice cream add 1 to 2 pounds of chopped nut meats at the freezer.

Maple Pecan

Same as above except use pecan meats.

Butter Pecan

Add 1.5 pounds of ground butter crunch candy plus 1 pound chopped pecans to 5 gallons mix.

Burnt Almond

Five gallons of mix plus 2 pounds burnt or roasted almonds. Almond flavor may also be added, as well as some burnt sugar or caramel color.

Pistachio

To 5 gallons of mix add 2 pounds of chopped pistachio nut meats, pistachio extract to taste and color to light green. Frequently English walnuts or pecan nut meats are used instead of pistachio nuts, in which case the pistachio flavor is secured from the extract.

Butter Crunch

Five gallons of mix plus 3 pounds of ground butter crunch candy.

Butterscotch

Four and one half gallons of mix and 2 quarts of butterscotch syrup; color to egg yellow.

Peppermint Stick

Crush or grind through a meat chopper 2 pounds of peppermint stick candy. Use this to flavor 5 gallons of mix.

Peanut Brittle

Crush or grind 2 to 3 pounds of peanut brittle. Add this at the freezer to 5 gallons of mix.

Bisque

This is a type of ice cream made by adding a bakery product to the partly frozen mix. To the full 5-gallon mix in the freezer add 2 to 4 pounds of either macaroons, sponge cake, lady fingers, grape nuts, chocolate chips or similar products broken into small pieces. The ice cream carries the name of the product used as the flavor.

Tutti-frutti

To 4.5 gallons of mix add 2 to 4 quarts of a mixture of several fruits. Color to light pink. Usually a prepared fruit mixture is used.

Frozen Pudding

Usually a prepared mixture is used. However, if nut meats and rum, or rum flavor are added to tutti-frutti ice cream, a frozen pudding flavor is the result.

Nesselrode Pudding

To 5 gallons of rich mix (similar to parfait mix), add 3 to 4 quarts of a special commercial fruit mixture suitable for Nesselrode Pudding. This should be added after the mix is partly frozen. Or prepare a mixture of the following fruits chopped into small pieces:

1 pint crushed pineapple
1 pint candied cherries
1 pint maraschino cherries
1 pint raisins
6 ounces candied orange peel
1 pound each of walnuts, almonds, and pecans chopped or coarsely ground. Color light orange.

Standard plain mix is often used instead of the richer mix in making puddings.

English Plum Pudding

To 5 gallons parfait mix to which has been added 1.5 pounds of chocolate syrup, add the following fruits and nuts after the mix is partly frozen:

1 pound figs	1 pound pecans
1 pound dates	3 teaspoons cinnamon
4 pounds mixed candied fruits	1 teaspoon each of ginger, allspice and
1 pound walnuts	cloves
4 ounces vanilla extract	

Fruits and nuts should be chopped and may be mixed with the spices before they are added to the partly frozen mix, or the spices may be added to the mix before freezing begins.

Parfait

This requires 4.5 gallons of high-fat (16 per cent) mix and 3.5 dozen fresh eggs. The eggs are added to about a gallon of the mix which is then cooked to a custard (about 160°F. for 30 minutes) and cooled to below 100°F. This custard is then added to the remaining part of the 4.5 gallons of high-fat mix. The resulting 5 gallons of parfait mix can be used like an ordinary ice cream mix to make any flavor desired, as vanilla, chocolate, strawberry, butterscotch and maple parfaits, etc.

Aufait

A molded ice cream and fruit combination consisting of two or more layers of ice cream with pectinized fruit spread between the layers. *Strawberry Aufait:* Fill a brick mold half full with vanilla ice cream; harden; spread over this a layer of pectinized strawberries (not too thick since it is difficult to cut through the fruit layer when it hardens); harden; and finish filling the mold with vanilla or strawberry ice cream. Many variations both as to number of layers and combinations of fruits are possible.

Aufaits are also made in bulk by gently stirring the pectinized fruit into the ice cream as it comes from the freezer. The fruit should be heavy enough and cold enough so that it will make a more or less continuous line in the ice cream giving a marbled effect.

Mousse

Whip 1 gallon of 40 per cent cream to a stiff consistency. Gently stir in 2 pounds sugar, a drop or two of desired color, and $1/2$ to 1 ounce of vanilla. Dates, nuts or fruits free from excessive juice, chopped into rather small pieces, can also be gently stirred in. The mixture is then placed in molds of the desired shape and is frozen in the hardening room without further agitation. This will yield about two and a half gallons of finished mousse.

Spumoni

A special spumoni cup should be used. Press one-fourth of a spumoni cupful of vanilla ice cream around the sides and bottom to line the cup. Add chocolate ice cream to half fill the cup. Finish filling with a mixture of fruit and whipped cream and then place in the hardening room. The fruit and whipped cream is prepared by whipping 1.0 pound confectioner's sugar with 1.0 gallon of heavy cream then gently stirring in the fruit from which excessive juice has been drained.

Variegated Ice Cream

As the plain vanilla ice cream is drawn from the freezer into the package, specially prepared syrups (such as chocolate, butterscotch, etc.) are added by means of a special nozzle so as to produce a marbled effect. Thus a stream of soft ice cream and a stream of the specially prepared syrup enter the package in the desired ratio and are slightly stirred to give a marbled effect. The syrups usually contain about one-half to one per cent stabilizer.

Rainbow Ice Cream

Carefully mix 6 or more different colored ice creams while they are soft (as drawn from the freezers) to give a marbled or rainbow colored effect. Then set in the hardening room to harden.

Fruit Salad

As generally made this consists of fairly large pieces of mixed fruits in combination with whipped cream or ice cream. Pineapple, sliced or cubed; red cherries, apricots, peaches, pears or prunes, properly pitted and sliced, are gently folded into the stiffly whipped cream which has been flavored to taste with a good brand of mayonnaise. This mixture is set to stiffen somewhat before it is placed in molds to harden.

A good formula is about as follows: One gallon fruit mixture to $2/3$ gallon whipped cream (mayonnaise-flavored). For variation $2/3$ gallon of softened vanilla ice cream may be substituted for the whipped cream.

Sherbet

Dissolve 11.0 pounds sugar and 4.0 ounces stabilizer in 2.75 gallons water. When cooled below 50°F. add 3.25 quarts of ice cream mix and 1.0 gallon of colorless corn syrup. At the freezer add 1.0 gallon of pureed fruit or fruit juices together with the desired amount of color and citric acid solution. When frozen, this mixture will yield about 9 gallons of finished sherbet.

Soufflé

This product is made from sherbet mixes, except that whole eggs are added and the freezing is done with sufficiently high overrun to give a fluffy product. The following formula is often used: 3.5 dozen eggs, 12 pounds sugar, 1 gallon strawberries (frozen pack), about 3 gallons skim milk or 3 gallons water. By substituting only the fruit used as flavoring many other soufflés can be made.

Lacto

This product is a milk sherbet made from cultured sour milk, buttermilk or fermented milk. For grape lacto use 3 gallons cultured sour milk, 9 pounds sugar, 12 eggs, 1.5 pints lemon juice, 1 quart grape juice. Dissolve the sugar in the milk. Add fruit juices and beaten egg yolks. Whip egg whites and add at the freezer. Other popular flavors can be made by substituting raspberry, cherry or orange juice for the grape juice.

Water Ice

Dissolve 8 pounds of sugar and 5 ounces of stabilizer in 3.5 gallons of water, and then add 1 gallon of colorless corn syrup. Cool to below 50°F. and add 1 gallon of pureed fruit or fruit juices together with the desired amount of color and citric acid solution. When frozen this mixture will yield about 8 gallons.

Granite

This is made from the same ingredients as an ice but is frozen much harder and with but little whipping or stirring during the freezing process. The result is a coarser textured product than an ice.

Frappé

Juice of 3 dozen lemons and 1 dozen oranges, 2 quarts of grape juice, 2 pounds of sugar and water enough to make 5 gallons. This is made in the same manner as an ice except that it is not hardened. Since frappés are served in a soft condition they ought preferably to be frozen just prior to serving. Many other fruit mixtures pleasing to taste can easily be developed.

Punch

An ice in which fruit juices have been reinforced with an alcoholic beverage. Often rum flavoring (non-alcoholic) is used instead of liquor. The following formula is used extensively: To about 7 gallons of water add 20 pounds sugar, 1 quart lemon juice, 1 quart grape juice and rum flavoring as desired. If it is to be served in frozen form, 5 ounces of stabilizer should be added.

Ice Milk

Thoroughly mix 4 ounces stabilizer with 6.75 pounds sugar. While stirring and heating 3.25 gallons of homogenized 4 per cent milk, slowly add the mixed sugar and stabilizer. Continue stirring and heating until a temperature of 120°F. has been maintained for 20 minutes. Then cool to about 80°F. and add 12 cans (14 ounces each) of evaporated milk. This will yield 45 pounds of ice milk mix to which any desired color and flavor may be added.

Frosted Malted

To 3.5 gallons of ice milk mix add 1 quart malt syrup (or 1 to 2 pounds of malted milk powder) and chocolate syrup made from 0.75 pound cocoa (or 1 pound chocolate liquor), 0.75 pound sugar and 1 to 1.5 quarts water. (Make syrup as directed for Chocolate Ice Cream.) Freeze and serve from freezer.

Diabetic Ice Cream (18 per cent fat, 7 per cent m.s.n.f., 4 per cent glycerin, 0.3 per cent egg yolk solids, 0.44 per cent gelatin, 26 per cent total solids). There is some call for an ice cream low in carbohydrate and sugar content for those who suffer from diabetes. The following formula may help meet this demand: For a 5-gallon mix use 3.25 gallons 30 per cent cream, 1.75 gallons skim milk, 7 fresh eggs, 3.5 ounces stabilizer, 35.0 grains = 2.26 gm. = 0.08 oz. saccharin, 1.75 pounds glycerin. The eggs, gelatin and saccharin are blended with the milk products, pasteurized and homogenized in the same manner as in making other ice cream mixes. The 1.75 pounds glycerin is added at the freezer when the desired color and flavor are added. It is imperative that the sugar content of the flavoring be held at a minimum; therefore vanilla, mint and lemon are most satisfactory. Fruits such as pineapple, peaches and apricots when well ripened can be used but are less satisfactory in this type of ice cream. Since the use of saccharin in ice cream is illegal in many states, special permission from health authorities must be secured.

Suggested Formula (Using Sorbitol) for Diabetics[1]

For 100 gallons: 400.2 lbs. 35 per cent cream; 234.9 lbs. 3.5 per cent milk, 139.2 lbs. Sorbitol solution (Arlex),[1] 3.5 lbs. stabilizer, 43.5 pounds whole eggs,[2] 48.7 lbs. of water and 43.5 gm. saccharin. This ice cream will contain 628 calories per pint at 80 per cent overrun.

---

[1] Sorbitol is used as a substitute for sucrose. Its chief value lies in the delay which occurs before the Sorbitol appears in the blood as glucose, and its low carbohydrate and insulin values.

[2] Or 12.75 lbs. powdered whole eggs plus 30.75 lbs. water.

Its composition will be as follows: 17 per cent milk fat, 5.1 per cent milk solids-not-fat, 16.0 per cent Sorbitol solution, 0.4 per cent stabilizer, 5.0 per cent liquid whole eggs, 5 gm. saccharin per 100-pound mix. (Tracy and Edman, 1950; Tracy, Turnbow and Rafetto, 1947.)

Other Formulas.—Many additional colors, flavors and styles of package are quite suitable for use as frozen desserts. The alert and ingenious ice cream maker, with the aid of his trade association publications and other suggestions picked up from here and there, will be able to develop new flavor combinations and more attractive style of packages. Supply houses are constantly offering new and interesting creations that should help him in increasing his sales and in successfully meeting competition.

FROZEN SUCKER FLAVORS WITH COLOR

Formula for Frozen Sucker Base—Yields 38 Dozen Suckers:

Water	10 gallons
Cane Sugar	15 pounds
Gelatin	5 ounces

Dissolve the sugar in 9.5 gallons of water. Do not use heat. Soak gelatin in small amount of cold water until it swells and becomes soft—then dissolve by stirring and adding sufficient hot water to make $1/2$ gallon of solution. Stir hot gelatin solution into sugar-water mix. Add flavor and acid as recommended below. No color to add. Color present in flavor. Add citric acid solution last. Flavored sucker base should be thoroughly agitated in mixing tank before pouring into the molds. Do not run through freezer. (See Fig. 41.)

Standard Acid Solution (50%) for Sherbets, Ices and Frozen Suckers—Citric or Tartaric Acid Crystals—4 pounds. Hot water to complete 1.0 gallon finished solution.

Orange: Orange (Natural), 4 to 5 ounces; Citric Acid Solution 50%, 6 to 7 ounces.

Limes: Limes Green (Natural), 4 to 5 ounces; Citric Acid Solution 50%, 14 to 15 ounces.

Grape: Grape Imitation, 4 to 5 ounces; Citric Acid Solution 50%, 8 to 10 ounces.

Raspberry: Raspberry Imitation, 4 to 5 ounces; Citric Acid Solution 50%, 5 to 6 ounces.

Lemon: Lemon Yellow (Natural), 4 to 5 ounces; Citric Acid Solution 50%, 10 to 11 ounces.

Cherry: Cherry Imitation, 4 to 5 ounces; Citric Acid Solution 50%, 6 to 8 ounces.

Pineapple: Pineapple Imitation, 4 to 5 ounces; Citric Acid Solution 50%, 5 to 6 ounces.

Strawberry: Strawberry Imitation, 4 to 5 ounces; Citric Acid Solution 50%, 5 to 6 ounces.

Banana: Banana Imitation, 1 to 2 ounces; Citric Acid Solution 50%, 4 to 5 ounces.

PLAIN MIX FORMULAS (TABLES 37 TO 44)

The ice cream maker who, for various reasons, does not care to calculate mixes as previously described, will find that the following formulas in "Mix Formulas" reprinted here from Commercial Ice Cream Formulas, BDIM Inf.11-USDA, will give quite satisfactory results.

The following eight tables present a great number of mix formulas for the production of ice cream ranging in fat content from 10% through 18%. Each table gives different combinations of milk products to be used. These are indicated in the heading at the top of the table.

Note that all these formulas are figured on a 100-pound basis which may be easily computed to other amounts.

For example: A batch of 500 gallons of mix is wanted. Multiply the 500 gallons by 9.2 pounds (average weight per gallon of mix) which results in 4600 pounds—the weight of a 500-gallon batch. Then multiply the amount of each ingredient specified in the formula by 46 to obtain the amount required for the batch.

Notice, also, that these mixes are complete except for color and flavor materials. The formulas in the first part of this chapter give the approximate amount of flavoring material to add to the unflavored mix to produce the desired ice cream. Process as described in Chapter 11. "Mix Processing."

TABLE 37

AMOUNTS OF CREAM OF VARIOUS FAT CONTENTS AND EITHER SKIM OR WHOLE MILK NECESSARY FOR MAKING DIFFERENT TYPES[1] OF ICE CREAM OF FAIRLY HIGH BUTTERFAT CONTENT WITHOUT THE USE OF CONCENTRATED MILK

	Ingredients in Various Types[1] of Ice Cream, Per Cent				
Ingredients	Type 14	Type 15	Type 16	Type 17	Type 18
Fat........................	14.00	15.00	16.00	17.00	18.00
Milk solids-not-fat...........	6.36	6.27	6.18	6.09	6.00
Sugar......................	15.00	15.00	15.00	15.00	15.00
Stabilizer..................	0.30	0.30	0.30	0.30	0.30
Total solids.............	35.66	36.57	37.48	38.39	39.30
Water.....................	64.34	63.43	62.52	61.61	60.70

EIGHT POSSIBLE COMBINATIONS OF MILK PRODUCTS AND OTHER INGREDIENTS FOR EACH TYPE OF ICE CREAM

	Percentage by Weight				
	Type 14	Type 15	Type 16	Type 17	Type 18
(1) Cream (50% fat)........	28.00	30.00	32.00	34.00	36.00
Skim milk..............	56.70	54.70	52.70	50.70	48.70
(2) Cream (40% fat)........	35.00	37.50	40.00	42.50	45.00
Skim milk..............	49.70	47.20	44.70	42.20	39.70
(3) Cream (30% fat)........	46.66	50.00	53.33	56.66	60.00
Skim milk..............	38.04	34.70	31.37	28.04	24.70
(4) Cream (20% fat)........	70.00	75.00	80.00	...	...
Skim milk..............	14.70	9.70	4.70	...	...
(5) Cream (50% fat)........	23.46	25.64	27.80	29.91	32.10
Whole milk (3.7% fat)....	61.24	59.06	56.90	54.79	52.60
(6) Cream (40% fat)........	29.92	32.69	35.45	38.18	40.94
Whole milk (3.7% fat)....	54.78	52.01	49.25	46.52	43.76
(7) Cream (30% fat)........	41.29	45.10	48.91	52.67	56.48
Whole milk (3.7% fat)....	43.41	39.60	35.79	32.03	28.22
(8) Cream (20% fat)........	66.61	72.76	78.91	...	...
Whole milk (3.7% fat)....	18.09	11.94	5.79	...	...
Add to any above combination:					
Sugar....................	15.00	15.00	15.00	15.00	15.00
Stabilizer...............	0.30	0.30	0.30	0.30	0.30
Total.................	100.00	100.00	100.00	100.00	100.00

[1] Type refers to the percentage of butterfat in ice cream.

TABLE 38

AMOUNTS OF CREAM OF VARIOUS FAT CONTENTS AND SKIM OR WHOLE MILK NECESSARY FOR
MAKING DIFFERENT TYPES OF ICE CREAM USING DRY SKIM MILK

Ingredients	Ingredients in Various Types of Ice Cream, Per Cent								
	Type 10	Type 11	Type 12	Type 13	Type 14	Type 15	Type 16	Type 17	Type 18
Fat....................	10.00	11.00	12.00	13.00	14.00	15.00	16.00	17.00	18.00
Milk solids-not-fat........	11.00	10.50	10.00	9.50	9.00	8.50	8.00	7.50	7.00
Sugar.................	15.00	15.00	15.00	15.00	15.00	15.00	15.00	15.00	15.00
Stabilizer..............	0.30	0.30	0.30	0.30	0.30	0.30	0.30	0.30	0.30
Total solids.........	36.30	36.80	37.30	37.80	38.30	38.80	39.30	39.80	40.30
Water..................	63.70	63.20	62.70	62.20	61.70	61.20	60.70	60.20	59.70

EIGHT POSSIBLE COMBINATIONS OF MILK PRODUCTS AND OTHER INGREDIENTS FOR EACH TYPE
OF ICE CREAM

	Percentage by Weight								
	Type 10	Type 11	Type 12	Type 13	Type 14	Type 15	Type 16	Type 17	Type 18
(1) Cream (50% fat)......	20.00	22.00	24.00	26.00	28.00	30.00	32.00	34.00	36.00
Skim milk............	59.70	58.20	56.70	55.20	53.70	52.20	50.70	49.20	47.70
(2) Cream (40% fat)......	25.00	27.50	30.00	32.50	35.00	37.50	40.00	42.50	45.00
Skim milk............	54.70	52.70	50.70	48.70	46.70	44.70	42.70	40.70	38.70
(3) Cream (30% fat)......	33.33	36.66	40.00	43.33	46.66	50.00	53.33	56.66	60.00
Skim milk............	46.37	43.54	40.70	37.87	35.04	32.20	29.37	26.54	23.70
(4) Cream (20% fat)......	50.00	55.00	60.00	65.00	70.00	75.00	80.00	...	...
Skim milk............	29.70	25.20	20.70	16.20	11.70	7.20	2.70	...	...
(5) Cream (50% fat)......	15.21	17.33	19.45	21.57	23.70	25.83	27.96	30.08	32.20
Whole milk (3.7% fat).	64.49	62.87	61.25	59.63	58.00	56.37	54.74	53.12	51.50
(6) Cream (40% fat)......	19.40	22.10	24.80	27.51	30.22	32.92	35.63	38.34	41.05
Whole milk (3.7% fat).	60.30	58.10	55.90	53.69	51.48	49.28	47.07	44.86	42.65
(7) Cream (30% fat)......	26.76	30.50	34.25	37.98	41.70	45.43	49.17	52.90	56.63
Whole milk (3.7% fat).	52.94	49.70	46.45	43.22	40.00	36.77	33.53	30.30	27.07
(8) Cream (20% fat)......	43.17	49.20	55.22	61.25	67.27	73.30	79.32	...	...
Whole milk (3.7% fat).	36.53	31.00	25.48	19.95	14.43	8.90	3.38	...	..
Add to any above combination:									
Dry skim milk[1]........	5.00	4.50	4.00	3.50	3.00	2.50	2.00	1.50	1.00
Sugar.................	15.00	15.00	15.00	15.00	15.00	15.00	15.00	15.00	15.00
Stabilizer.............	0.30	0.30	0.30	0.30	0.30	0.30	0.30	0.30	0.30
Total...............	100.00	100.00	100.00	100.00	100.00	100.00	100.00	100.00	100.00

[1] 95 per cent solids.

TABLE 39

AMOUNTS OF CREAM OF VARIOUS FAT CONTENTS AND SKIM OR WHOLE MILK NECESSARY FOR MAKING DIFFERENT TYPES OF ICE CREAM USING UNSWEETENED CONDENSED SKIM MILK

Ingredients	Ingredients in Various Types of Ice Cream, Per Cent								
	Type 10	Type 11	Type 12	Type 13	Type 14	Type 15	Type 16	Type 17	Type 18
Fat...................	10.00	11.00	12.00	13.00	14.00	15.00	16.00	17.00	18.00
Milk solids-not-fat........	11.00	10.50	10.00	9.50	9.00	8.50	8.00	7.50	7.00
Sugar.................	15.00	15.00	15.00	15.00	15.00	15.00	15.00	15.00	15.00
Stabilizer...............	0.30	0.30	0.30	0.30	0.30	0.30	0.30	0.30	0.30
Total solids..........	36.30	36.80	37.30	37.80	38.30	38.80	39.30	39.80	40.30
Water..................	63.70	63.20	62.70	62.20	61.70	61.20	60.70	60.20	59.70

EIGHT POSSIBLE COMBINATIONS OF MILK PRODUCTS AND OTHER INGREDIENTS FOR EACH TYPE OF ICE CREAM

	Percentage by Weight								
	Type 10	Type 11	Type 12	Type 13	Type 14	Type 15	Type 16	Type 17	Type 18
(1) Cream (50% fat)......	20.00	22.00	24.00	26.00	28.00	30.00	32.00	34.00	36.00
Skim milk...........	41.00	41.25	41.50	41.80	42.10	42.40	42.70	42.95	43.19
(2) Cream (40% fat)......	25.00	27.50	30.00	32.50	35.00	37.50	40.00	42.50	45.00
Skim milk...........	36.00	35.75	35.50	35.30	35.10	34.90	34.70	34.45	34.19
(3) Cream (30% fat)......	33.33	36.66	40.00	43.33	46.66	49.99	53.33	56.66	60.00
Skim milk...........	27.67	26.59	25.50	24.47	23.44	22.41	21.37	20.29	19.19
(4) Cream (20% fat)......	50.00	55.00	60.00	65.00	70.00	...	...	...	...
Skim milk...........	11.00	8.25	5.50	2.80	0.10				
(5) Cream (50% fat)......	16.73	18.70	20.68	22.66	24.63	26.61	28.59	30.57	32.53
Whole milk (3.7% fat).	44.27	44.55	44.82	45.14	45.47	45.79	46.11	46.38	46.66
(6) Cream (40% fat)......	21.33	23.85	26.37	28.89	31.41	33.93	36.45	38.97	41.50
Whole milk (3.7% fat).	39.67	39.40	39.13	38.91	38.69	38.47	38.25	37.98	37.69
(7) Cream (30% fat)......	29.44	32.92	36.40	39.82	43.35	46.82	50.30	53.77	57.25
Whole milk (3.7% fat).	31.56	30.33	29.10	27.98	26.75	25.58	24.40	23.18	21.94
(8) Cream (20% fat)......	47.49	53.10	58.72	64.32	69.92	...	...	...	...
Whole milk (3.7% fat).	13.51	10.15	6.78	3.48	0.18	...	...	...	...
Add to any above combina-tion:									
Unsweetened condensed skim milk[1]..........	23.70	21.45	19.20	16.90	14.60	12.30	10.00	7.75	5.51
Sugar................	15.00	15.00	15.00	15.00	15.00	15.00	15.00	15.00	15.00
Stabilizer.............	0.30	0.30	0.30	0.30	0.30	0.30	0.30	0.30	0.30
Total...............	100.00	100.00	100.00	100.00	100.00	100.00	100.00	100.00	100.00

[1] Concentration 3 to 1; contains 27 per cent milk solids-not-fat.

TABLE 40

AMOUNTS OF CREAM OF VARIOUS FAT CONTENTS AND SKIM OR WHOLE MILK NECESSARY FOR MAKING DIFFERENT TYPES OF ICE CREAM USING SWEETENED CONDENSED SKIM MILK

Ingredients	Ingredients in Various Types of Ice Cream, Per Cent								
	Type 10	Type 11	Type 12	Type 13	Type 14	Type 15	Type 16	Type 17	Type 18
Fat....................	10.00	11.00	12.00	13.00	14.00	15.00	16.00	17.00	18.00
Milk solids-not-fat........	11.00	10.50	10.00	9.50	9.00	8.50	8.00	7.50	7.00
Sugar..................	15.00	15.00	15.00	15.00	15.00	15.00	15.00	15.00	15.00
Stabilizer...............	0.30	0.30	0.30	0.30	0.30	0.30	0.30	0.30	0.30
Total solids.........	36.30	36.80	37.30	37.80	38.30	38.80	39.30	39.80	40.30
Water..................	63.70	63.20	62.70	62.20	61.70	61.20	60.70	60.20	59.70

EIGHT POSSIBLE COMBINATIONS OF MILK PRODUCTS AND OTHER INGREDIENTS FOR EACH TYPE OF ICE CREAM

	Percentage by Weight								
	Type 10	Type 11	Type 12	Type 13	Type 14	Type 15	Type 16	Type 17	Type 18
(1) Cream (50% fat)......	20.00	22.00	24.00	26.00	28.00	30.00	32.00	34.00	36.00
Skim milk...........	54.74	53.63	52.68	51.59	50.56	49.53	48.49	47.45	46.40
(2) Cream (40% fat)......	25.00	27.50	30.00	32.50	35.00	37.50	40.00	42.50	45.00
Skim milk...........	49.74	48.18	46.63	45.09	43.56	42.03	40.49	38.95	37.40
(3) Cream (30% fat)......	33.33	36.66	40.00	43.33	46.66	49.99	53.33	56.66	60.00
Skim milk...........	41.41	39.02	36.63	34.26	31.90	29.54	27.16	24.79	22.40
(4) Cream (20% fat)......	50.00	55.00	60.00	65.00	70.00	...	...	...	...
Skim milk...........	24.74	20.68	16.63	12.59	8.56	...	...	...	...
(5) Cream (50% fat)......	15.63	17.71	19.79	21.87	23.96	26.04	28.13	30.21	32.30
Whole milk (3.7% fat).	59.11	57.97	56.84	55.72	54.60	53.49	52.36	51.24	50.10
(6) Cream (40% fat)......	19.93	22.58	25.24	27.89	30.55	33.20	35.86	38.53	41.20
Whole milk (3.7% fat).	54.81	53.10	51.39	49.70	48.01	46.33	44.63	42.92	41.20
(7) Cream (30% fat)......	27.51	31.17	34.83	38.49	42.16	45.82	49.49	53.13	56.80
Whole milk (3.7% fat).	47.23	44.51	41.80	39.10	36.40	33.71	31.00	28.32	25.60
(8) Cream (20% fat)......	44.69	50.44	56.19	62.10	68.00	73.91	79.83	...	...
Whole milk (3.7% fat).	30.05	25.24	20.44	15.49	10.56	5.62	0.66	...	...
Add to any above combination:									
Sweetened condensed skim milk[1]...........	17.22	15.57	13.92	12.27	10.61	8.96	7.31	5.65	4.00
Sugar...............	7.74	8.45	9.15	9.84	10.53	11.21	11.90	12.60	13.30
Stabilizer.............	0.30	0.30	0.30	0.30	0.30	0.30	0.30	0.30	0.30
Total...............	100.00	100.00	100.00	100.00	100.00	100.00	100.00	100.00	100.00

[1] Contains 30.0 per cent milk solids-not-fat, 42 per cent sugar, 28 per cent water.

TABLE 41

AMOUNTS OF CREAM OF VARIOUS FAT CONTENTS AND SKIM OR WHOLE MILK NECESSARY FOR
MAKING DIFFERENT TYPES OF ICE CREAM USING UNSWEETENED CONDENSED SKIM MILK AND
LIQUID SUGAR

Ingredients	Ingredients in Various Types of Ice Cream, Per Cent								
	Type 10	Type 11	Type 12	Type 13	Type 14	Type 15	Type 16	Type 17	Type 18
Fat....................	10.00	11.00	12.00	13.00	14.00	15.00	16.00	17.00	18.00
Milk solids-not fat.........	11.00	10.50	10.00	9.50	9.00	8.50	8.00	7.50	7.00
Sugar..................	15.00	15.00	15.00	15.00	15.00	15.00	15.00	15.00	15.00
Stabilizer...............	0.30	0.30	0.30	0.30	0.30	0.30	0.30	0.30	0.30
Total solids..........	36.30	36.80	37.30	37.80	38.30	38.80	39.30	39.80	40.30
Water..................	63.70	63.20	62.70	62.20	61.70	61.20	60.70	60.20	59.70

EIGHT POSSIBLE COMBINATIONS OF MILK PRODUCTS AND OTHER INGREDIENTS FOR EACH TYPE
OF ICE CREAM

	Percentage by Weight								
	Type 10	Type 11	Type 12	Type 13	Type 14	Type 15	Type 16	Type 17	Type 18
(1) Cream (50% fat)......	20.00	22.00	24.00	26.00	28.00	30.00	32.00	34.00	36.00
Skim milk...........	30.42	30.70	30.99	31.29	31.59	31.86	32.14	32.39	32.65
(2) Cream (40% fat)......	25.00	27.50	30.00	32.50	35.00	37.50	40.00	42.50	45.00
Skim milk...........	25.42	25.20	24.99	24.79	24.59	24.36	24.14	23.89	23.65
(3) Cream (30% fat)....	33.33	36.66	40.00	43.33	46.66	49.99	53.33	56.66	60.00
Skim milk..........	17.09	16.04	14.99	13.96	12.93	11.87	10.81	9.73	8.65
(4) Cream (20% fat)......	...	...	...	...	...	...	...	...	...
Skim milk...........	...	...	...	...	...	...	...	...	...
(5) Cream (50% fat)......	17.61	19.57	21.54	23.51	25.48	27.47	29.46	31.43	33.40
Whole milk (3.7% fat).	32.81	33.13	33.45	33.78	34.11	34.39	34.68	34.96	35.25
(6) Cream (40% fat)......	22.42	24.95	27.49	30.03	32.57	35.08	37.59	40.16	42.74
Whole milk (3.7% fat).	28.00	27.75	27.50	27.26	27.02	26.78	26.55	26.23	25.91
(7) Cream (30% fat)......	30.90	34.39	37.88	41.25	44.62	48.20	51.78	55.34	58.90
Whole milk (3.7% fat).	19.52	18.31	17.11	16.04	14.97	13.66	12.36	11.05	9.75
(8) Cream (20% fat)......	...	...	...	...	...	...	...	...	...
Whole milk (3.7% fat).	...	...	...	...	...	...	...	...	...
Add to any above combination:									
Unsweetened condensed skim milk[1]...........	27.28	25.00	22.71	20.41	18.11	15.84	13.56	11.31	9.05
Liquid sugar[2]..........	22.00	22.00	22.00	22.00	22.00	22.00	22.00	22.00	22.00
Stabilizer..............	0.30	0.30	0.30	0.30	0.30	0.30	0.30	0.30	0.30
Total...............	100.00	100.00	100.00	100.00	100.00	100.00	100.00	100.00	100.00

[1] Concentration 3 to 1; contains 27 per cent milk solids-not-fat.
[2] 68.1 per cent concentration; i.e., 1 gallon = 11 pounds containing 7.5 pounds sugar.

TABLE 42

AMOUNTS OF CREAM OF VARIOUS FAT CONTENTS AND SKIM OR WHOLE MILK NECESSARY FOR
MAKING DIFFERENT TYPES OF ICE CREAM USING SWEETENED CONDENSED SKIM MILK AND
LIQUID SUGAR

Ingredients	Ingredients in Various Types of Ice Cream, Per Cent								
	Type 10	Type 11	Type 12	Type 13	Type 14	Type 15	Type 16	Type 17	Type 18
Fat......................	10.00	11.00	12.00	13.00	14.00	15.00	16.00	17.00	18.00
Milk solids-not-fat.........	11.00	10.50	10.00	9.50	9.00	8.50	8.00	7.50	7.00
Sugar..................	15.00	15.00	15.00	15.00	15.00	15.00	15.00	15.00	15.00
Stabilizer...............	0.30	0.30	0.30	0.30	0.30	0.30	0.30	0.30	0.30
Total solids...........	36.30	36.80	37.30	37.80	38.30	38.80	39.30	39.80	40.30
Water...................	63.70	63.20	62.70	62.20	61.70	61.20	60.70	60.20	59.70

EIGHT POSSIBLE COMBINATIONS OF MILK PRODUCTS AND OTHER INGREDIENTS FOR EACH TYPE
OF ICE CREAM

	Percentage by Weight								
	Type 10	Type 11	Type 12	Type 13	Type 14	Type 15	Type 16	Type 17	Type 18
(1) Cream (50% fat)......	20.00	22.00	24.00	26.00	28.00	30.00	32.00	34.00	36.00
Skim milk...........	50.65	49.25	47.86	46.44	45.02	43.59	42.16	40.82	39.48
(2) Cream (40% fat)......	25.00	27.50	30.00	32.50	35.00	37.50	40.00	42.50	45.00
Skim milk...........	45.65	43.75	41.86	39.94	38.02	36.09	34.16	32.32	30.48
(3) Cream (30% fat)......	33.33	36.66	40.00	43.33	46.66	50.00	53.33	56.66	60.00
Skim milk...........	37.32	34.59	31.86	29.11	26.36	23.59	20.83	18.16	15.48
(4) Cream (20% fat)......	50.00	55.00	60.00	65.00	70.00	...	...	...	...
Skim milk...........	20.65	16.25	11.86	7.44	3.02	...	...	...	...
(5) Cream (50% fat)......	15.95	18.07	20.19	22.28	24.37	26.49	28.62	30.75	32.89
Whole milk (3.7% fat).	54.70	53.18	51.67	50.16	48.65	47.10	45.54	44.07	42.59
(6) Cream (40% fat)......	20.32	23.01	25.70	28.39	31.09	33.79	36.50	39.17	41.84
Whole milk (3.7% fat).	50.33	48.24	46.16	44.05	41.93	39.80	37.66	35.65	33.64
(7) Cream (30% fat)......	28.11	31.81	35.51	39.19	42.87	46.63	50.39	54.10	57.81
Whole milk (3.7% fat).	42.54	39.44	36.35	33.25	30.15	26.96	23.77	20.72	17.67
(8) Cream (20% fat)......	46.24	51.81	57.38	63.25	69.13	...	...	...	...
Whole milk (3.7% fat).	24.41	19.44	14.48	9.19	3.89	...	...	...	...
Add to any above combination: Sweetened condensed skim milk[1]............	18.43	16.88	15.32	13.76	12.21	10.67	9.14	7.53	5.93
Liquid sugar[2]..........	10.62	11.57	12.52	13.50	14.47	15.44	16.40	17.35	18.29
Stabilizer...............	0.30	0.30	0.30	0.30	0.30	0.30	0.30	0.30	0.30
Total.................	100.00	100.00	100.00	100.00	100.00	100.00	100.00	100.00	100.00

[1] Contains 30.0 per cent milk solids-not-fat, 42 per cent sugar, 28 per cent water.
[2] 68.1 per cent concentration: i.e., 1 gallon = 11 pounds containing 7.5 pounds sugar.

TABLE 43

AMOUNTS OF CREAM WITH 50 PER CENT OF THE FAT ADDED IN THE FORM OF BUTTER,
UNSWEETENED CONDENSED OR DRY SKIM MILK, AND WATER OR WHOLE MILK NECESSARY
FOR MAKING DIFFERENT TYPES OF ICE CREAM

Ingredients	Ingredients in Various Types of Ice Cream, Per Cent								
	Type 10	Type 11	Type 12	Type 13	Type 14	Type 15	Type 16	Type 17	Type 18
Fat....................	10.00	11.00	12.00	13.00	14.00	15.00	16.00	17.00	18.00
Milk solids-not-fat........	11.00	10.50	10.00	9.50	9.00	8.50	8.00	7.50	7.00
Sugar...................	15.00	15.00	15.00	15.00	15.00	15.00	15.00	15.00	15.00
Stabilizer	0.30	0.30	0.30	0.30	0.30	0.30	0.30	0.30	0.30
Total solids	36.30	36.80	37.30	37.80	38.30	38.80	39.30	39.80	40.30
Water..................	63.70	63.20	62.70	62.20	61.70	61.20	60.70	60.20	59.70

EIGHT POSSIBLE COMBINATIONS OF MILK PRODUCTS AND OTHER INGREDIENTS FOR EACH TYPE
OF ICE CREAM

	Percentage by Weight								
	Type 10	Type 11	Type 12	Type 13	Type 14	Type 15	Type 16	Type 17	Type 18
(1) Cream (40% fat)......	12.50	13.75	15.00	16.25	17.50	18.75	20.00	20.25	22.50
Unsweetened condensed skim milk[1]..........	24.40	22.30	20.20	17.90	15.60	13.40	11.20	8.97	6.75
Water..............	41.70	41.95	42.20	42.65	43.10	43.42	43.75	44.10	44.45
(2) Cream (40% fat)......	12.50	13.75	15.00	16.25	17.50	18.75	20.00	21.25	22.50
Dry skim milk[2]........	5.00	4.55	4.10	3.65	3.20	2.75	2.30	1.85	1.40
Water	61.10	59.70	58.30	56.90	55.50	54.07	52.65	51.22	49.80
(3) Cream (20% fat)......	25.00	27.50	30.00	32.50	35.00	37.50	40.00	42.50	45.00
Unsweetened condensed skim milk[1]..........	24.40	22.30	20.20	17.90	15.60	13.40	11.20	8.97	6.75
Water..............	29.20	28.20	27.20	26.40	25.60	24.67	23.75	22.85	21.95
(4) Cream (20% fat)......	25.00	27.50	30.00	32.50	35.00	37.50	40.00	42.50	45.00
Dry skim milk[2]........	5.00	4.55	4.10	3.65	3.20	2.75	2.30	1.85	1.40
Water..............	48.60	45.95	43.30	40.65	38.00	35.32	32.65	29.97	27.30
(5) Cream (40% fat)......	8.25	9.47	10.70	11.85	13.00	14.30	15.60	16.90	18.20
Unsweetened condensed skim milk[1]..........	24.40	22.30	20.20	17.90	15.60	13.40	11.20	8.97	6.75
Whole milk (3.7% fat).	45.95	46.23	46.50	47.05	47.60	47.87	48.15	48.45	45.75
(6) Cream (40% fat)......	6.23	7.65	9.08	10.44	11.80	13.15	14.50	15.80	17.10
Dry skim milk[2]........	5.00	4.55	4.10	3.65	3.20	2.75	2.30	1.85	1.40
Whole milk (3.7% fat).	67.37	65.80	64.22	62.71	61.20	59.67	58.15	56.67	55.20
(7) Cream (20% fat)......	18.50	21.20	23.90	26.55	29.20	32.00	34.80	37.40	40.00
Unsweetened condensed skim milk[1].....	24.40	22.30	20.20	17.90	15.60	13.40	11.20	8.97	6.75
Whole milk (3.7% fat).	35.70	34.50	33.30	32.35	31.40	30.17	28.95	27.95	26.95
(8) Cream (20% fat)......	14.10	17.10	20.10	23.10	26.10	29.10	32.10	35.15	38.20
Dry skim milk[2]........	5.00	4.55	4.10	3.65	3.20	2.75	2.30	1.85	1.40
Whole milk (3.7% fat).	59.50	53.35	53.20	50.05	46.90	43.72	40.55	37.32	34.10
Add to any above combination:									
Butter[3]	6.10	6.70	7.30	7.90	8.50	9.13	9.75	10.38	11.00
Sugar.................	15.00	15.00	15.00	15.00	15.00	15.00	15.00	15.00	15.00
Stabilizer	0.30	0.30	0.30	0.30	0.30	0.30	0.30	0.30	0.30
Total...............	100.00	100.00	100.00	100.00	100.00	100.00	100.00	100.00	100.00

[1] 27 per cent milk solids-not-fat.   [2] 95 per cent solids.   [3] 82 per cent butterfat.

TABLE 44

AMOUNTS OF CREAM OF VARIOUS FAT CONTENTS AND SKIM OR WHOLE MILK NECESSARY FOR
MAKING DIFFERENT TYPES OF ICE CREAM USING UNSWEETENED CONDENSED SKIM MILK AND UP
TO HALF THE NORMAL SUCROSE REPLACED BY CORN SYRUP WHILE MAINTAINING A SWEETNESS
OF 13.5[1]

	Ingredients in Various Types of Ice Cream, Per Cent								
Ingredients	Type 10	Type 11	Type 12	Type 13	Type 14	Type 15	Type 16	Type 17	Type 18
Fat	10.00	11.00	12.00	13.00	14.00	15.00	16.00	17.00	18.00
Milk solids-not-fat	11.00	10.50	10.00	9.50	9.00	8.50	8.00	7.50	7.00
Sucrose	7.50	7.50	7.50	7.50	7.50	7.50	7.50	7.50	7.50
Corn syrup solids	10.00	10.00	10.00	10.00	10.00	10.00	10.00	10.00	10.00
Stabilizer	0.30	0.30	0.30	0.30	0.30	0.30	0.30	0.30	0.30
Total solids	38.80	39.30	39.80	40.30	40.80	41.30	41.80	42.30	42.80
Water	61.20	60.70	60.20	59.70	59.20	58.70	58.20	57.70	57.20

EIGHT POSSIBLE COMBINATIONS OF MILK PRODUCTS AND OTHER INGREDIENTS FOR EACH TYPE
OF ICE CREAM

	Percentage by Weight								
	Type 10	Type 11	Type 12	Type 13	Type 14	Type 15	Type 16	Type 17	Type 18
(1) Cream (50% fat)	20.00	22.00	24.00	26.00	28.00	30.00	32.00	34.00	36.00
Skim milk	33.42	33.71	34.00	34.27	34.55	34.83	35.11	35.41	35.70
(2) Cream (40% fat)	25.00	27.50	30.00	32.00	35.00	37.50	40.00	42.50	45.00
Skim milk	28.42	28.21	28.00	27.77	27.55	27.33	27.11	26.91	26.70
(3) Cream (30% fat)	33.33	36.66	40.00	43.33	46.66	49.99	53.33	56.66	60.00
Skim milk	20.09	19.05	18.00	16.94	15.89	14.84	13.78	12.75	11.70
(4) Cream (20% fat)	50 00	...	...	...	...	...	...	...	...
Skim milk	3.42	...	...	...	...	...	...	...	...
(5) Cream (50% fat)	17.28	19.26	21.24	23.21	25.19	27.17	29.15	31.13	33.11
Whole milk (3.7% fat)	36.14	36.45	36.76	37.06	37.36	37.66	37.96	38.28	38.59
(6) Cream (40% fat)	22.11	24.63	27.16	29.68	32.20	34.71	37.22	39.74	42.26
Whole milk (3.7% fat)	31.31	31.08	30.84	30 59	30.35	30.12	29.89	29.67	29.44
(7) Cream (30% fat)	30.50	34.03	37.56	40.99	44.43	47.90	51.37	54.84	58.31
Whole milk (3.7% fat)	22.92	21.68	20.44	19.28	18.12	16.93	15.74	14.57	13.39
(8) Cream (20% fat)	49.21	...	...	...	...	...	...	...	...
Whole milk (3.7% fat)	4.21	...	...	...	...	...	...	...	...
Add to any above combination:									
Unsweetened condensed skim milk[2]	26.28	23.99	21.70	19.43	17.15	14.87	12.59	10.29	8.00
Sucrose	7.50	7.50	7.50	7.50	7.50	7.50	7.50	7.50	7.50
Corn syrup[3]	12.50	12.50	12.50	12.50	12.50	12.50	12.50	12.50	12.50
Stabilizer	0.30	0.30	0.30	0.30	0.30	0.30	0.30	0.30	0.30
Total	100.00	100.00	100.00	100.00	100.00	100.00	100.00	100.00	100.00

[1] The amount of sugar used is calculated to be that amount which will make the finished mix as sweet as one
containing 13.5 per cent sucrose.

[2] Concentration 3 to 1; contains 27% milk solids-not-fat.

[3] Corn syrup containing 80.3 per cent solids. High equivalent syrup of 82 per cent solids of greater sweetness
can be used in compounding these mixes by adding from 3 to 6 pounds of water to 100 pounds of syrup.

CHAPTER 18

Defects, Scoring and Grading

Quality and price are two major factors in determining not only the volume of current business but also the future of the entire ice cream industry. Since quality is so vital in establishing price, it is necessary to understand the cause and remedy of defects in quality. The manufacturer and connoisseur both realize that defects in quality are the result of faults in flavor, body and texture, melting characteristics, color and package, bacterial content or composition. In their effort to improve the quality they assume an ideal of perfection for each of these characteristics. This ideal standard is embodied in a score card which is used to measure the degree of perfection, and the deductions which should be made for the various defects of the ice cream.

The scoring of ice creams, sherbets and ices presents some difficulties not encountered in scoring other dairy products. In the first place, the ideal flavor is far more variable than the ideal flavor for other dairy products, since it depends not only on the flavoring material used but also on the presence of other substances which blend with and modify the added flavoring material. Such a blend or combination, even if it be unintentional, is not always displeasing. Consequently, the ideal standard is a blend of two ideal flavors: the ideal flavor in the dairy products and the ideal flavor in the added flavoring material.

The common defects in ice cream cause diminished consumer good will, sales and income to the manufacturer. The ideal product should be packaged in an attractive container, possess a typical, pleasant and desirable flavor, have a close, smooth, uniform body and texture, have desirable melting properties, possess a uniform natural color and have a low bacterial count. The ice cream score card is as follows:

(a) flavor—45 points
(b) body and texture—30 points
(c) bacteria—15 points
(d) color and package—5 points
(e) melting quality—5 points

FLAVOR DEFECTS

Sources of flavor defects are: (a) dairy products of poor quality—with common off-flavors of old ingredient, oxidized, acid, cooked or unclean; (b) sweetness—excessive or deficient; (c) flavoring—excess, deficient or

246

not typical; (d) blend—may not be pleasing; or (e) serving conditions—too hard or too soft.

The qualities of flavor imparted by the flavoring material may be designated as high, low, delicate, harsh and unnatural.

High flavor is characterized by the presence of large amounts of the flavoring material. In some cases an excess of flavoring material will impart a sharp or bitter flavor to the ice cream. A poor quality of flavoring may have the same effect; hence it is quite important to determine, if possible, whether the bitter flavor is due to poor quality or to large amounts of flavoring material, although both are undesirable defects.

Low flavor refers to an insufficient amount of flavoring material; that is, not enough to make the flavor easily recognized. It may be due to insufficient or weak flavoring material, to some other substance obscuring the flavor, or to the ice cream mix being cooked after the volatile flavoring material is added. However, low flavor should not be confounded with delicate flavor.

Delicate flavors are, as a rule, the most pleasing and desirable and most easily blended, and they do not readily clog the appetite. Natural flavors, such as fruit and nut flavors, are delicate and pleasing to taste but they are also readily dissipated by careless handling.

Harsh flavors are sharp and lingering, such as ginger, onion and vinegar. A good illustration of this defect in ice cream is obtained when quite large quantities of lemon or orange extract are used, giving a flavor entirely due to the lemon or orange oil. Harsh flavors are usually due to the use of inferior flavoring substances, but in some cases may result from the use of too much flavoring extract. Inferior and artificial extracts lack the fine, delicate qualities of the high grade extracts and frequently give a very pronounced, but not pleasing, flavor to the ice cream.

Unnatural flavors are considered as defects, but the extent to which the score is reduced will depend upon the source of that flavor. For example, because of its acidity lemon juice is sometimes added to reinforce certain fruit flavors. However, should any of the oil from the rind of the lemon find access to the mixture, it is likely to impart a lemon flavor where it is not wanted. In such a case, the resulting blended fruit flavor would be "unnatural" but not of a particularly undesirable sort. Similarly a pronounced vanillin flavor in vanilla ice cream, caramel flavor in maple ice cream colored with caramel, and synthetic flavors that are not perfect imitations of the true flavors are considered unnatural. Flavors due to poor cream, poor gelatin, fermented syrups, overripe or unsound fruit and rancid nuts are unnatural flavors to which a lower score should be given.

Fruit and fruit juices may impart undesirable flavors if the fruit is unsound or the juice fermented. The naturally delicate flavor imparted by sound fruit may be quite easily distinguished from the artificial flavors. An artificial flavor, being somewhat unnatural, is not entitled to as high a score as a natural flavor.

Nut flavors are to be judged in the same way as fruit flavors. The way in which the nuts have been prepared should also receive attention. It should be noted whether or not the nuts have been blanched, finely chopped and evenly distributed through the ice cream.

Syrups and sugar may be used in excess, making the mixture too sweet. When an insufficient amount is used the ice cream has a flat flavor. Sometimes a sour or yeasty flavor may be imparted by the use of a syrup which has begun to ferment.

The flavors imparted by the dairy products are the most important from an hygienic standpoint. The flavor given to ice cream by good, pure dairy products is rich, creamy and delicate. Flavor defects usually described as "cooked" and "feed" (when due to normal feeds) are not of a particularly undesirable sort. Lower scores should be given for flavors due to the use of tainted dairy products. These flavors may be grouped under such terms as "feed" (due to weeds, etc.), "high acid," "old ingredient" such as yeasty, cheesy, musty, bitter, etc., "oxidized," "rancid," "salty" (when due to "salty" cream), and "unclean."

Defects Caused by Chemical Changes.—Flavor defects described as "storage" (stale) and "oxidized" (resembling cardboard or tallow) sometimes develop in ice cream as the result of chemical changes and are particularly objectionable. An especially unpleasant flavor, suggesting a stale and unclean flavor, may be absorbed from the air of the hardening room when moisture-soaked wood is exposed through lack of paint or cracked paint. This absorbed flavor defect is usually most noticeable in the whipped cream decorations of specialties being hardened without wrapping.

Lack of fine flavor is a minor flavor defect. It may be corrected by using fresh dairy products and true flavoring materials.

Acid flavor is caused by the presence of an excessive amount of lactic acid. It can be remedied by (a) using fresh dairy products; (b) prompt, efficient cooling of the mix; and (c) avoiding prolonged storage of the mix at high storage temperatures.

Bitter flavor results from the use of inferior products and may be prevented by (a) using true extracts; (b) avoiding use of dairy products stored for long periods at low temperatures, as certain types of bacteria produce bitter flavor under these conditions; and (c) using products free from off-flavors.

Cooked flavor is caused by overheating the mix or using overheated concentrated dairy products. This defect can be prevented by (a) carefully controlling the pasteurization process; and (b) by using concentrated products free of cooked flavor.

Flat flavor is a result of the use of insufficient flavor, sugar or milk solids. The defect can be remedied by increasing the amount of these materials.

Unnatural flavor indicates the presence of a flavor not typical to ice cream. This condition can be remedied by (a) using high quality flavoring products; (b) using high quality dairy and non-dairy products.

Metallic flavor is caused by copper contamination and in some cases may be the result of bacterial action. It may be prevented by (a) avoiding copper contamination of the mix during processing; (b) avoiding the use of products having a metallic flavor.

Salty flavor may be due to (a) the use of more than 0.1 per cent salt in the mix, or (b) too high milk solids-not-fat content of the mix.

Old ingredient flavor may be prevented by using only clean, fresh dairy products.

Oxidized flavor is also sometimes known as tallowy or cardboard. It may be avoided by (a) using fresh dairy products; (b) using only stainless steel equipment; (c) using antioxidants; (d) pasteurizing the mix at high temperatures (170°F.).

BODY AND TEXTURE DEFECTS

The body of ice cream pertains to its firmness and resistance or consistency. Ice cream texture is dependent upon the number, size, shape and arrangement of the ice crystals and other particles. The body and texture characteristics are closely associated and are important in influencing consumer acceptance of ice cream and related products. Ice cream texture should be smooth, uniform and present a pleasing reaction when the ice cream is consumed. Body defects are commonly described as crumbly, soggy and weak while the common texture defects are coarse, icy, fluffy, sandy and buttery.

The internal structure factors that influence body and texture include: (1) size, shape and distribution of ice crystals, (2) size, shape and distribution of air cells, (3) amount and distribution of unfrozen material.

The photographs presented in Fig. 45 were taken of ice cream samples having different body and texture characteristics.

Sources of common body and texture defects are: (a) improper composition of mix; (b) improper processing methods; (c) improper storage conditions. Composition affects body and texture in general through increase or decrease in total solids of the mix.

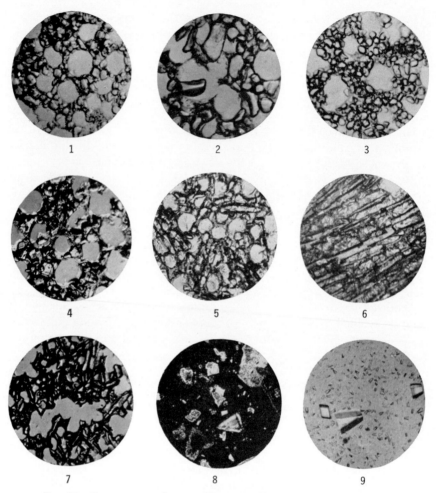

FIG. 45.   PHOTOGRAPHS SHOWING BODY AND TEXTURE CHARACTERISTICS
OF ICE CREAM

(1) close, smooth, (2) coarse, open, (3) short, fluffy, (4) soggy, (5) coarse, icy, due
to temperature fluctuation, (6) coarse, icy, flaky, due to slow freezing without agitation, (7) coarse, icy surface heat shock, (8) lactose crystals from sandy ice cream,
(9) lactose crystals.

Body may be said to be that quality which gives weight and substance
to the product and enables it to stand up well.   Thus it refers to consistency ("chewiness") or firmness and to the melting character of ice cream.
The ideal body is that which is produced by the correct proportion of milk
solids (both butterfat and milk solids-not-fat) together with the proper
overrun, and which melts fairly rapidly at room temperature to a smooth

liquid similar in appearance and consistency to sweet cream containing about 40 per cent fat. It results from the proper combination of composition and processing, each being somewhat limited by the other.

A "crumbly" body lacks cohesion and pulls or breaks apart very easily— a common defect of sherbets and ices where it is less serious than in ice cream. It is frequently associated with a low total solids content, insufficient stabilization, excessive overrun, low homogenization pressure, large air cells and imperfect homogenization. Factors (such as improper salt balance, enzymatic improvers and certain gum stabilizers) which limit the hydration of the proteins are thought to cause "crumbliness." It is similar to the defect sometimes referred to as "dry" body which results from excessive use of emulsifiers, egg yolk solids, certain types of vegetable stabilizers, excessive homogenization pressure or the addition of dry milk solids at the freezer.

Crumbly body is a condition in which the ice cream does not hold together properly. It may be remedied by (a) increasing the solids content; (b) increasing the stabilizer; or (c) decreasing the overrun.

A "soggy" body is dense and may be somewhat "wet" in appearance. In some market areas this defect is not too objectionable. It is due to a low overrun (especially if the total solids content is high), a high concentration of sugars that lower the freezing point, hand packaging after hardening the ice cream or excessive concentration of stabilizer. It is frequently confused with defects described as "gummy," "doughy," "sticky" and "gluey." Excessive stabilization or a high total solids content produces a "chewy" or "gummy" body while syrups and certain types of gum (pectin, oatgum, etc.) favor a "pasty," "sticky" or "gluey" body. Sogginess and its related defects contribute to high melting resistance.

A "weak" body lacks firmness or "chewiness" and is invariably accompanied by rapid melting. It should not be confounded with "fluffy" or "snowy" texture and excessive overrun. A weak body is particularly undesirable from the consumer's viewpoint and should receive a very low score. The defect is due to a low total solids content combined with insufficient stabilization, and results, therefore, in a thin mix—a mix of weak consistency.

Texture refers to the grain or to the finer structure of the product, and depends upon the size, shape and arrangement of the small particles. Ice cream having an ideal texture will be very smooth, the solid particles being too small to be detected in the mouth.

"Buttery" texture refers to lumps of butterfat large enough to be easily detected in the mouth. When a lump of butterfat is chewed, the sensation is different from that obtained from ice crystals or from lactose crystals. This defect is due to churning (usually during the freezing process), which results from incomplete homogenization, high fat content, mix entering the freezer at too high a temperature and slow freezing.

"Coarse" or icy texture indicates that the ice crystals are large or not uniform in size, or that the air cells are too large. The coarseness due to large air cells should not be confused with high overrun obtained by small air cells. This is the most common texture defect and is affected by many factors. For example, large air cells may be due to the type of freezer used, or to a mix of low whipping ability. Large ice crystals are favored by (1) insufficient stabilizer, (2) slow freezing in the freezer, (3) slow freezing in the hardening room (such as happens after partial melting before entering, and refreezing in the hardening room or when storage temperatures fluctuate and slightly softened ice cream is re-hardened) and (4) insufficient hydration of the protein (lack of aging, high acidity, poor salt balance, etc.). The defect "coarse and icy" also includes the presence of ice pellets, which should receive a low score. These pellets are caused by droplets of water getting into the ice cream, frequently from the retailer's scoops. Coarse texture is the most common texture defect. This defect may be controlled by avoiding (a) low solids mixes; (b) insufficient stabilizer; (c) high drawing temperatures at the freezer; (d) slow hardening; (e) heat shocking and (f) prolonged storage.

"Fluffy" texture is readily detected by the large air cells and open texture. It is due to the incorporation of an excessive amount of air either as large or small air cells. This defect may be expected when the total solids content is not more than one-third of the overrun. When the air cells are large and the amount of air is excessive the texture is sometimes described as "snowy" or "flaky." Such a condition might be more properly scored as both "fluffy" and "coarse." It may be corrected by (a) decreasing the overrun; (b) increasing solids; (c) decreasing the amount of emulsifier.

"Sandy" texture is readily detected by a roughness like sand in melted ice cream not only when rubbed against the roof of the mouth but also when chewed. Sandy texture should receive a very low score since it jeopardizes the marketability of the ice cream. It is due entirely to fairly large lactose crystals which are slow to dissolve. Conditions favoring the development of a sandy texture include a high lactose content (usually expressed as high milk solids-not-fat content), high and perhaps fluctuating temperatures (as in retail cabinets), or high temperature when drawn from freezer, low viscosity of the unfrozen liquid phase, and perhaps the presence of substances which initiate crystal formation.

Sandy texture is caused by lactose crystallization. This defect may be controlled by (a) reducing the milk solids-not-fat content of the mix; (b) acid standardization; (c) replacing part of the cane sugar content with dextrose; and (d) maintaining uniformly low storage temperature. **The factors affecting texture include:** (1) mix composition, (2) ingredients used, (3) physical and chemical characteristics of mix, (4) methods of processing, (5) method of freezing, (6) rate of hardening and (7) storage conditions.

Increased total solids content of the mix as resulting from increasing the percentage of any of the mix constituents may produce a smoother texture because: (1) there is a reduced amount of water to be frozen, (2) there is an increased concentration of mix causing mechanical obstruction to crystal growth and air incorporation during the freezing process or (3) the freezing point may be lowered.

Fat content (Table 45) influences texture by its ability to: (1) reduce ice crystal size through mechanical obstruction, and (2) produce a lubricating effect causing a smooth sensation in mouth. The effect on ice crystal size is shown as follows:

TABLE 45

EFFECT OF FAT CONTENT ON CRYSTAL SIZE

Fat Content	Ice Crystal Size[1]
per cent	microns
10	82.6 × 60.8
16	47.2 × 38.0

[1] Arbuckle (1940).

Milk solids-not-fat (m.s.n.f.) (Table 46) affects texture by: (1) reducing freezing point, (2) increasing the amount of unfrozen material, (3) mechanical obstruction to ice crystal and air cell formation and (4) holding a portion of the water as water of hydration.

TABLE 46

EFFECT OF MILK SOLIDS-NOT-FAT ON THE INTERNAL STRUCTURE OF ICE CREAM[1]

Milk Solids-Not-Fat Content of Ice Cream	Average Ice Crystal Size	Average Air Cell Size	Cell Wall Thickness	Texture Observations
per cent	microns	microns	microns	
9	55.8	176.6	165.4	Slightly coarse
11	52.3	188.4	148.7	Medium smooth
13	39.4	158.0	116.6	Smooth
15	32.2	103.2	124.0	Very smooth

[1] Arbuckle (1940).

Increased milk solids-not-fat shows a pronounced effect upon the texture resulting in smaller ice crystals, smaller air cells and a reduced thickness of the air cell walls. The occurrence of smaller air cells with increased amounts of milk solids-not-fat is significant in that milk solids-not-fat is probably the constituent present in the mix which has the greatest influence in the air cell size. These factors also influence the body characteristics.

Increasing the sugar content (Table 47) causes a smoother texture because: (1) the freezing point is lowered and the amount of unfrozen material is increased, and (2) sugar holds a portion of the water.[1]

TABLE 47

EFFECT OF SUGAR CONTENT ON CRYSTAL SIZE

Sugar Content	Ice Crystal Size
per cent	microns
12	67.5 × 51.0
18	48.8 × 35.5

Added increments of corn sugar may decrease ice crystal size because of lowering the freezing point of the mix. The unfrozen material is increased and the body characteristics may show improvement.

The percentage overrun (Table 48) is an important factor influencing body and texture of ice cream. The influence of overrun on ice crystal and air cell size and distribution[1] is shown as follows:

TABLE 48

EFFECTS OF OVERRUN

Overrun	Ice Crystal Size	Air Cell Diameter	Unfrozen Material
per cent	microns	microns	microns
85	62.7 × 51.2	165.2	11.2
100	53.9 × 47.3	142.3	10.0
115	50.4 × 44.1	109.0	8.5
130	49.8 × 43.1	104.0	7.0

The effect of 1 per cent increase of mix components in decreasing ice crystal size may be as follows:[2]

---

[1] In the above data mixes of average composition were studied with the variable component listed. Arbuckle (1940).

[2] In the above data mixes of average composition were studied with the variable component listed. Arbuckle (1940).

TABLE 49

EFFECTS OF COMPONENT INCREASE ON CRYSTAL SIZE

	Ice Crystal Size Reduction
	microns
1% fat	4.5
1% m.s.n.f.	4.3
1/2% fat and 1/2% m.s.n.f.	5.8
1% sugar in 11% m.s.n.f.	2.8
1% sugar in 13% m.s.n.f.	2.4
10% overrun	1.6

It seems that after the texture reaches a certain degree of closeness further changes of components of the mix have little influence upon ice crystal size.

The acidity of the mix (Table 50) influences texture characteristics.[2]

TABLE 50

EFFECT OF ACIDITY ON CRYSTAL SIZE

Acidity	pH	Ice Crystal Size
per cent		
0.24	6.5	50.7 × 42.5
0.18	6.8	42.5 × 37.4
0.12	7.5	49.2 × 44.3

The viscosity or thickness of mix has little relationship to the body and texture characteristics of the finished ice cream.

Stabilizers are effective in producing a smooth texture through their ability to combine with a portion of the water of the mix. This results in mechanical obstruction to ice crystal formation and smaller ice crystals. Stabilizers also prolong whipping time which provides for a more uniform distribution of internal structure components.[3]

Emulsifiers (Table 51) produce smooth stiff ice cream with smaller ice crystals and more evenly distributed and somewhat smaller air cells. Egg yolk solids produce similar but usually not as pronounced effects.[4]

Special products such as sodium caseinate, calcium sulfate, delactosed milk solids, have various effects on body and texture. Sodium caseinate improves whipping properties and affects air cell and ice crystal distributions. Calcium sulfate produces a dry stiff ice cream and has little effect on smoothness.[5]

Mix processing procedures most effective in influencing body and textures are pasteurization, homogenization and aging.

---

[3] Arbuckle (1948).
[4] Arbuckle (1948).
[5] Arbuckle (1953).

TABLE 51

EFFECT OF EMULSIFIERS ON TEXTURE[1]

Product	Ice Crystal Diameter	Air Cell Diameter	Comments
	microns	microns	
Gelatin	38	188	Very slightly coarse
Gelatin plus lecithinated products	32	156	Medium smooth
Gelatin plus mono and diglycerides	36	151	Medium smooth
Gelatin plus fatty acid esters	31	122	Smooth
Gelatin plus polyoxalkylene derivatives	35	135	Smooth

[1] Arbuckle, *Ice Cream Trade J.* (1950).

Pasteurization temperature may range from 150°F. to 300°F. The effect of higher temperatures on mix components is to produce a smoother product.[6,7]

Effective homogenization results in smooth ice cream—excessive pressure may produce adverse results. Aging or storing of mix two to four hours allows stabilizer and other mix constituents to become oriented.

Rate of freezing and hardening affects texture. Fast freezing produces small ice crystals. Rate of hardening is important.

Such factors as container size, air circulation, hardening room temperature, and use of air blast in tunnel, influence rate of hardening and the resulting texture of the product. Uniform hardening room temperature is extremely important in maintaining uniformity of texture. Hardening room temperature as high as —5°F. may produce good results if fluctuations are avoided. Partial melting and re-hardening should always be avoided.

Lactose crystallization in the finished product results in a sandy texture defect. Rapid turnover of the product, the use of delactosed milk solids and mineralized solids have been proposed to prevent this.

The effect of stabilizers of the fruit (Table 52) on the texture characteristics of strawberry ice cream is shown as follows:[8,9]

TABLE 52

EFFECTS OF FRUIT STABILIZERS ON TEXTURE

Kind of Berry Preparation Used	Texture Observations
Frozen berries stabilized by fruit packer	Smooth, berries firm, ice crystals not detectable
Frozen berries thawed and stabilized (by the ice cream plant)	Slightly coarse, berries tend toward coarseness
Frozen strawberries not stabilized	Medium coarse, berries icy

[6] Arbuckle (1951).
[7] Arbuckle (1955).
[8] Arbuckle, Ice Cream Field (1950).
[9] Arbuckle (1952).

Fruit particle size used in ice cream is important. It is difficult to get smoothness in large fruit portions. Too small particles result in good texture but poor flavor appeal.

It is quite essential to avoid the presence of undissolved particles of any of the mix constituents if a desirable body and texture is maintained. The importance of body and texture should never be overlooked in the production of ice cream that will have maximum consumer acceptance.

MELTING QUALITY DEFECTS

Desirable melting qualities are shown when the melted ice cream is very similar in characteristic to that of the original mix.

The melting appearance of ice cream is sometimes distinctly foamy. This should be considered a defect and is due particularly to large air cells and large amounts of egg solids. Emulsifiers or excess gelatin in low solids mixes, as well as a heavy mix consistency, are likely to augment the condition.

"Curdy" meltdown includes not only the finely divided particles of protein in watery liquid, but also a dull, finely wrinkled, scum-like surface on the melted ice cream. This defect leads the consumer to assume that inferior ingredients were used. Actually it is the result of protein destabilization which may be caused by anyone or any combination of the following: excess acidity, low concentration of citrates and phosphates in proportion to the calcium and magnesium content, melting and refreezing even in the freezer, the use of enzymatic improvers, the use of certain stabilizers, excessive homogenization pressures, long storage at low temperatures and shrinkage of the ice cream.

Curdled meltdown indicates high acidity in the mix or any other factor that might cause instability of milk protein. The condition may be corrected by (a) using fresh dairy products; (b) avoiding the use of any product that might disturb the natural salt balance of the mix; or (c) avoiding high acid mixes.

"Does not melt" includes not only the ice cream which retains its shape when warmed but also the various degrees of slow melting to a liquid. It frequently accompanies body defects described as "soggy," "gummy," "doughy" and "sticky." The conditions causing these body defects also contribute to high melting resistance. Other factors producing this melting defect include a high fat content, drawing at a low temperature from continuous freezers, a high freezing point and excessive viscosity resulting from slow cooling, the use of calcium neutralizers or certain types of stabilizer.

Slow melting indicates over-stabilization or improper processing of the mix. The condition can be corrected by (a) reducing the amount of stabilizer or emulsifier; (b) using fresh dairy products; or (c) homogenizing at proper temperature and pressure.

Whey leakage occurs during the melting of ice cream when the mix is of poor quality or if the mix is improperly balanced or stabilized. This defect can be remedied by (a) using high quality dairy products: (b) balancing the constituent of the mix carefully; or (c) using a more effective stabilizer.

Foamy meltdown is caused by the incorporation of too much air in the ice cream. The foamy defect may be corrected by (a) reducing the overrun; (b) reducing the amount of emulsifier or egg product used.

COLOR AND PACKAGE DEFECTS

Color and package aid in presenting the tempting appearance essential in a food or dessert. Therefore, good workmanship as evidenced by delicate, appropriate colors, uniformity of colors, not only the uniformity of layers but also the clearness of object outlines in molded ice creams and the cleanliness and neatness of packages should receive consideration. The ideal color is characteristic of the flavor, true in shade and neither too pale nor too intense. For example, vanilla ice cream should be the color of cream produced on early pasture.

Uniform, natural color is desirable in ice cream. Excessive color is the result of adding too much artificial color to the mix. An uneven color results if the color is not properly added and also if care is not exercised when changing flavors. An unnatural color is caused by (a) carelessness in adding the color; (b) improper use of colors; or (c) use of foreign materials.

"Unnatural" color describes defects due to insufficient (pale) color, excess (intense) color and colors that are not characteristic (true in shade) of the flavor. Examples of defective shades are the tannish brown of caramel instead of the reddish brown of chocolate, or egg yellow for annatto color in vanilla ice cream or a dull, grayish appearance (due to neutralization of the mix) in vanilla ice cream, and a slight bluish tint (due to lack of acidity) in cranberry ice cream.

Other defects such as uneven color, no parchment lining of cans, rusty cans and unclean cans are too obvious to need discussion here.

COMPOSITION AND BACTERIAL DEFECTS

Standards for composition and bacterial content are now adopted by nearly all communities, so that the public may be assured of a safe, healthful product. These standards represent the lowest quality (i.e., the least expensive) permissible for market, and should not be interpreted as either optimum or ideal quality. As yet there is no widely accepted procedure for scoring variations in either bacterial content or composition except to require compliance with local legal standards.

"Sediment" designates insoluble foreign material. It proves extreme carelessness and therfore is very objectionable. It may enter as part of the ingredients, when the ingredients are carelessly produced or stored (as in open containers) or it may be due to carelessness while manufacturing.

The disadvantages of strainers and filters for removing foreign materials are (1) it is almost impossible to sanitize these utensils after they are assembled for use, (2) they encourage the operator to use contaminated ingredients, erroneously thinking that strainers and filters will remove bacterial contamination and (3) they tend to encourage carelessness on the part of the operator. However, in commercial practice they have some advantages such as (1) preventing serious damage to expensive equipment by bolts, wrenches, rings, buttons, etc., dropping into vats or ice cream hopper either accidentally or through carelessness of employees, and (2) catching such other foreign substances as should not, but sometimes do, get into the milk, cream or ice cream mix.

But foreign substances such as buttons, hairpins, jewelry, etc., sometimes gain access to the hardened ice cream after it leaves the factory, when lids are removed while handling cans for storage in retail cabinets or for dispensing the ice cream over the counter. Hence precautions against these mishaps should be taken at every step from the factory to the consumer.

"Pancakes" (a taffylike deposit at the bottom of the package) is similar to the defect "bleeding" in ices and sherbets. When hardened these so-called pancakes are very coarse and unpalatable. Conditions favoring this defect are (1) storage at too high a temperature, near the melting point of the ice cream, (2) draining the freezer too completely, i.e., collecting unfrozen mix, (3) a weak body due to an improper balance of the mix constituents, such as a high sugar content, low concentration of stabilizer and low total solids content. Although not specifically mentioned on the score card, this defect is serious and greatly reduces the score.

"Shrinkage" adequately describes a particularly vexatious defect. After well-filled packages are hardened, the volume of the ice cream shrinks leaving a space either at the top or side of the package which then appears "not full." It is probably a special type of the "weak" body defect combined with a texture defect (therefore closely associated with whipping ability) and becomes apparent with certain temperature changes or types of package. (See Fig. 46.)

Although it has been widely studied, and many factors have been

Courtesy of D. J. Hankinson, University of Massachusetts

FIG. 46.   APPEARANCE OF SHRINKAGE DEFECT IN ICE CREAM

suggested as causes, it is still difficult to produce at will; in fact, frequently it occurs in only a portion of the packages frozen under similar conditions from the same batch of mix.   Conditions accepted as probable causes include: (1) neutralization[1] of the mix or some of the ingredients used; (2) containers that are porous to air, such as paper not properly waxed on the side in contact with the ice cream; (3) abnormally low temperatures either when freezing, drawing from the freezer, hardening in tunnels or hardening by dry ice before storage; (4) conditions favoring bleeding or pancakes; (5) excessive overrun as in fluffy texture (though the product may not appear fluffy the air content may be greater than can be contained at conditions to which the product is exposed); (6) excessive smoothness (the texture is too fine grained) possibly results from an unusual combination of conditions, such as too rapid freezing, which favor the formation of small-sized particles, and conditions arising from a combination of emulsifiers, as yet not too well understood, but which seem to favor very small air cells; (7) texture that favors curdy melt down—i.e., partially destabilized protein.   Shrinkage, although not specifically mentioned on the score card, might be expected in ice cream receiving severe criticism for weak body.

THE SCORE CARD
(Table 53)

Ice cream as yet is not sold on the basis of score.   However, the score card is a convenient tool or guide with which to measure the degree

---

[1] Neutralization of mix or ingredients is not permitted in any case.

TABLE 53

THE OFFICIAL ICE CREAM SCORE CARD[1]

Write scores opposite the rating for perfect score.   Check criticisms in the space opposite
the defects noted and in the proper sample column.

Perfect Score	Criticisms	Sample Number			
		1	2	3	4
Flavor 45	No criticism 40–45 Normal range 31–40				
	Cooked Egg Feed High acid Lacks fine flavor Lacks flavoring Lacks freshness Lacks sweetness Metallic Neutralizer Old ingredient Oxidized Rancid Salty Storage Unclean Unnatural flavoring				
Body and texture 30	No criticism 29.5–30 Normal range 25–29.5				
	Buttery Coarse or icy Crumbly Fluffy Sandy Soggy Weak				
Melting quality 5	No criticism 5 Normal range 4–5				
	Curdy Does not melt				
Color and package 5	No criticism 5 Normal range 3–5				
	Color uneven Color unnatural No parchment Rusty can Unclean can				
Bacteria 15					
Total 100	Total score of each sample				

[1] Example of a typical score card.   Minor changes are made from time to time, and for specific purposes.

TABLE 54

THE USE OF THE SCORE CARD

Defect or Criticism	Flavor Scores						
	40–45	38.5–39.5	37.5–38.0	36.0–37.0	34.5–35.5	33.0–34.0	31.0–32.5
Cooked	...	Slight	Definite	Definite	Pronounced	...	...
Egg	...	Definite	Pronounced	...	...	...	...
Feed	...	...	...	Slight	Definite	Pronounced	Pronounced
High Acid	...	...	...	Slight	Definite	Pronounced	Pronounced
Lacks fine flavor	...	Definite	Pronounced	...	...	...	...
Lacks flavoring	...	Definite	Pronounced	...	...	...	...
Lacks freshness	...	Definite	Pronounced	...	...	...	...
Lacks sweetness	...	Definite	Pronounced	...	...	...	...
Metallic	...	...	...	Slight	Definite	...	...
Neutralizer	...	...	...	...	...	Slight	Definite
Old ingredient	...	...	...	Slight	Definite	Pronounced	Pronounced
Oxidized	...	...	...	Slight	Definite	Definite	Pronounced
Rancid	...	...	...	...	...	Slight	Definite
Salty	...	...	...	Slight	Definite	Pronounced	Pronounced
Storage	...	...	...	Slight	Definite	Pronounced	Pronounced
Too high flavor	...	Definite	Pronounced	...	...	...	...
Too sweet	...	Definite	Pronounced	...	...	...	...
Unclean	...	...	...	...	...	Slight	Definite
Unnatural	...	...	...	Slight	Definite	Pronounced	...

Defect or Criticism	Body and Texture Scores				
	29.5–30	29.0–27.5	27.0–26.5	26.0–25.5	25.0
Buttery	...	...	Slight	Definite	Pronounced
Coarse or icy	...	Slight	Definite	Pronounced	Pronounced
Fluffy	...	Slight	Definite	Pronounced	Pronounced
Sandy	...	...	Slight	Definite	Pronounced
Soggy	...	Slight	Definite	...	...
Weak	...	Slight	Definite	Pronounced	Pronounced

	Melting Quality Scores		
	5	4.5	4.0
Curdy	...	Slight	Definite
Does not melt	...	Slight	Definite

	Color and Package Scores			
	5	4.5	4.0–3.5	3.0
Color uneven	...	Slight	Definite	Pronounced
Color unnatural	...	Slight	Definite	Pronounced
No parchment	...	...	Definite	...
Rusty can	...	...	Slight	Definite
Unclean can	...	Slight	Definite	Pronounced

of perfection of any given ice cream. The ideal or standard as indicated by the highest score on the score card serves as the measuring stick by which to compare or judge the ice cream. Some practice in the use of the score card should be valuable in improving the quality of ice cream. The reliability of the score depends partly upon the judge's conception of the ideal standard and partly upon his ability to recognize very slight defects. The degree of perfection or score may or may not agree with the acceptability of the ice cream in a certain market area, although there is usually a rather close agreement.

TABLE 55

A SUGGESTED CLASSIFICATION OF MARKET GRADES FOR ICE CREAM, SHERBETS AND ICES

	Market Grades[1]					
Factors	1st Quality	2nd Quality	3rd Quality	4th Quality	5th Quality	No Grade[2]
Fat content[3]	Not less than 14.0%	Not less than 11.0%	Not less than 10.0%	Not less than 10.0%	Not less than 8.0%	
Flavor score	Not less than 40.0	Not less than 37.5	Not less than 36.0	Not less than 33.0	Not less than 30.0	
Sum of scores on body and texture, melting quality, color and package	Not less than 39.5	Not less than 37.0	Not less than 34.5	Not less than 33.0	Not less than 30.0	
Plate count ratio[4]	Not less than 4.0	Not less than 2.0	Not less than 1.5	Not less than 1.0	Not less than 0.9	
Coli test	Negative	Negative	Negative	Negative	Positive	

[1] To be admitted to a certain grade the requirements for each factor must be met.
[2] Any ice cream that does not conform to the requirements of higher grades.
[3] Values are for plain ice cream. Fruit and nut ice creams might be 2 per cent lower—i.e., 12 per cent for first quality.
[4] This ratio is determined by dividing the legal standard by the actual plate count of the ice cream.

The Use of the Score Card.—The purpose of scoring ice cream is to emphasize the degree of perfection and the opportunity for improvement. Table 54 is an approximate summary of the relative significance of the defects as described in previous paragraphs of this chapter. For example, a slight feed flavor would score between 36 and 37 points, while a definite feed flavor would score between 34.5 and 35.5 points. Similarly, ice cream criticised for unclean flavor should not be scored above 34.5 points.

A defect is considered (1) "slight" when recognized by the connoisseur but not detectable by most consumers; (2) "definite" when detectable by many consumers; (3) "pronounced" when detectable by most consumers. Usually the defects are scored to the nearest half point, and a product with a score below the "normal range" should generally be considered unsalable.

MARKET GRADES

Market grades or classes have not as yet been accepted in the ice cream industry in spite of the fact that many consumers would welcome a system of market grades. The fluid milk or market milk industry has a widely accepted system of market grades in which the methods of producing and handling the milk receive more emphasis than does the score, i.e., its degree of perfection. These market grades of milk are closely associated with the relative value of the milk not only to the consumer but also as determined by the cost of production and distribution. Similarly the market grades of butter are closely associated with the score, even though the distinction between the grades is based primarily upon the relative value of the butter to the consumer. A similar system of market grades based primarily upon the relative value to the consumer might be beneficial to the ice cream industry.

Suggested Market Grades for Ice Cream.—Table 55 suggests a possible system of market grades together with the approximate correlation to the ice cream score. It should be recognized that the score primarily measures differences in degree of perfection which may not represent significant differences in value to the consumer—the latter differences being the primary distinction in market grades. Therefore, a market grade will include a range of scores all of which will represent the same market value to the consumer.

CHAPTER 19

Sanitation and Quality Control

A high quality ice cream can be made only from good mix ingredients properly balanced to produce a desirable composition, along with proper processing, freezing, hardening and distribution, under proper sanitary conditions. All of these factors are important and must be carefully controlled if the most acceptable product is to be produced. It must be remembered that product inferiority constitutes one of the greatest menaces to the success and progress of the ice cream industry. The consumer has learned to depend upon ice cream as a safe, enjoyable, energy-giving, nourishing and refreshing food. The consumer is definitely interested in the quality of ice cream and this interest is one of the industry's greatest assets.

Although the quality of ice cream is usually judged by the flavor, body and texture, melting quality, package, color and keeping quality characteristics, it is the bacterial content that plays an important role in determining sanitary quality.

The usual methods of measuring sanitary quality include the sediment test, the standard plate count for bacteria, the coliform test and the usual tests for proper pasteurization. The combined tests will help indicate whether there has been contamination with pathogenic (disease producing) bacteria and careless methods of handling. However, they do not measure toxic (poisonous) materials resulting from certain types of spoilage or from the use of ingredients containing them. There are also some unsanitary practices such as straining out foreign materials, or contamination with undesirable soluble materials which are not easily detected. The hygienic quality of poor ingredients cannot be entirely corrected even though pasteurization does destroy whatever pathogenic bacteria are present. Therefore, the need for conscientious, constant detailed attention is apparent.

Factors of ultimate importance to the ice cream manufacturer in producing a finished product of high sanitary quality include the following: (1) clean, healthy, employees who are quality minded; (2) quality ingredients; (3) proper processing methods; (4) proper plant sanitation; (5) good equipment; and (6) proper distribution methods.

Almost as important as the quality of the finished product are clean, healthy employees who are industrious and quality minded, of good character and integrity, with a knowledge of the business and an appreciation for laboratory facilities and quality control.

The highest quality ice cream can be made only from good, clean, fresh raw materials. The extensive use of dairy products of questionable quality or products held for long storage periods may result in a finished product of less desirable quality. Standards are given in Table 56.

TABLE 56

RECOMMENDED MICROBIOLOGICAL STANDARDS FOR INGREDIENTS

Product	Used in Raw State	Used in Pasteurized Condensed, Evaporated or Dried State
Ingredients derived from:	*Plate count per gram:*	*Plate count per gram:*
Milk	Not to exceed 200,000	Average of 50,000
Cream	Not to exceed 400,000	Average of 50,000
Ingredients not derived from milk:		*Mold and Yeast count per gram:*
Egg products	Not to exceed 200,000	Not exceeding 100
Flavor and color materials	Not to exceed 10,000	Not exceeding 100

Coliform micro-organisms not to exceed 10 per gram in any product.

Mix ingredients that may usually be expected to have low bacterial counts include butter, milk, sugar, vanilla, preserved fruits, non-fat dry milk solids and stabilizers or emulsifiers. Products that may have higher counts or be a source of off-flavor are cream, bulk condensed milk, fresh or frozen fruits, raw nuts and, sometimes, liquid color.

The processing methods or equipment may be responsible for wide variations in bacterial counts. Proper pasteurization will give effective bacterial reduction. The homogenization process may increase the count as a result of breaking up bacterial clumps or because the machine has not been properly cleaned. The cooler, freezer and especially the packaging machine may also increase the count. Prolonged storage in the storage tank may be an important cause of a high count. Maintenance of all equipment in good repair, free from dented surfaces and leaks will help avoid high counts due to equipment.

Plant sanitation is essential in order to: (1) comply with legal requirements and (2) produce a product free from objectionable bacteria. Effective bacterial control promotes health protection; product popularity; quality; and less spoilage loss. A high count may be due to any one or more of the following: (1) high count in raw products; (2) ineffective processing methods; (3) ineffective sanitizing methods; (4) carelessness; or (5) prolonged storage of mix.

The types of micro-organisms important in the sanitary quality of dairy products include bacteria, yeast and molds.

Bacteria are unicellular microscopic organisms belonging to the plant kingdom, classed as coccus, which are spherical shaped; bacillus, which are rod-shaped; or spirillum, which are spiral shaped. They reproduce by fission or division. Yeast are unicellular, but are larger than bacteria. They reproduce by budding. Molds are multicellular branched fungi which produce visible surface growth.

Factors affecting micro-organism growth include: (1) temperature; (2) light; (3) chemicals; (4) food materials; (5) oxygen; and (6) moisture. The types of fermentation that may be produced by these organisms are acid, gas, sweet curdling, proteolytic and color.

SANITARY EQUIPMENT

Washing and Rinsing.—The importance of thorough washing and rinsing cannot be over-estimated in making equipment hygienic. Either sterilizing or sanitizing is very difficult, if not impossible, when the equipment is not thoroughly cleaned. Thorough washing also offers an excellent opportunity to inspect the equipment for wear, loss of tinned surface, rust, pitting, etc. The first step in washing any piece of equipment is *rinsing with lukewarm* (80° to 110°F.) *water* to remove milk remnants. *Soaking* may be necessary when the milk film has been allowed to dry. Rinsing should be followed by *vigorous scrubbing* with a stiff-bristled brush and hot (115° to 120°F.) water containing a washing powder (cleaning agent). Extra effort should be applied to corners and any other places that are difficult to reach. This scrubbing is essential for removing the film that remains after the visible milk, fat or foreign material has been removed. A stream of washing solution under pressure can be as effective as a brush. The outside of the equipment also should receive the same careful washing treatment. When the surface has been scrubbed to a high polish with washing solution, it should be *rinsed* again with clean, warm water (100° to 110°F.), sufficiently rinsed to remove the thin film of washing solution. When this process is carefully done, the equipment will have a bacteria count not exceeding that of the final rinse water.

In-place cleaning of ice cream processing equipment is becoming more popular. The success of the in-place cleaning procedure depends upon the following:

    (1) The effectiveness of the in-place cleaning installation.
    (2) The temperature and velocity of cleaning solution.
    (3) The use of proper detergent solutions and adequate circulation time.
    (4) The proper adaptability of the processing equipment to in-place cleaning.

The steps which should be considered in the in-place cleaning procedure are as follows:

(1) Rinse system with water (100°F. or less) until rinse water runs clear. This rinse should be directed to sewer.
(2) Use centrifugal pump to circulate cleaning solution containing sufficient acid (phosphoric and hydroxyacetic) to give from 0.15 to 0.6 per cent acidity, at 150° to 160°F., and 5 to $7^1/_2$ feet per second velocity for 20 to 30 minutes.
(3) Rapidly drain and rinse system with water at 145°F. for 5 to 7 minutes.
(4) Flush for 20 to 30 minutes with 150° to 160°F. water containing 1 to $1^1/_4$ pounds alkali detergent for each 10 gallons of water.
(5) Rinse with cold water until equipment is cool.

Washing powders (cleaning agents) should contain no soap because this ingredient leaves a surface film which is difficult to rinse away. Free alkalis, as sodium hydroxide and caustic, should not be used on metallic surfaces if corrosion is to be prevented   Sodium metasilicate, sodium carbonate (washing soda) and tri-sodium phosphate are satisfactory types of cleaning agents. The effectiveness of these materials is improved by a small amount of so-called "wetting agents" (i.e., materials like sulfonated alcohols sold under various trade names like "Dreft," "Syntex beads," etc.). Water containing appreciable amounts of calcium or magnesium is described as "hard" water. The use of such water is a contributing cause of a deposit known as "milkstone" on the surface of the equipment. This can be avoided by adding a "water-softening" agent (such as pyrophosphate or metasilicate) to the washing compound, but these are not necessary when "soft" water is used. A very satisfactory cleaning agent for use in hard water may be prepared by thoroughly mixing 100 lbs. trisodium phosphate with 20 lbs. tetra-sodium pyrophosphate and 2 lbs. Syntex beads. Where soft water is available, excellent results are obtained from a mixture of 40 lbs. tri-sodium phosphate, with 60 lbs. sodium carbonate and 2 lbs. Syntex beads. Preparing these mixtures is somewhat troublesome even though it frequently is more economical. There are many similar mixtures available under trade names, and these may give equally good results.

Sterilizing of the equipment should follow the washing and rinsing process. Ideally, sterilizing will kill all organisms on the equipment—a goal that is desirable and not impractical. However, most commercial workers and many milk sanitarians are satisfied with merely preventing "public health hazards" and therefore substitute sanitizing for sterilizing.

Sanitizing kills all pathogenic organisms but may leave a few bacteria (so-called "reasonably small number" or "insignificant number"). It is a less expensive, less exacting and less time-consuming process than sterilizing, although the same two groups of agents are used. For example: Heat (as hot water) of 170°F. for ten minutes will sanitize, while heat (as steam under 15 lbs. pressure) of 240°F. for 15 minutes will sterilize.

Sanitizing Agents.—The recommended sanitizing agents together with their advantages and the precautions to be observed in using them may be outlined as follows:

1. **Heat** is the most reliable agent, especially when both temperature and time are carefully controlled. Its main advantages are its penetrating ability and the fact that it facilitates drying of the equipment.

    (a) Dry heat at 240°F. for 5 minutes sanitizes.
    (b) Steam under pressure (15 lbs. or 240°F.) for 5 minutes sanitizes.
    (c) Steam at zero pressure (212°F.) for 10 minutes sanitizes.
    (d) Hot (so-called "boiling") water (180° to 212°F.) for 10 minutes sanitizes.

Lower temperatures or shorter times at that temperature will not properly sanitize nor leave the equipment dry.

2. **Chemical agents** are effective only under four conditions: (1) When the surface is entirely clean, (2) when the surface is in intimate contact with the chemical, (3) when there is sufficient concentration of the active constituent of the chemical and (4) when there is sufficient time of contact with the surface. The first three requirements are difficult to satisfy. Many mechanical washers do not clean the surface sufficiently for chemical sanitizing agents. Furthermore, pipe lines may appear to be completely filled with sanitizing solution and yet contain air pockets which will prevent complete sanitization. This is especially true of fittings, joints and pumps. Also, vat covers may not come in contact with the chemical agent. The concentration of the solution will change if the chemical agent is not properly stored, or if it is used repeatedly or if it is used for too many pieces of equipment.

Temperatures of 110°F. or more usually cause rapid loss of concentration, and therefore volatile chemical sanitizing agents should be used and stored at lower temperatures. Since low temperatures are used, the equipment is seldom left dry. This is a serious objection, for moisture even without the chemical will favor corrosion of the equipment. However, this low-temperature sanitizing has three advantages: (1) It permits sanitizing immediately before the equipment is to be used, when hot equipment would be injurious to the quality of the milk. (2) It avoids excessive strain on equipment which occurs by expansion and contraction when high temperatures are used. This is particularly important in freezers and equipment having stuffing boxes, as in pumps. (3) It encourages the flushing out of equipment immediately before use, thereby removing any possible dust that may have entered the cans or equipment.

Types of Chemical Sanitizing Agents.—Only three types of chemical sanitizing agents have sufficiently pleasing odors to permit their use; all others have odors which are objectionable in dairy products. There are many trade-named products containing one of these three types as the active ingredient.

(a) **Hypochlorites,** usually sodium hypochlorite, are rapid in action, lose strength easily and are rather corrosive on equipment. Sanitizing solution should contain not less than 50 parts (many recommend as much as 200) of available chlorine per million parts of solution. The solution should be in contact with the surface for at least 15 seconds.

Sodium hypochlorite is prepared by the electrical decomposition of salt in a slightly alkaline solution and many preparations are available under trade names.

It may also be prepared in a stone crock as follows: To 4 lbs. of "chloride of lime" add 5 gallons of water, and to this add $1^1/_2$ lbs. of washing soda. Thoroughly mix with a wooden paddle and allow to stand until the lime settles to the bottom. Then drain off the clear solution into a bottle. Use one-half pint of this solution to 2 gallons of water for a sanitizing solution.

(b) **Chloramines** are available under many trade names. Chlorine is the active ingredient as in the hypochlorites. These are less rapid in action, lose strength less rapidly and are less corrosive than the hypochlorites. Sanitizing solutions should contain not less than 50 parts of chlorine (many recommend as much as 200) per million parts of solution. The solution should be in contact with the surface for at least one minute.

(c) **Quaternary Ammonium Compounds.**—Several compounds of this type are available on the market, but their advantages and limitations are not yet well established. However, at the present time investigational work indicates some probable special advantages, such as: (1) a less objectionable odor, (2) less severe corrosive action, (3) less loss of efficiency in the presence of small quantities of organic matter, (4) greater stability when used at temperatures of 120° to 150°F. and (5) greater efficiency in the presence of alkali cleaning agents. The addition of a chemical sanitizing agent to the wash water containing a cleaning agent appeals to the uninformed person who would like to wash and sanitize in one operation. However this would seem to be an absurd practice since the purpose of using a sanitizing agent demands that it be used after (instead of while) the equipment is cleaned and rinsed. Therefore an attempt to combine the two operations is as erroneous as an attempt to dry the equipment while spraying it with rinse water. Among the probable limitations are (1) a recommended concentration of not less than 200 parts per million, and (2) less efficiency for certain individual organisms (whether these are commonly found in dairy plants is not yet known).

Iodophors are products which are a combination of iodine with a non-ionic wetting agent. This sanitizer has been developed in recent years and as a result is not used as extensively as other sanitizers. Iodophors are used at the rate of $12^1/_2$ to 100 ppm in sanitizing solutions at the pH of 5 or lower at temperatures of 120°F. or lower for best results.

Wetting agents are synthetic organic compounds which improve the wetting of particles and penetration of washing solutions. These agents are of the anionic, non-ionic and cationic types. The cationic type is not used extensively because of expense.

Drying is the last process in sanitization. It should be accomplished by heat and ventilation; never by the use of a cloth or towel of any kind. While sanitization is not complete without drying, the drying process may be omitted when the equipment is to be immediately re-filled with a dairy product. Drying is essential to reduce deterioration and corrosion. It also inhibits the growth of organisms that may find access to the properly cleaned, rinsed and sterilized surface. Drying should also be accompanied by ventilation in so far as this is possible without recontamination. Re-sanitizing with a chemical agent immediately before the dried equipment is put into use again is advisable.

SANITARY SURROUNDINGS

Equipment can be kept more uniformly hygienic in sanitary surroundings, i.e., in rooms having hygienic construction and kept sanitary by hygienic personnel. All rooms, even toilets and locker rooms, of the factory should be kept sanitary by the same method described for producing hygienic equipment.

Hygienic construction is probably more important than hygienic methods, since it encourages hygienic practices, especially at an economical cost. The essential factors in hygienic construction are very similar for utensils, equipment, work rooms, buildings and surroundings. They may be listed as:

1. Surfaces should be smooth and free from scratches and grooves. This is particularly essential for surfaces coming in contact with the product, such as the inside of utensils and equipment. Floors of work rooms are the only exception, and these should be slightly rough (like the commonly known "wood finish" on concrete) to prevent accidents by slipping on the wet floor.

2. Surfaces should be sloping and free from depressions that do not drain quickly and completely. This is desirable not only in equipment but also for all floors, window sills, ledges, shelves, etc.

3. Corners should be rounded and large enough to permit scrubbing with a brush. Sharp corners and crevices must be avoided in surfaces which come in contact with dairy products. In walls, floors, the outer surface of equipment, etc., sharp corners and crevices are objectionable because they are difficult to get completely clean.

4. All surfaces should be easily accessible for scrubbing. Pipe fittings should be tees, never elbows, and easily dismantled to permit visual inspection for cleanliness. Coils in vats should not interfere with scrubbing the entire surface of the coil and the vat. Equipment should be mounted on the floor so as to permit scrubbing the floor instead of leaving corners and floor space under the equipment that cannot be scrubbed daily.

5. Materials used in construction should be impervious to moisture and free from objectionable odors. Certain woods and paints have odors that are easily absorbed by dairy products. Some metals tend to dissolve in the product and to cause undesirable flavors which are frequently described as "cardboard," "tallowy" or "metallic." This injurious effect can be avoided by covering the metal with a film or coating of tin. When such tinned equipment is used it should be frequently inspected for small spots where the tin coating has been removed by scratching or wear. Most modern equipment is made from stainless steel which has no injurious effect on the flavor of dairy products.

6. Light is essential for proper cleaning. It should be available especially during cleaning operations without interfering with the operation (i.e., the operator should not have to stand in the light and cast a shadow on the surface being scrubbed).

7. Ventilation with fresh, clean air is essential. All equipment, utensils, and all rooms, cupboards, etc., should be constructed to permit thorough ventilation without contamination. This not only avoids undesirable odors but reduces the objectionable moisture in the atmosphere.

8. Rodents and insects should have no place to collect or hide. Dark places, moist places and unclean places attract rodents, ants, roaches, flies, etc. Removal of all such places eliminates the pests. Sprays, poisons, screens and traps should be used only as a temporary measure, preferably not at all. Neither the pest nor the usual "control measures" belong in a respectable dairy, and either one is evidence of careless methods.

9. Segregation of operations is necessary in the construction of buildings. There should be separate rooms for unpasteurized or raw products to avoid contamination of equipment and possible mixing of unpasteurized with pasteurized products; for products with pronounced odors that may be easily absorbed by other products; for wash rooms, for cans,

bottles, etc.; for boilers, engines, refrigeration compressors, etc.; for all storage rooms whether refrigerated or not; and for rest rooms (toilets) and locker rooms.

10. Special facilities are necessary in the construction of buildings and work rooms. Conveniently located facilities for obtaining an ample supply of both hot and cold water are most essential. The supply of both hot and cold water should be unrestricted if cleanliness is expected. Mixing outlets, permitting adjustment of temperature, should be located for convenience in applying an ample supply of water to all parts of every room. Floor drains in each room are equally essential. They should be located so as to drain the floor completely and not leave even shallow puddles. When possible it is desirable to locate them at the sides or at least out of the traffic lanes, but they must be easily accessible for cleaning when they become clogged; for this reason they are often located in the center of the room. A most important special feature of each room is a lavatory, i.e., a small basin for washing hands. This lavatory should be equipped with a mixing faucet for hot and cold water, soap or cleaning agents, a cold water drinking fountain and single service (paper) towels. Thus personal cleanliness is encouraged, and the improper use of equipment (such as sinks for washing utensils, drinking from a hose, contamination by handling equipment with dirty hands) is avoided.

Hygienic personnel is probably the most important factor not only in obtaining but also in maintaining healthful quality in the product. Every person associated with dairy products should be hygienic-minded and constantly observant of sanitary details. This applies to such persons as mechanics, electricians, janitors, stenographers, truck drivers, etc., as well as to persons actually operating equipment for processing the dairy product. The three characteristics of hygienic personnel may be listed as follows:

1. Hygienic conscience, or a subconscious desire to employ only healthful practices and habits as well as a determined conscious effort to correct errors in hygienic behavior.

2. Physical health, especially freedom from contagious diseases. Medical examination for contagious diseases (particularly typhoid which supports "carriers") should be required once a year. Rigid isolation should be practiced even in the event of less fatal contagious diseases such as common colds.

3. Hygienic habits including innumerable personal details such as the following:

(a) Hands and nails should be clean. The hands should be washed before touching dairy products or clean utensils; especially after touching unsterile cans, shaking hands with anyone, coughing against the hand, wiping the nose, scratching, visits to the toilet, etc.

(b) Insanitary practices such as coughing in or near the equipment, spitting on the floor, etc., should be avoided.

(c) A net or cap should be worn to prevent loose hair from contaminating the product or equipment.

(d) Clothes should not be worn longer than one full day between launderings, and should be changed oftener when they become untidy. Clothes worn on the street or outside of the work-room should not be worn while handling the product. Footwear used while cleaning larger vats that must be entered should not be worn elsewhere, even on the floor of that room.

(e) Wounds or sores should be bandaged to prevent any possible contact with the equipment or product. Wet equipment may make contact by soaking through the bandage. When this cannot be avoided the person should not touch the equipment or product.

The recontamination problem is very complex because (1) the product is exposed to so much equipment, some of which is difficult to sanitize, and (2) the product is exposed to human contact. Hygienic ingredients can be reasonably assured by obtaining bacterial counts on all products used in the ice cream. Bacterial counts and coliform tests on samples of ice cream taken at various places between the pasteurizer and the retailer aid in discovering recontamination. Wherever possible human contact should be eliminated, and where it cannot be avoided the health of the worker should be supervised and he should be compelled to practice hygienic habits. Some sanitarians believe that:

1. Every employee should be required to have a complete medical examination by a competent physician and submit the necessary samples of blood, feces and urine for laboratory examination, together with any other test necessary, at the time he is employed and semi-annually thereafter. If the Board of Health does not require such an examination, the employer should require it for his own protection.

2. Supplementing the above examination and as an added protection, all employees coming in direct contact with food, milk or other dairy products should be examined regularly by a nurse, foreman or some other competent person for evidence of contagious diseases. By means of education and intelligent application, many causes of potential or actual disease may be found in this way.

3. Whether this system or any other is used in trying to find persons suffering from contagious disease, employees must not be penalized by being discharged or temporarily laid off without due compensation.

4. Only persons who are inherently clean should be employed in the

food or dairy industry. All new employees should be watched carefully until they have been so classified.

QUALITY CONTROL PROCEDURES FOR FINISHED PRODUCTS

Finished product control procedures are extremely important in the production of a good product.

Comply with all composition standards for all products by testing bi-weekly. Fat content should not vary more than 0.2 per cent and total solids not more than 1 per cent.

Weekly bacteriological analyses should be made for all regular flavors and the results should comply with Health Department standards.

Weekly examinations should be made for quality of each product manufactured. These examinations should include: flavor—natural, typical, clean; body and texture—smooth, close; color—uniform, typical of flavor represented, not extreme; appearance—uniform, even distribution of flavor materials such as fruit, nut or candy particles.

Packages should be clean, neat and properly labeled.

Weight control of packages is important. Usually gallon units should weigh within 4 ounces, $2^1/_2$ gallon units within 5 ounces and 5 gallon units within 8 ounces of the standard desired.

Routine checks on processing procedures including mix preparation, homogenization, flavoring, and flavoring and coloring materials, freezing, packaging, storage and distribution play an important role in producing the best product. The rate of turnover of products in the hardening room should be as rapid as possible. The maximum time should not exceed six weeks.

Spillage, broken packages, and overaged products should be kept at a minimum and this material should be discarded rather than used as a re-run.

Products showing defects in periodic examinations may be given prompt corrective attention. In this manner, products may be maintained at the desired standards.

CHAPTER 20

Refrigeration

Refrigeration is the removal of heat from a substance and therefore is concerned with heat exchange (i.e., heat transfer). The excess heat in the substance being cooled (refrigerated) is transferred to a cooler substance which becomes heated. Therefore "refrigeration" is the reverse of "heating," both occurring simultaneously and being dependent upon the same principles and factors of heat exchange. However, the ice cream industry uses the term "refrigeration" to mean cooling to temperatures below 40°F., mainly between 40° and —30°F.

METHODS OF REFRIGERATION

The Ice and Salt Method.—Natural ice, in very early times, was harvested from ponds and stored to be used for refrigeration. Since ice melts at 32°F., lower temperatures could be obtained only by mixing ice and salt. This method, now called "the ice and salt" method, is being used when only a small amount of refrigeration is required. Under usual conditions it is not practical to obtain temperatures below 0°F. by this method, although theoretically —6°F. is possible when using 1 lb. of salt to 3 lbs. of ice.

The lowest temperature obtained by this method depends upon the proportion of ice and salt, the rate at which heat is supplied, the density of the brine, the original temperature of ice and salt before mixing and the size of both the ice and salt particles. Smaller lumps of ice and more concentrated brine favor rapid cooling and are used when the rate of heat transfer is high.

Mechanical refrigeration is now almost universally used and has the advantages of: requiring less labor, being less cumbersome, having lower temperatures and more uniform temperature control available. It is also more rapid, cleaner and drier. It is based on the principle that a liquid absorbs heat when it vaporizes, as in the case of water changing into steam; the vapor can be collected, cooled to a liquid and used again. The particular liquid, called the "refrigerant," to be used in a mechanical refrigeration system depends upon many factors. Some of the more important of these factors are: (1) the boiling point of the liquid, (2) pressure characteristics (the pressures under which it can be used), (3) the latent heat of vaporization (amount of heat absorbed when the refrigerant vaporizes), (4) the ease with which a leak is detected, (5) its corrosive

276

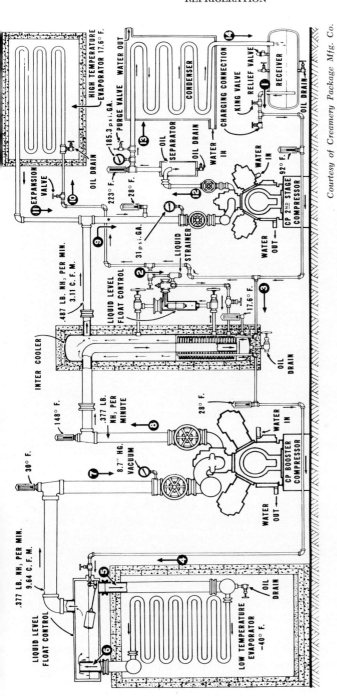

Courtesy of Creamery Package Mfg. Co.

FIG. 47. FLOW DIAGRAM OF BOOSTER COMPRESSION REFRIGERATION SYSTEM

1—liquid refrigerant leaving receiver
2—liquid refrigerant passing through float control to intercooler
3—liquid refrigerant passing to liquid cooling coil in intercooler
4—sub-cooled liquid refrigerant passing through float control to low temperature evaporator
5—liquid refrigerant from accumulator circulating through low temperature evaporator
6—refrigerant liquid and vapor mixture circulating from evaporator to accumulator
7—low pressure refrigerant vapor entering booster compressor
8—hot intermediate pressure refrigerant vapor leaving compressor and entering intercooler
9—cold intermediate pressure refrigerant vapor leaving intercooler and entering second-stage compressor
10—liquid refrigerant passing through expansion valve to high temperature evaporator. (Optional)
11—intermediate pressure refrigerant vapor leaving high temperature evaporator and entering second-stage compressor. (Optional)
12—high pressure refrigerant vapor leaving second-stage compressor and entering oil separator
13—high pressure refrigerant vapor leaving oil separator and entering condenser
14—liquid refrigerant returning to receiver

action on metals used in the system and (6) its toxicity. (See Figs. 47 and 48.)

TYPES OF REFRIGERANTS COMMONLY USED

Of the many and various refrigerants, only two have been found sufficiently satisfactory to be widely used in the ice cream industry; ammonia, which has been used a long time, and "Freon-12," a representative of the non-toxic refrigerants used in ice cream cabinets, in small installations (home refrigerators, counter freezers, etc.), and where very low temperatures are not required.

Courtesy of Delvale Dairies, Inc.

FIG. 48. BOOSTER COMPRESSORS AT DELVALE DAIRIES, INC., BALTIMORE, MARYLAND

The most important advantages of ammonia are: (1) it absorbs a large amount of heat when vaporizing, (2) operating pressures are reasonably convenient, (3) leaks are easily detected, (4) its toxicity is not great in low concentrations though its odor is very pungent, and it has a very pronounced irritating effect on mucous membranes and wet skin and (5) it usually operates at pressures above atmospheric, thereby keeping foreign gases and liquids out of the system.

Its main disadvantages are: (1) it is very corrosive to brass and other copper alloys (since only iron and steel can be used in the system, the equipment is rather bulky), (2) the relatively large volume of gas requires large compressors, (3) mechanical automatic operation is difficult to obtain, (4) maintenance of temperature within a narrow range is difficult (the last two of these disadvantages are due to the large amount of heat absorbed during vaporization but are not significant in many installations) and (5) for some installations the objectionable odor from even minor leaks becomes very important.

Freon-12 (dichlorodifluoromethane) is one of the many Freon refrigerants. The advantages of these refrigerants are: (1) they require lower operating pressures, (2) their odor is neither objectionable nor toxic, (3) they are not injurious to food materials, (4) they are not corrosive to usual metals, although alloys containing magnesium must be avoided, (5) smaller and more compact refrigeration systems can be used because of the lower pressures and the use of copper alloys (hermetically sealed units are becoming popular), (6) they are carriers for oil thus facilitating the lubrication of compressors, (7) mechanical automatic operation is fairly simple and (8) more uniform temperatures can be maintained.

The main disadvantages of Freon refrigerants are: (1) they must be free of moisture, (2) leaks are not easily detected (a special Halide torch which gives a pink flame in the presence of Freon can be used to detect leaks), (3) the system must be tighter than for ammonia to avoid leaks (small leaks are not noticeable and the refrigerant may be lost just when it is most needed) and (4) they are less satisfactory than ammonia for very low temperatures.

PRINCIPLES OF MECHANICAL REFRIGERATION

The mechanical refrigeration system consists of only three essential parts: (1) the compressor, (2) the "high pressure side" and (3) the "low pressure side." The compressor consists of one or two cylinders, usually surrounded by a water-jacket for cooling, and containing pistons, similar to those of a gasoline engine, operated by a crankshaft that runs in oil in the crank case. The compressor is usually belt-driven from a motor, engine or other source of power. The purpose of the compressor is to concentrate the vapor. It takes the vapor from the "low pressure side" of large volume at low pressure and low temperature, and discharges it into the "high pressure side." Thus the compressor occupies one of the two positions dividing the high and low sides. The "high pressure side" extends from the compressor to the so-called "expansion valve" and includes the "condenser" and "receiver." The hot vapor leaving the compressor passes through the condenser, i.e., coils of pipe which are cooled by water or air. This cooling in the condenser changes the vapor into a liquid at about room temperature and still under a high pressure, the liquid being collected in a tank (the "receiver"). This liquid refrigerant passes on to the "expansion valve" which is the other position dividing the high and low sides. The "low pressure side" extends from the expansion valve to the compressor. The expansion valve is usually an ordinary needle valve permitting fine adjustment and may be operated manually. It derives its name from the fact that the liquid refrigerant passes through the valve and then expands into a vapor. The liquid refrigerant is under high pressure at room temperature before passing through the valve, and under low pressure at low temperature as it leaves the expansion valve to go through the "expansion coils," i.e., coils of pipes located where refrigeration is to be produced, and leading back to the compressor. In this way the refrigerant is used repeatedly, being compressed, condensed and expanded. The refrigerant never wears out, but slight leaks invariably occur making it necessary to replenish the supply. The refrigeration or cooling is obtained by means of the expansion coils since in these coils the liquid refrigerant absorbs heat while vaporizing. The pressure in these expansion coils determines the lowest temperature obtainable, and this pressure is often called the "suction pressure" or "back pressure" of the system. The expansion coils may be located in the hardening room, in a tank of water or brine, in the ice cream freezer, etc., to give refrigeration in that particular place.

A large amount of heat is absorbed as the liquid changes to a vapor, and a smaller amount of heat is absorbed by the vapor when it expands further. This heat which is absorbed in the expansion coils is carried in the vapor to the compressor and on to the condenser where the heat is transferred from the hot refrigerant vapor to the cooling water or air around the condenser coils. Sometimes this cooling water is used only once and wasted, in other places it is more economical to re-use this water. In these cases the water is pumped to the top of a "cooling tower" (usually on the roof) and allowed to trickle down over the tower, being cooled by partial evaporation in the process. This proves very economical where the cost of water is high. In some Freon systems the condenser is air cooled, usually by a fan blowing air around the condenser coils that have fins to facilitate radiation of the heat.

Although the principle involved in the mechanical refrigeration system is rather simple, the construction and installation is too complicated for a brief discussion. Usually it is more economical to obtain the services of a refrigeration engineer to supervise the planning and installation of the system.

OPERATING PRECAUTIONS

Precautions to observe in operating refrigeration systems are:

1. When opening valves on refrigerant lines, open them slowly.
2. Keep the suction pressure as high as possible. It must be sufficiently low to give the desired temperature. The pressure on the low side should correspond to an ammonia boiling point 10°F. lower than the

temperature of the brine (or other medium surrounding the expansion coils) for maximum efficiency. A lower back pressure than this reduces the refrigeration capacity. There is a temperature drop of about 10°F. between the brine and the ammonia due to the wall of the expansion coil. This is the same principle as in a milk cooler. The cooling medium must always be cooler than the temperature to which it is desired to cool the milk. Table 57 shows the boiling point of ammonia at different gauge pressures.

TABLE 57

THE RELATION OF GAUGE PRESSURE TO BOILING POINT OF AMMONIA

Gauge Pressures	Boiling Point of Ammonia	Minimum Brine Temperature
lbs. per sq. in.	°F.	°F.
+1.17	−25	−15
+3.45	−20	−10
+5.99	−15	−5
+8.77	−10	−0
+10.93	−5	+5
+15.37	−0	+10
+19.17	+5	+15
+23.55	+10	+20
+27.93	+15	+25
+32.95	+20	+30
+38.43	+25	+35
+44.41	+30	+40

To illustrate: If a minimum brine temperature of ten below zero is wanted, the pressure on the low pressure gauge should be that at which ammonia will boil at −20°F. or 3.45 lbs. per sq. in. Table 57 shows that it is not necessary to carry a vacuum on the low side unless extremely low temperatures are desired. Head pressures are determined by the temperature of the refrigerant in the condenser.

3. Keep the "head pressure" or pressure on the high side as low as possible. This saves power. The head pressure depends on (a) size of the condenser, (b) temperature of water used for cooling the condenser, (c) amount or volume of water flowing through the condenser, (d) impurities in the refrigerant (mainly oil and air), (e) cleanliness of the condenser outside as well as inside.

4. Avoid operating the compressor at zero suction pressure or under vacuum, since this favors oil passing out of the compressor into the condenser.

5. Avoid having frost on the compressor. The suction pipe at the compressor should carry frost up to the compressor when operating most efficiently.

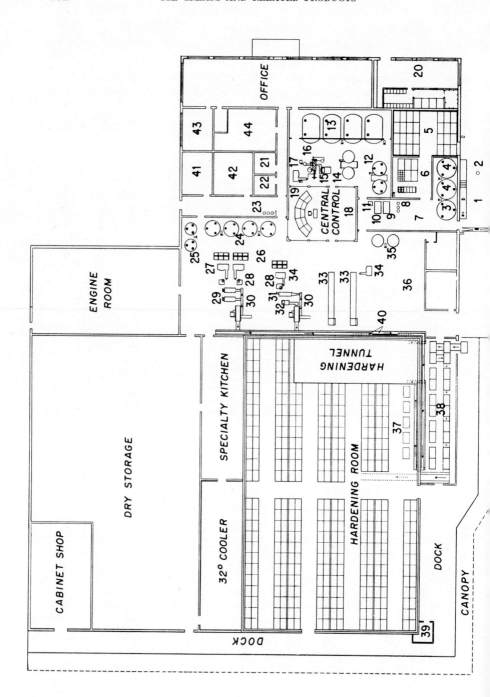

Fig. 49. Ice Cream Plant Layout

1—receiving
2—tank truck manhole
3—corn syrup tank (500 gal)
4—sugar syrup tank (500 gal)
5—butter and plastic cream storage
6—melting room
7—storage
8—CIP tanks
9—non-fat dry milk hopper
10—cocoa hopper
11—stabilizer hopper
12—mix assembly tanks (1000 gal)
13—raw products tanks (4000 gal)
14—batch pasteurizing tanks (500 gal)
15—homogenizer
16—UHT–HTST pasteurizer
17—mix cooler
18—laboratory
19—auto control panel
20—drivers' room
21—air condition unit
22—cold water unit

23—CIP tanks
24—mix storage tanks (2000 gal)
25—mix storage tanks (1000 gal)
26—flavor tanks
27—freezers
28—fruit feeder
29—1/2-gallon fillers
30—Hayssen bundler
31—pint filler
32—cup filler
33—Vita freeze (500 doz)
34—freezer
35—pop supply tank
36—chocolate bar and novelty area
37—palletizing area
38—palletizing room
39—receiving, shipping
40—belt conveyor
41—coffee lounge
42—men's locker room
43—women's locker room
44—conference room

6. Inspect and drain all oil traps regularly. Some oil always passes along with the refrigerant and collects at low spots in the system. Valves at these points permit the oil to be drained out, thereby improving the efficiency of the heat transfer. Worn piston rings favor oil passing into the refrigerant.

7. Keep air out of the system. Air and some other gases do not condense into a liquid, but collect at high spots in the system. Valves at these points permit the removal of the air. Air decreases the efficiency of the condenser, causing excessive head pressures. Usually the air is removed at the high point of the condenser; this operation is called "purging."

8. Keep the expansion coils as free from frost as possible. This is especially important in hardening rooms, since frost and ice beyond a certain thickness reduce the rate of heat transfer.

DEFROSTING METHODS

Common methods of defrosting are:

1. Brushing the coils with a stiff or wire bristled brush. This is not very effective as it may leave a thin layer of ice which gradually increases in thickness.

2. Scrubbing with hot water. A wet, messy, disagreeable operation leaving much moisture in the room and warming up the entire hardening room. However, it is nearly always used when the expansion coils are in a separate cabinet through which the hardening room air is circulated.

3. Passing hot liquid refrigerant through the coils. This requires extra valves and pipes in the installation, but does not raise the temperature of the room much. The frost and ice are easily removed from the quickly heated coils before the ice melts.

4. Passing hot refrigerant vapor or gas through the coils. This is similar to the use of hot liquid refrigerant.

5. Using a brine drip or spray over the coils. A trough containing calcium chloride crystals is placed above the coil so that as the crystals absorb moisture the brine drips down over the coil to collect in a pail at the bottom.

METHODS OF COOLING

The brine method of cooling, sometimes called the "brine system," represents the first application of mechanical refrigeration. The expansion coils of the mechanical refrigeration system are immersed in a large tank of brine (a calcium chloride solution) to cool the brine. Then the brine is pumped through pipes to the freezer (or other place where refrigeration is desired) and back to the brine tank to be cooled again. This method involves additional investment in brine tank, brine solution, pumps, pipes, etc. It is less efficient since the heat removed for refrigeration must be transferred to the brine and then to the mechanical refrigeration system. Other disadvantages are the corrosiveness of the brine, the difficulty in obtaining very low temperatures and the more bulky installation. The most important advantages are that it permits storing up of refrigeration and can be used where ammonia leaks would be dangerous. Although it has been largely replaced in modern factories, it continues to find application in certain operations such as making ice cream novelties and in making artificial ice.

The care of brine systems is important and may be summarized as follows:

1. Test the brine every month for concentration, alkalinity and ammonia.

2. Keep the concentration of the brine high enough to give a freezing point at least 10 degrees lower than the lowest temperature to which it will be cooled (see Table 57). Otherwise, the brine will freeze onto the expansion coil and this ice will act as insulation preventing the heat in the brine from penetrating the expansion coil.

3. Adjust the alkalinity by adding a solution of sodium hydroxide (caustic soda) or of lime until the brine is neutral to litmus or phenolphthalein. If the brine is acid to litmus it is too corrosive.

4. Use only one metal, preferably a pure grade of cast iron, in contact with the brine. Two different metals favor corrosive action.

5. Immerse a bar or strip of zinc in the brine to decrease the corrosion when two different metals are used in the system.

6. Add a solution of sodium dichromate and caustic soda to reduce corrosion; however, this will cause irritation of the skin. Care must therefore be used in handling the dichromate, as well as the brine containing it. To make the solution, thoroughly dissolve, by stirring, a mixture of 5 lbs. commercial dichromate, 1.4 lbs. caustic soda, in one gallon of water. This amount will be sufficient to treat 375 gallons of brine the first time. Once a year it will be necessary to add from one fourth to one half of the original amount.

7. Avoid air coming in contact with the brine since air makes the brine acid and more corrosive. Keep the brine tank covered, and avoid bubbling air through the brine or spraying the brine.

8. Avoid ammonia leaks from the expansion coils which cause the brine to become more alkaline. They can be detected by boiling a sample of brine in a narrow-necked flask and testing the vapors with red litmus

paper. If the red litmus paper turns blue the steam from the boiling brine contains ammonia.

The "direct expansion" method of cooling has replaced the brine method in many installations, since it represents increased efficiency and a saving in investment. In this method the brine pipes in the freezer (or other place where refrigeration is desired) are replaced by the expansion coils of the mechanical refrigeration system. These expansion coils may or may not contain much liquid refrigerant in addition to the refrigerant vapor.

The "flooded system" or method of cooling is a special case of the direct expansion method in which the liquid refrigerant collects in the expansion coils nearly filling the coils. The compressor draws off the vapor as the absorbed heat vaporizes the liquid. Thus in the operation of this flooded system the liquid refrigerant under high pressure and room temperature passes through a valve (usually controlled by a float) to the expansion coils where it is a liquid under a lower pressure and lower temperature. As heat is transferred to the liquid refrigerant evaporation takes place; the vapor from this evaporation is constantly removed by the compressor and the liquid level maintained by the float.

The important advantages of the flooded system are: (1) it is more efficient, since heat is more readily transferred between liquids than between vapors, gas or liquid to gas, (2) less cooling surface or coil surface is needed, (3) there is less fluctuation in temperature. The fact that float valves occasionally stick causing liquid refrigerant to enter and damage the compressor is the main disadvantage.

DEFINITIONS OF TERMS USED IN REFRIGERATION

1. "B.t.u.": British thermal unit or the amount of heat required to raise the temperature of one pound of water through one degree Fahrenheit when water has its greatest density (at about 39°F.). Roughly the amount of heat required to raise the temperature of one pound of water from 39° to 40°F.

2. "Latent Heat of Vaporization": The amount of heat (in B.t.u.) required to change one pound of liquid into one pound of vapor without changing the temperature or pressure.

3. "Latent Heat of Fusion": The amount of heat (in B.t.u.) required to change one pound of liquid into a solid without changing the temperature or pressure.

4. "Ton of Refrigeration": 288,000 B.t.u. per 24 hours or the amount of heat required to melt one ton of ice per day at 32°F. without changing the temperature or pressure. Other convenient "ton of refrigeration"

equivalents are: 12,000 B.t.u. per hour = 1 ton; 200 B.t.u. per minute = 1 ton.

5. "Ton Refrigeration Machine": A compressor or machine that will produce a "ton of refrigeration" during 24 hours of continuous operation under a particular set of conditions. (For example, 5°F. suction vapor and 86°F. condenser.)

Refrigeration compressors are frequently rated in "tons of refrigeration at a certain suction pressure" and this numerical figure is approximately one-half of the horsepower rating of the motor driving the compressor. However, many engineers find it more satisfactory to list the size of compressor in terms of piston diameter and length of piston stroke, since the following factors affect the size of motor and capacity of a compressor:

(a) The refrigerant used. Compressors are made for a particular refrigerant.

(b) The diameter of the cylinder. This influences the volume of refrigerant vapor that can be handled at one stroke.

(c) The length of the piston stroke, which also determines the volume of refrigerant vapor handled at one stroke.

(d) The speed, which determines the volume of refrigerant vapor handled per minute, hour or day.

(e) The suction pressure or pressure on the low pressure side, which determines the weight of refrigerant vapor per volume handled by the cylinders.

(f) Volumetric efficiency of machine—i.e., the ratio between the piston displacement and the actual amount of gas delivered.

The first four of these factors are usually constant in a particular installation, but the capacity of the compressor decreases rapidly with a decrease in the suction pressure. Also it should be remembered that the pressure on the "high pressure side" has almost no influence on the capacity of the compressor, although it does greatly affect the power consumption of the motor.

CHAPTER 21

Some Laboratory Tests Often Used in Ice Cream Plants

Proper laboratory control is important for efficient operation and for maintaining uniform quality of ice cream. It consists of both chemical and bacteriological analyses of the ingredients used, of the finished product and of other samples which are taken in the attempt to remedy undesirable conditions. Sometimes arrangements are made with a competent commercial laboratory to make these analyses on the basis of a fixed price per sample, or a flat price per month. However, it is generally desirable and economical to have at least the most essential routine testing done in the plant by its own personnel.

A few of these tests, such as are described later, can be made in a small laboratory containing the simplest and least expensive equipment, and the operator needs only a small amount of specialized training.

TEST FOR FLAVOR AND AROMA

This is perhaps the most essential routine test. It is one of the best and most accurate measures of quality. The aroma (or odor) is best observed in a place where there are no strong odors, and when the observation is made immediately after the sample bottle is opened. The flavor is obtained by taking a small portion (about a teaspoonful) into the mouth, allowing it to warm and then carefully rolling it to the back of the mouth without swallowing any of it. After the flavor has been observed the portion is delivered into a sink or garbage receptacle instead of being swallowed. Then the next sample may be tested. Care is necessary to avoid contaminating the product.

THE BABCOCK TEST FOR FAT IN MILK

Taking the Sample.—Whether the sample to be tested is milk, cream, butter or ice cream, it is equally important that it be taken in such a manner as to make absolutely sure that it is a fair and representative sample of the product to be tested. Otherwise time and money are wasted in proceeding with the details of the test. Therefore a considerable portion of the product to be tested should be carefully and thoroughly mixed before the sample is taken.

Apparatus and Reagents: Standard Babcock Test Equipment.

Procedure: By means of the 17.6 ml. pipette transfer to the milk test bottle 18 gm. of the sample which has been previously cooled to a tem-

288

perature of 60° to 70°F. and thoroughly mixed, being sure to drain the pipette completely by blowing out the last drop. Add 17.5 ml. of commercial sulfuric acid, at the same temperature as above, pouring it down the side of the neck of the bottle in such a way as to wash any traces of milk into the bulb. Mix the milk and acid thoroughly, first by a rotary motion and finally by vigorous shaking, until all traces of curd have disappeared. Then transfer the bottle to the tester; counterbalance it; and after the proper speed has been attained, whirl for 5 minutes. Add soft water, at 140°F. or above, until the bottle is filled to the neck. Whirl the tester again, this time for 2 minutes. Add hot water until the fat is brought well within the scale on the bottle neck. Whirl again, this time for 1 minute. Transfer the bottle to a water bath maintained at a temperature of 130° to 140°F. Immerse it to the level of the top of the fat column, allowing it to remain for 5 minutes. Remove bottle from the bath; wipe it; with a pair of dividers measure the fat column, in terms of percentage by weight, from its lower surface to the highest point of the upper meniscus.

At the time of measurement, the fat column should be translucent, of a golden yellow or amber color, and free from visible suspended particles. All tests in which the fat column is milky or shows the presence of curd or of charred matter, or in which the reading is indistinct or uncertain should be rejected and the test repeated.

BABCOCK TEST FOR FAT IN CREAM

Taking the Sample.—In collecting the sample of cream, the same general procedure is followed as in sampling milk. The cream to be tested should be warmed to a temperature of 100° to 110°F. just before it is mixed. After the cream is warmed it should be thoroughly mixed and all lumps broken up. Precaution should be taken to avoid overheating or allowing the sample to stand too long at 110°F. which would cause it to "oil off."

Apparatus and Reagents: Standard Babcock Test Equipment.

Procedure: Use the cream test scales and weigh 9 gm. of prepared sample into a 9-gm. cream test bottle, or 18 gm. into an 18-gm. bottle. Proceed by one of the following methods.

Method 1. After the cream has been weighed into the test bottle, add 8 to 12 ml. of sulfuric acid in the case of the 9-gm. bottle, or 14 to 17 ml. in the case of the 18-gm. bottle; or add acid until the mixture of cream and acid, after shaking, has assumed a chocolate-brown color. Then shake the bottle with a rotary motion until all lumps have completely disappeared and add 5 to 10 ml. of soft water at a temperature of 140°F. or above. Transfer the bottle to the tester, counterbalance and, after the proper speed has been attained, whirl it for 5 minutes. Add hot water until the fat column is brought well within the graduated scale on the bottle neck. Whirl 1 minute longer. Transfer the bottle to the water bath as in the testing for fat in milk, immersing the bottle to the level of the fat column and allowing it to remain for 5 minutes. Now place 2 or 3 drops of glymol on the surface of the fat column, care being taken to allow the glymol to run down the side of the neck in order to prevent its splashing and getting beneath the fat column. Remove the bottle from the bath. With the aid of the dividers measure the fat column from its lowest surface to the line of division between the fat column and the glymol.

Method 2. (For use with only the 9-gm. bottle.) After the cream has been weighed into the test bottle add 9 ml. of soft water and mix thoroughly; add 17.5 ml. of sulfuric acid and shake with a rotary motion until all lumps have completely disappeared. Transfer the bottle to the tester, counterbalance and, after the proper speed has been attained, whirl for 5 minutes. Fill the bottle to the neck with hot water and whirl again, for 2 minutes. Add hot water until the fat column is well within the graduated scale on the bottle neck. Whirl for 1 minute longer. Transfer to the water bath and continue as in Method 1.

As in the test for fat in milk, the fat column, at the time of reading, should be translucent, of a golden yellow or amber color and free from visible suspended particles. All tests in which the fat column is milky or shows the presence of curd or charred matter, or in which the reading is indistinct or uncertain, should be rejected and the test repeated.

MODIFIED BABCOCK TESTS FOR ICE CREAM

The original Babcock test is not satisfactory for testing ice cream because the strong sulfuric acid used reacts with the sugar in the product and the charred material is formed to such an extent that it is impossible to obtain an accurate test. The ice cream mix is homogenized which also makes the fat more difficult to separate. It has been necessary then to develop modifications of the Babcock test for testing ice cream. Numerous modified tests have been recommended. The modifications which have become most popular include the Minnesota, Nebraska, Pennsylvania, Illinois and Glacial acetic-sulfuric acid tests. The Pennsylvania and Minnesota tests have probably gained the greatest acceptance; however, all of the above tests, according to various investigators, check within ±0.3 per cent of the ether extraction method.

The main use of the modified tests is to serve as a guide as to whether the mix complies to the legal composition standard or to the composition standard which the manufacturer wishes to meet.

In general, the modified Babcock tests which employ sulfuric acid of a reduced strength require a base such as ammonium hydroxide to aid in digesting the protein present and alcohol or ether or both to aid in freeing the butterfat. The modified tests which employ alkaline reagents also require an alcohol or ether to help dissolve and free the fat.

Pennsylvania Test.—This test employs three reagents which are easily obtainable. The method employs a diluted sulfuric acid to complete the digestion after ammonium hydroxide and alcohol have been added to the sample. This procedure gives clear fat columns and ranks high from the standpoint of accuracy.

Preparation of Sample: Melt the ice cream at room temperature and, if necessary, heat to eliminate the foam. Warm ice cream mix to approximately 70°F. Reduce large particles in fruit and nut ice cream to a finely divided state.

Apparatus and Reagents: Regular Babcock equipment and glassware, including ice cream test bottles. Ammonium hydroxide (28 to 29% NH_3). Correct strength is important. Normal butyl alcohol (b.p. 117°C.). Diluted commercial sulfuric acid (approximate specific gravity 1.72 to 1.74 at 68°F.). The acid is prepared by adding $3^1/_2$ parts, by volume, of commercial sulfuric acid (specific gravity 1.82 to 1.83) to one part of water in a heat resisting container.

Procedure: Weigh 9 gm. of the representative sample into a 9-gm. 20% ice cream test bottle, care being taken to keep the fruit or nut ice cream thoroughly mixed. Add 2 ml. ammonium hydroxide (preferably from a burette). Mix for approximately one-half minute. Add 3 ml. of butyl alcohol. Mix for approximately one minute (samples containing chocolate require additional mixing). Add 17.5 ml. of the diluted sulfuric acid. Mix thoroughly until digestion is completed. Centrifuge the bottles for 5 minutes. Add water (130° to 140°F.) to bring the contents to within one-fourth inch of the base of the neck of the bottle. Centrifuge for 2 minutes. Add enough water (130° to 140°F.) to keep the fat within the graduated portion of the neck of the bottle until read. Centrifuge 1 minute.

Place the bottles in a water bath at 130°F. for 5 minutes. Allow a few drops of glymol to run down the inside of the neck of the bottle just before reading. Measure the length of the fat column from the bottom of the lower meniscus to the sharp line of demarcation between the glymol and the fat.

Precaution: The small amount of sample which adheres to the inside of the neck of the bottle should be washed into the bottle by the reagent; otherwise it may collect at the base of the fat column and make the correct reading of the fat column difficult. Other precautions of the method include (1) use care in transferring ammonium hydroxide—add to test bottle from burette, (2) be sure chemicals are of proper purity and strength, (3) use care in preparation of dilute acid, (4) use precautions observed in testing milk by the Babcock test.

Minnesota Test.—This is an alkaline test. It requires four chemicals which are available at chemical supply houses or the ready mixed reagent can be obtained.

The precautions to be observed by this method include (1) those observed for testing milk by the Babcock test, (2) store reagent in glass stoppered bottle to prevent evaporation and absorption of CO_2 but use caution to prevent glass stopper from sticking in bottle, (3) store reagent in cool place, (4) use proper water bath temperatures and times, (5) mix samples frequently during heating period. Use care to prevent the alcohol from boiling out of test bottle during this period.

Procedure:

1. Weigh 9 gm. of the well-mixed melted ice cream into 20% ice cream test bottles. An 8%, 18-gm. milk test bottle may be used, but the fat reading must be multiplied by 2.

2. Add 15 ml. of the Minnesota reagent and shake thoroughly. (Prepare Minnesota reagent by mixing the following dry materials: 645 gm. sodium salicylate, 355 gm. potassium carbonate and 160 gm. sodium hydroxide. Add three quarts of water and after solution is complete add one quart of isopropyl alcohol (Petrohol). The reagent is then ready for use. Store in glass and stopper to prevent evaporation and absorption of CO_2).

3. Digest in water bath at 180°F. or above until the fat layer at the surface is clear and well-defined. Do not shake the tests vigorously and no more than is absolutely necessary to cause complete digestion. The digestion period usually requires about 12–15 minutes.

4. Centrifuge one-half minute.

5. Add hot water (135°–140°F.) to bring the fat into reading scale of bottle.

6. Centrifuge one-half minute.

7. Place bottles in a water bath at 133° to 137°F. for five minutes.

8. Read test in same manner as for cream, using glymol; multiply the reading by 2 if the whole milk test bottle is used.

THE BABCOCK TEST FOR FAT IN BUTTER

Taking the Sample.—All that has been said about the need for care in sampling milk applies equally, or even more, to the sampling of butter because the sample must be taken so as to represent the composition of the whole batch to be tested. A butter trier is used to take the samples or "plugs" as they are called, from various places in the butter container.

and from top to bottom of the butter in the container. The sample may be prepared in several different ways but the following method is quite generally used: Place the "plugs," as they are taken, in a clean, dry, tightly stoppered sample jar. Warm only enough to soften the butter so that it can be stirred easily. Using an electric food mixer of the double beater type, with shafts attached to a metal screw cover to fit the sample jar, insert the beaters into the jar; screw cover down tight; mix contents at high speed for about three minutes. Rotate the jar until all portions of the contents are incorporated in the mixture. Remove the beater and proceed with test.

Precaution: If for any reason the testing is not done within a few hours, or if the sample has been allowed to become so warm that it melts, re-mix the sample just before the test is to be made.

Apparatus and Reagents: Standard Babcock Test Equipment including a 90% Butter Test Bottle.

Procedure: Weigh 9 gm. of the prepared sample into the 90% butter test bottle. (Fat clinging to the neck of the bottle may be melted by holding the bottle neck under the warm water tap till the fat melts and runs into the bottle.) Add about 9 ml. of the sulfuric acid (sp.g. 1.82 to 1.83). Mix thoroughly by gently rotating the bottle. Centrifuge and complete the test as described for testing cream.

The Babcock test is not quite as accurate for butter as for cream. It is generally thought to read about one-half per cent too high. There are more accurate tests such as the "Kohman" and the "Mojonnier" which the operator with more experience may wish to use.

Mojonnier Analysis for Fat and Total Solids in Ice Cream

Apparatus: Mojonnier tester and equipment including:

Balance
Fat dishes—solid dishes
Tongs
Dish contact maker
Extraction flasks
Pipettes—1, 2 and 5

Reagents:
Distilled water—free from residue.
Ammonia—chemically pure—about 26° Baumé, sp. gr. 0.8164 at 60°F.
Ethyl ether—not more than 4 per cent water, free from residue, sp. gr. from 0.713 to 0.716 at 77°F. Boiling point about 95°F.

Petroleum ether—free from residue—sp. gr. 0.638 to 0.660 at 70°F. Boiling point not over 120 to 140°F.

Alcohol—95 per cent—190 proof, 0.8164 sp. gr.

Procedure for Fat:

1. Prepare a representative sample and mix thoroughly by pouring from one container to another.

2. Weigh a 5 gm. sample into a properly labeled extraction flask.

3. Add 5 to 6 ml. of water.

4. Add 1.5 ml. of ammonia. Mix thoroughly.

5. Add 10 ml. of 95 per cent alcohol. Insert the cork and shake one-half minute. Keep finger over cork.

6. Add 25 ml. of ethyl ether. Insert cork and shake for one-half minute.

7. Add 25 ml. of petroleum ether. Insert cork and shake for one-half minute.

8. Centrifuge thirty turns, taking one-half minute.

9. Pour off the ether mixture containing the extracted fat into previously tared and weighed fat dishes. Use care to avoid getting any of the residue into the dish.

Second extraction.

10. Add 5 ml. of alcohol to the flask.

11. Add 25 ml. each of ethyl and petroleum ether. Insert the cork and shake for 30 seconds after each reagent.

12. Centrifuge 30 turns, taking one-half minute.

13. Pour off the other mixture into the same fat dishes used in the first extraction.

14. Evaporate the ether from the fat dishes on an electric hot plate at 135°F.

15. Place dishes in vacuum oven at 135°F. for five minutes with not less than 20 inches of vacuum.

16. Cool the dishes in the cooling desiccator for seven minutes.

17. Weigh dishes and fat rapidly and record weight of fat. Weights should be recorded to the fourth decimal place.

$$\% \text{ Fat} = \frac{\text{Weight of Fat}}{\text{Weight of Sample}} \times 100$$

Procedure for Solids:

1. Mix the sample thoroughly by pouring several times from one container to another.

2. Weigh a 1 gm. sample into a solids dish which has been previously heated for five minutes in a solids oven at 212°F. and then cooled for five

minutes in a solids cooling desiccator. Make weighings to the fourth decimal place with cover on the dish.

3. Record the weight of the dish and the weight of the sample.

4. Add 1 ml. water.

5. Tilt the dish in order to spread the mix in a thin film over the entire bottom of the dish.

6. Place the dish on the hot plate at 350°F. and heat until the residue begins to turn a light brown. Use the contact maker to insure uniform evaporation.

7. Place the dish into the solids vacuum oven at 212°F. and heat for ten minutes under not less than 20 inches vacuum.

8. Cool for 5 minutes in the cooling desiccator.

9. Weigh the dish and solids. Record the weight.

$$\% \text{ Total Solids} = \frac{\text{Weight of Solids}}{\text{Weight of Sample}} \times 100$$

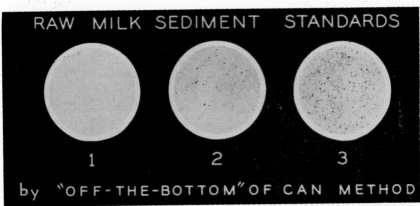

Courtesy of American Dry Milk Institute

FIG. 50. SEDIMENT STANDARDS

These can be used for checking for sediment in nonfat milk solids much the same as in milk and cream.

TOTAL SOLIDS—OFFICIAL

Into a round flat bottom dish not less than 5 cm. in diameter, weigh quickly 1–2 gm. of sample. (Sample may be weighed by means of short, bent, 2 ml. measuring pipette.) Heat on steam bath 30 min., then in air oven at 100°C. for 3.5 hours. Cool in desiccator and weigh quickly to avoid absorption of moisture.

THE ACIDITY TEST FOR MILK

This test is a means of measuring the percentage of acidity in milk.

Taking the Sample.—Samples for this test should be taken in the same careful manner as mentioned for fat tests.

Apparatus and Reagents: 17.6 ml. pipette as for the Babcock test; 9 ml. pipette; white porcelain cup; glass stirring rod; burette graduated to read to 0.1 ml.; alkali solution (0.1 normal); indicator (1.0% phenolphthalein).

Procedure: By means of the 17.6 ml. pipette transfer 18 gm. of the sample to the white cup. Add three to five drops of the indicator. Then fill the burette with alkali solution, making sure that no air bubbles remain in the tip of the burette when it is filled to the zero mark. Slowly titrate the milk with the alkali solution until a faint pink color appears. (This color should persist for about 30 seconds.) Read to the nearest 0.1 ml. the number of milliliters of alkali solution used. Divide the number of milliliters of alkali used by 20 to get the percentage of acidity in the milk.

THE ACIDITY TEST FOR CREAM AND PLAIN ICE CREAM MIX

Taking the Sample.—Proceed as for testing acidity in milk.

Apparatus and Reagents: The same as for testing acidity in milk.

Procedure: By means of the 9 ml. pipette transfer 9 gm. of sample to the white cup. Add 9 ml. of distilled water, and three to five drops of the indicator. Then titrate with the alkali solution as described for milk, and read the number of milliliters of alkali solution used. The percentage acidity is obtained by dividing the number of milliliters used by 10.

Protein Stability Test.—Place 5 ml. of mix in a test tube. Add distilled water and then alcohol (95%) in various proportions, starting with 9 ml. water and 1 ml. alcohol; then 8 ml. water and 2 ml. alcohol in the next test tube, etc. The total volume of alcohol plus water should always equal 10 ml. Mix by closing the tube with the thumb and slowly inverting three times. Vary the amount of alcohol used until a slight precipitate can be seen on the wall of the test tube as the mix drains away. Record the ml. of alcohol necessary to form the slight precipitate. (See Fig. 50.) This is a simple test to indicate the protein stability of an ice cream mix.

TESTING GELATIN

The Dahlberg Test, sometimes called the test-tube test, serves as a guide in determining the amount of gelatin needed in the mix, and in comparing the stabilizing ability of different gelatins when used in ice cream.

Apparatus: Butter moisture scales, or scales of equal accuracy; set of weights, 1 to 100 gm.; a 250 ml. beaker (for weighing skim milk); one-liter Erlenmeyer flask; 2 dozen test tubes—12 to 14 mm. diameter; a test tube rack; 2 pipettes, capacity 10 ml. in 0.1 ml. graduations.

Reagents: Gelatin sample and at least a quart of fresh skim milk.

Procedure: Weigh and put into the flask exactly 495 gm. fresh skim milk, below 80°F. Weigh exactly 5 gm. gelatin, and add it to the skim milk in the flask, thus obtaining a 1.0% gelatin solution. Allow to soak for 30 minutes. Then, using a water bath, heat the gelatin solution to 145°F. and hold at this temperature for 15 minutes, keeping the flask stoppered to prevent evaporation while heating, etc. Cool the solution to room temperature. Now put at least ten clean, dry test tubes in a rack, and number them. Then using one pipette for the gelatin-skim milk solution, and another for the fresh skim milk, prepare the following series of solutions as shown in Table 58:

TABLE 58

THE DAHLBERG TEST FOR GELATIN STRENGTH

Tube No.[1]	Gelatin-Skim Milk	Skim Milk	Factor
	ml.	ml.	
1	10.0	0	1.00
2	9.5	0.5	0.95
3	9.0	1.0	0.90
4	8.5	1.5	0.85
5	8.0	2.0	0.80
6	7.5	2.5	0.75
7	7.0	3.0	0.70
8	6.5	3.5	0.65
9	6.0	4.0	0.60
10	5.5	4.5	0.55
11	5.0	5.0	0.50
12	4.5	5.5	0.45

[1] Additional tubes may be needed for some gelatins.

Mix each tube by inverting it, and then set them in ice water for 18 to 20 hours. Then examine each tube in turn by placing a thumb over the top of the tube and quickly inverting the tube, holding the inverted tube still for 30 seconds. Do not allow the hand to warm the tube. Record the number of the tube in which the solution just fails to break when inverted for 30 seconds. The "Factor" (the percentage gelatin in the tube) corresponding to this tube is used to calculate the amount of this sample of gelatin needed in an ice cream mix as follows:

$$\% \text{ gelatin in the mix} = \text{Factor} \times \frac{100 - \% \text{ total solids in mix}}{100 - \% \text{ serum solids in skim milk}}$$

The skim milk used in the gelatin test contained 8.7% serum solids. When the tubes were inverted for 30 seconds the solutions in tubes Nos. 10 and 11 broke and ran down, but the solution in tube No. 9 failed to break. The factor corresponding to tube No. 9 is 0.60. Therefore,

$$\% \text{ gelatin in the mix} = 0.60 \times \frac{100 - 36.09}{100 - 8.7} = 0.42\%$$

which is the percentage of gelatin to use in this ice cream mix provided no other ingredients used act as a stabilizer.

When using the Dahlberg test to compare different gelatins, the following conditions must be kept uniform for all gelatins: (1) the quality, i.e., acidity, of the skim milk; (2) the soaking time, heating time and temperature in making the solutions; and (3) the temperature and time of the ice water bath.

This test is not satisfactory for the gum type of stabilizers. In fact, there is, as yet, no really accurate test of stabilizing ability for either the gelatin type or the gum type of stabilizer.

TESTS FOR AMMONIA LEAKS

Apparatus and Reagents: A clean tumbler; a piece of glass large enough to cover it. Ammonia test papers purchased from refrigeration companies. Similar papers may be prepared from heavy white paper strips (about 1 by 5 inches). These are dipped in phenolphthalein solution (the indicator solution used for acidity tests). If dried and stored for future use these test papers must be moistened with distilled water when used.

Procedure: Pass a strip of the test paper along the ammonia pipes, valves or compressor head suspected of having leaks. If there is a leak, the phenolphthalein treated paper will turn pink where it comes in contact with the escaping ammonia.

Ammonia leaking into the brine or the cooling water may be detected as follows: Fill a tumbler half full of the suspected brine or cooling water and add about one-eighth teaspoonful of dry caustic soda or lye, whichever is available. Cover with the piece of glass. Insert right under the cover, but not in the solution, a small strip of the phenolphthalein treated paper. If paper becomes pink after a few minutes it indicates that ammonia has been escaping into the brine or cooling water.

OTHER TESTS USED IN A QUALITY CONTROL PROGRAM

Other chemical tests, and bacteriological tests require more elaborate equipment and a more skilled operator. However, their use is important in any well-organized quality control program. Among these tests are the Mojonnier Test for fat and total solids; the Phosphatase Test for detecting improper pasteurization; the Coliform Test used as a measure of the sanitary handling of dairy products; the Sediment Test used to detect the presence of insoluble foreign matter that does not properly belong in dairy products; tests for antibiotic and pesticide residues.

Directions for these and other analytical tests can be found in Standard Methods for the Examination of Dairy Products published by the American Public Health Association, 1790 Broadway, New York 19, New York; and in Official and Tentative Methods of Analysis published by the Association of Official Agricultural Chemists, Box 540, Benjamin Franklin Station, Washington 4, D.C.

CHAPTER 22

Sales Outlets

In recent years, as competition for ice cream business has become keen, the wise ice cream manufacturer, as a security measure, tries to assure himself of a dependable market for his product. There are several types of market from which he may choose.

1. He may wholesale to drug stores and confectionery stores, to frozen foods stores (supermarkets) and to dairy stores.

2. He may retail directly from his factory to his customers.

3. He may have his own special outlets in the form of ice cream stores, dairy bars or one of the newer types of drive-in stores (parlors).

WHOLESALING

If the first type of outlet is chosen, the drug store will usually be a good market for bulk and may carry some packaged ice cream. The frozen food store will be an excellent market for the take home package. In the large cities dairy stores are quite common and usually have developed a reputation for high quality ice cream in addition to other high-quality dairy products such as cottage cheese, other well-cured cheese, dependably good butter, cream, cultured sour milk, etc.

FACTORY RETAILING

Factory retailing has been somewhat facilitated in recent years by the availability, in most commercial centers, of dry ice, and by use of single-service containers and light cardboard packing cases. These conveniences make it possible to use light-weight trucks and side-delivery motorcycles for making deliveries from factory to consumer and thus reduce expense to some extent.

DRIVE-IN STORE

The main requirement for the drive-in store, second only to the store itself, is, of course, plenty of parking space for customers' cars. If possible the site chosen should have a pleasing background and a good view, and the parking area should be kept neat and tidy. Since it has been estimated that about 75 per cent of ice cream business is in repeat orders, obviously the drive-in store should be on the edge of the residential area and preferably near and in view of a well-traveled highway.

The store itself should be attractive, well-lighted, well-arranged and convenient for service. It should be kept clean and sanitary in every detail, even to toilets for the public and for employees.

The manager of such a store, of any food store, should make it a first rule to become familiar with his state and local community health regulations and insist that all his employees and persons delivering food products to his establishment comply with such regulations.

Courtesy of American Dairy Association

Fig. 51. Eye Appealing and Taste Tempting Ice Cream Service

THE TAKE-HOME PACKAGE SECTION

Perhaps there is no better way to expand an ice cream business through retail channels than by encouraging customers to take home a package of ice cream. For quick service have it neatly packaged in pint, quart and half-gallon sizes of such shapes that they will fit neatly into the consumer's home refrigerator or deep freeze compartment. These packages should be stored in the cabinet ready to be placed in insulated bags to hand to the customer. Promoting take-home packages surely helps to get more people in the habit of eating ice cream oftener. Emphasize

FIG. 52.   A MODERN SODA FOUNTAIN

The installation includes wall fountain, liberal ice cream storage facilities and low temperature display and storage case in which frozen ice creams can be displayed unwrapped, in all their attractiveness; a very effective sales medium.

again and again how easy it is and how time-saving, to serve ice cream at home as compared with other desserts. Stress the food value and palatability of this truly great American dessert.

THE SODA FOUNTAIN

Soda fountain service is a profitable addition to many of the types of outlet mentioned. However this kind of business should be ventured into only if there is sufficient capital to do a good and attractive job of installation, and only if the management is soda fountain-minded and sufficiently interested to become familiar with the many phases of this kind of merchandising.

If rightly equipped and managed, and staffed with perfectly trained personnel there is no doubt that the soda fountain can be a great help in selling ice cream. Keep in mind, however, that service must be given in an accommodating, eye-appealing and taste-tempting manner. The ice cream dispenser, and the soda fountain itself, should have a neat, well-cared-for appearance. Over all and about everything connected with the fountain and its environment there must be that intangible atmosphere which suggests wholesomeness, cleanliness and sanitation. (See Fig. 52.)

General Housekeeping.—Both the inside and the outside of the fountain need regular attention both as to cleaning and upkeep. For sanitary reasons, the inside must be kept scrupulously clean. Keeping it clean both inside and outside also retards corrosion of the metal linings and thus prolongs the life of the fountain. Keep in mind too that a spotless general appearance has definite customer appeal and generally pays off handsomely in additional profits.

Glass or Paper Dishes.—At the fountain either glass or paper cups and serving dishes may be used. Many people prefer glass serviceware but if it is used great care must be taken to prevent breakage and to keep dishes sanitary. With glass there is also the danger that chips of glass may fall into the open ice cream cans, and there is always the extra work of cleaning dirty dishes. When paper cups and dishes are used, good housekeeping is made easier, the serving can be more sanitary and there is no danger of broken glass and no expensive delay for dishwashing.

PERSONNEL

Remember that soda fountain success is quite definitely dependent upon the selection and training of just the right type of personnel for giving good service. This applies equally well to dairy bar or dairy store personnel. The men and women behind the counter should be schooled to follow a well-planned routine regarding the best form of greeting and approach to customers in taking the order, in serving the food, in making suggestions for increasing the order, in presenting the customer's bill or check and in cleaning the counter before the next customer is served, etc. In short, the good dispenser, or sales person, will cultivate cheerfulness, meet customers with a smile, be dignified and quiet, give quick, accurate and gracious service and be dependable and honest.

Health Habits.—The public is becoming more and more health conscious and therefore persons handling and serving food should be trained to live up to definite and rigid health standards. The hair should be well groomed; women employees should wear hair nets; men should be clean shaven; teeth should be well cared for, hands and fingernails clean and trim; uniforms should be clean and neat and shoes clean and polished. Soap and water should be easily accessible and used as freely as common-sense sanitary regulations dictate.

Keep Hands Clean.—"Hands," someone has said, "are the tools of the food worker," essential tools in many operations in filling orders. The following rules about cleanliness of the hands must be observed by all operators: Keep them clean. Always assume they may carry germs. Wash them before handling tableware and food. Wash them after each visit to the lavatory; after coughing or sneezing, or combing the hair; and after handling refuse or waste of any kind. Always be sure they are clean before they touch food.

TRAINING FOR FOUNTAIN SERVICE

Quite likely the retailer's principal interest in the soda fountain is to increase his profits. To do this he must have more and more customers. In order to attract customers and have them come back for repeat orders, he must be sure that his ice cream is of high quality, that good cream and good flavoring substances are used in making it, and that equally good quality of syrups and toppings are used to combine with the ice cream at the fountain. Generally it is best to buy and use only the best and most palatable materials for toppings and syrups and then be familiar with the "how" and "when" to use them most effectively. Therefore it would pay the retailer to train his workers so that they will sell more ice cream and thereby make larger profits.

The dispenser, the man in charge of the fountain, should have some special training in soda fountain work until he has thoroughly mastered the "know-how" of what and how to serve. He should be familiar with the best methods of preparing toppings and of blending fruits, nuts and toppings with simple syrups. He should also know how to dip ice cream most economically, and know the most attractive ways in which the variously colored and flavored ice creams should be served.

How to Dip Ice Cream.—While it may seem like an easy thing to do it really takes practice and planning to dip ice cream properly. To lower the ice cream surface evenly in the can, to cut from the highest surface of the ice cream and to keep the can stationary while dipping the ice cream for the cone, requires skill that comes only with practice. Experienced fountain operators (dispensers) have found that it is best to press the ball of ice cream gently on the side of the cone with the outside of the dipperbowl, pressing just enough to make it stick but not enough to spoil its shape or to break the cone. The dispenser should learn early at what temperature ice cream will dip or cut easily and still not be so soft as to spoil the texture and cause shrinkage. He will get this "feel" for dipping only by practice. (See Figs. 50 and 51.)

The dipped package usually refers to carry-out packages filled by the

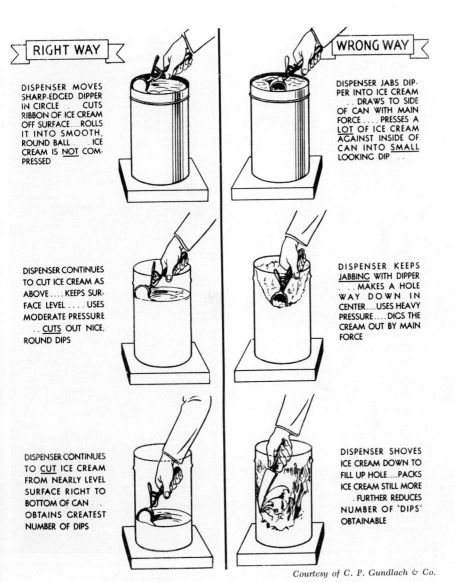

RIGHT WAY

DISPENSER MOVES SHARP-EDGED DIPPER IN CIRCLE . CUTS RIBBON OF ICE CREAM OFF SURFACE....ROLLS IT INTO SMOOTH, ROUND BALL . ICE CREAM IS NOT COMPRESSED

DISPENSER CONTINUES TO CUT ICE CREAM AS ABOVE....KEEPS SURFACE LEVEL .... USES MODERATE PRESSURE . CUTS OUT NICE, ROUND DIPS

DISPENSER CONTINUES TO CUT ICE CREAM FROM NEARLY LEVEL SURFACE RIGHT TO BOTTOM OF CAN . OBTAINS GREATEST NUMBER OF DIPS

WRONG WAY

DISPENSER JABS DIPPER INTO ICE CREAM . . DRAWS TO SIDE OF CAN WITH MAIN FORCE .... PRESSES A LOT OF ICE CREAM AGAINST INSIDE OF CAN INTO SMALL LOOKING DIP . .

DISPENSER KEEPS JABBING WITH DIPPER . . . MAKES A HOLE WAY DOWN IN CENTER....USES HEAVY PRESSURE....DIGS THE CREAM OUT BY MAIN FORCE

DISPENSER SHOVES ICE CREAM DOWN TO FILL UP HOLE....PACKS ICE CREAM STILL MORE . FURTHER REDUCES NUMBER OF 'DIPS' OBTAINABLE

Courtesy of C. P. Gundlach & Co.

FIG. 53.   ICE CREAM—HOW TO DIP

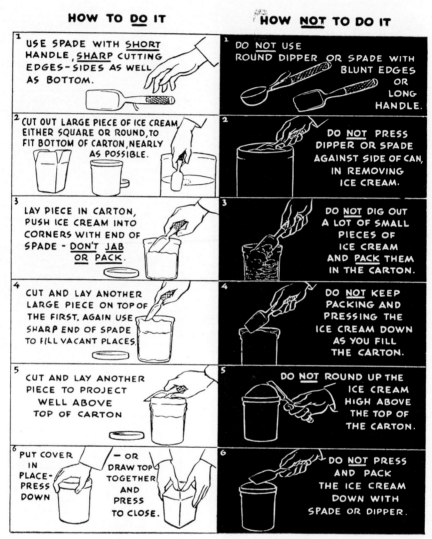

FIG. 54. DIPPING ICE CREAM INTO CARRY HOME PACKAGES

retailer who dips the hardened ice cream from a bulk package in his cabinet and presses it into the new container.

It is common knowledge that the volume of ice cream after dipping is less than the volume before dipping. This decrease in volume is due to air being compressed or expelled from the ice cream with a corresponding loss in overrun. It is impossible for the retailer to sell the same volume of ice cream that he manufactures or receives from the manufacturer as he sustains what is known as a dipping loss. Several factors may affect dipping losses among which are overrun, dipping temperature and composition. These factors were studied in detail by H. R. Bierman several years ago and reported in the Maryland Agr. Exp. Sta. Bull. 293, the findings still offer valuable information.

The percentage overrun is important in determining the number of quarts or servings which the ice cream dealer can dip from a container of ice cream. Table 59 shows the effect of overrun on dipping losses.

TABLE 59

HOW OVERRUN AFFECTS DIPPING LOSSES AND WEIGHT PER QUART[1]

Average Overrun	Dealer Dips from 20-Quart Containers	Average Dipping Loss	Weight per Quart	
			Before Dipping	After Dipping
per cent	quarts	per cent	ounces	ounces
60.3	16.96	15.18	22.95	27.05
80.6	15.37	23.14	20.37	26.52
100.8	14.07	29.66	18.30	26.25
118.6	13.45	32.76	16.81	25.14
Average	14.96	25.18	19.61	26.24

[1] From Bierman (1927).

The most uniform weight quarts were dipped from ice cream containing from 80 to 100 per cent overrun. The percentage dipping loss increases as the overrun of the ice cream increases. If the dealer observes this fact, he will be in a better position to establish proper dispensing procedures.

The dipping temperature (Table 60) influences the number of servings which can be dipped from a container of ice cream. The table shows the effect of dipping temperatures on losses.

It appears from the above results that if dipping losses are to be kept at a minimum, ice cream of average composition (15 per cent sugar) should be dipped at 8°F. or lower. The dipping temperature should be varied inversely 1.0° to 1.5°F. for each one per cent differences in sugar content and, to make dipping practical at 8°F. or lower, the ice cream should contain approximately 90 per cent overrun.

TABLE 60

HOW DIPPING TEMPERATURE AFFECTS DIPPING LOSSES AND WEIGHT PER QUART[1]

Dipping Tempera-ture	Average Overrun	Dealer Dips from 20-Quart Containers	Average Dipping Loss	Weight Per Quart	
				Before Dipping	After Dipping
°F.	per cent	quarts	per cent	ounces	ounces
3–8	90	15.33	23.35	19.34	25.72
9–16	90	14.65	26.75	19.34	26.82
17–20	90	15.86	20.70	19.34	24.46

[1] Compiled from Md. Agr. Exp. Sta. Bul. No. 293.

The proper dipping temperature is determined by different factors. It must be low enough to keep dipping losses to a minimum and yet afford easy dipping. This is affected by the overrun and composition, especially the sugar content of the product.

Composition has only a slight effect on dipping losses when compared to the effect of overrun and dipping temperature. The dipping losses in high fat content ice cream are slightly less than in average or low fat ice cream. The loss encountered in high milk solids-not-fat ice cream is greater than in a low milk solids-not-fat product when dipped at the same temperature. This is caused by the increased sugar (lactose) content introduced in the mix when the milk solids-not-fat content is increased. Ice cream with a high sugar content has a greater dipping loss than ice cream containing a lower per cent of sugar unless the dipping temperature is varied so as to give equal hardness to the ice cream and then the dipping loss will be approximately the same regardless of the sugar content.

Dipping studies indicate that there are two factors influencing the weight of ice cream dipped. One of these is the resistance offered by the ice cream which prevents the expulsion of the air. The second factor is the amount of force applied to push the dipper into the ice cream.

Dipping temperature of 8°F. or lower, overrun of 80 to 90 per cent and ice cream of average composition all tend to keep dipping losses at a minimum and maintain uniformity in the portion of ice cream dispensed.

The advantages of hand packing ice cream are completely outweighed by such **disadvantages** as:

1. The greater chance for unintentional contamination by the retailer.

2. The wide variation in the amount of ice cream placed in containers of equal size. The main factors influencing this variation are:

(a) Temperatures of ice cream (3° to 8°F. is generally recommended to make dipping easy but it varies with freezing point, etc., of the ice cream).

(b) Individuality. Variation from person to person doing the dipping is great.

(c) The composition and air content of the ice cream.

3. The inevitable delay in serving customers.

4. The necessarily higher temperature of the ice cream when it leaves the retail store. It has to be softer for dipping and therefore does not reach the home in as good condition.

5. The damaged quality, especially in body and texture of the ice cream.

6. The inability of the retailer to control operating costs. Since it is impossible for the retailer to completely fill equal-sized containers with equal weights of dipped ice cream, it is impossible for him to operate on a narrow margin or to estimate his profits.

A similar practice of dipped packaging is employed when making fancy molds; i.e., fancy shapes resembling animals, flowers, etc.

Metal molds are filled with ice cream dipped from bulk packages because the molds do not hold enough ice cream to be filled from the freezer. Most of the disadvantages listed above are equally applicable here. An additional disadvantage, in this case, lies in the fact that using too much pressure in order to force the ice cream into the corners of the mold, will pack the ice cream so solidly that it must be melted before it can be cut with a spoon for eating. Such hard ice cream is especially undesirable in "center-molds."

Employees as Sales Representatives.—The men and women employed for fountain service are the principal contact the retailer has with the public who buy his products. It is really a waste of money to advertise, build and equip a fine building, and manufacture or buy high quality ice cream if the employees who represent the establishment are sloppy, or lazy or if, in general, they create an unfavorable impression on the public —the consumer who is counted upon to buy this delicious product.

All that has been said about employees' training, ability and qualifications has been said simply to emphasize the fact that these employees really reflect the business and managerial ability of the proprietor. If he is a good manager his business should prosper. In case the business is larger than he can handle personally, much will depend on the store or fountain manager he chooses to help run the business for him.

Choosing a Manager.—The manager should be chosen with great care —not on the spur of the moment. His references should be carefully checked to make sure that he is all he represents himself to be. As a guide in checking his qualifications the following suggestions may be helpful: he must be honest; be conscientious; be able to handle personnel, to work with them and yet be their leader; he must be efficient in the duties he is hired to perform and have some administrative ability; he must have enough originality to be able to develop new sales ideas; and finally he must be 100 per cent loyal to the proprietor or organization which hires him. When the person with the right qualifications has been found, he should be paid what he is worth, his boss should back him up to the nth degree, and see that life is made pleasant for him especially until he is thoroughly initiated into his new job.

If the staff of store and fountain is to "click" as would be expected in a well-integrated organization, training for the job is necessary for all employees. The work expected of them should be carefully explained, better still, ably demonstrated to them. Employees should be given a chance to ask questions and these questions should be very patiently answered so that the employee will thoroughly understand his work and that of the others with whom he must work.

The management which has thus thoroughly trained its representatives, i.e., its employees, for their respective jobs, should be well on the way toward a profitable business.

"SPECIALS" FOR SPECIAL OCCASIONS—SEASON MINDED

One of the best ways of promoting sales is by featuring "specials" and being "season-minded" about them. Some especially appetizing and attractive reminders of Spring when Winter is about to take leave and equally attractive features for the other seasons will tempt the public to choose ice cream more often. There are many special days in every season which will suggest to the imaginative ice cream maker or soda fountain dispenser new ideas for taste-tempting formulas and decorative schemes. The variety thus introduced will make his product so attractive that sales are bound to mount. He must, of course, not only make these specials but see to it that they are well advertised so the public will know about them well in advance of the special day that is featured. For instance, consumers should know well in advance of Easter what attractive special ice creams they may have for dessert and for decorative effects for that special day. So, with Fourth of July, World Series days, Thanksgiving, Christmas Day, New Year's and Valentine's Day, to name only a few. Then there are birthday specials and anniversary specials to fit the season in which such family or club events occur. All these should be very good sales outlets for the manufacturer who is looking for extra business. (See Chapter 16, Fancy Molded Ice Creams, Novelties and Specialties.)

CHAPTER 23

Formulas for Soda Fountain Use

From George W. Hennerich's excellent book (Hennerich 1947), "Let's Sell Ice Cream,"[1] we are quoting by permission[2] certain definitions of soda fountain terms, and soda fountain formulas. In this book Mr. Hennerich offers valuable detailed information not only regarding the many and varied combinations of Ice Cream and Toppings used to produce the sundaes and other specialties which have helped many to secure added business, but has also suggested the type of glassware and the quantity of each ingredient. Your own serviceware, either glass or paper, may of course be substituted. He stresses the importance of putting the various ingredients into the glass or paper service in the order listed.

SODA FOUNTAIN TERMS

Following are a few of the most commonly used soda fountain terms. The ambitious dispenser should lose no time in acquiring a handy reference book giving full details of this phase of his work.

Ades—Drinks containing the juice of citrus fruits, sweetened, to which plain or carbonated water is added.

Baumé Hydrometer—Used to determine the degree of sugar concentration in simple syrup.

Bon-Bon—Similar to a sundae. Usually made in a 6- or 7-ounce fancy stem glass. Candied fruit in the bottom of glass, a combination of ice cream, sherbet, flavor or fruit.

College Ice—This name was given to a sundae in a college town and was originally applied to sundaes topped with whipped cream.

Cooler—A drink made of fruit or fruit flavors in combination with ice, carbonated or plain water and topped with sherbets. Frequently made up complete and dispensed from punch bowl, adding ice and sherbet.

Double Sundae—Ice cream and topping of the same flavor—as for example chocolate ice cream and chocolate topping.

Egg Phosphate—A glass of carbonated water in which have been carefully blended, flavor, acid phosphate and an egg.

---

[1] Former managing director of the Ice Cream Merchandising Institute, Inc., Washington, D.C. Affiliate of the International Association of Ice Cream Manufacturers.

[2] By permission of the Ice Cream Merchandising Institute, Inc., affiliate of the International Assoc. of Ice Cream Manufacturers.

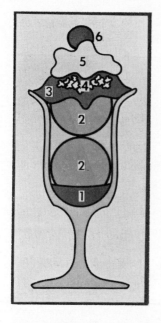

Fig. 55.   The Sundae

Ingredients:

    6—*cherry*
    5—*whipped cream*
    4—*nuts*
    3—*1 oz. crushed, sliced or whole fruit*
    2—*ice cream—two dippers*
    1—$^{1}/_{2}$ *oz. crushed, sliced or whole fruit*

Fizz—Originally applied to tart drinks to which was added powdered sugar to give the fizzing effect. This name is applied to many egg drinks.

Float—An ade, freeze, ricky, milk shake or other drink on the top of which fruit ice, sherbet or ice cream is floated.

Frappé—Frozen or partly frozen fruit juices. It is applied to whipped combinations of ice cream, syrup, fruits, nuts and whipped cream.

Frosted Chocolate—Another name for a chocolate milk shake made with ice cream.

Frosty—A milk shake made with sherbet or fruit ice.

Glacé (glä-say)—Frozen or iced fruits, nuts, etc. Drinks with an overlay of fruits or nuts, usually made very cold with ice. Also applied to sundaes on which glossy surfaced fruits and sugared nuts are served.

Ice Cream Soda—A combination of fruit syrup or other flavor, ice cream and carbonated water.

Royal—Applied to unusual ice cream combinations—generally those in which sliced fruit covers the bottom of the dish, and is topped with ice cream, fruits, toppings, nuts, etc.

Shakes—Originally applied to any drink that was shaken to mix it. Now applied to milk drinks made with ice cream, and mixed on drink mixer.

Soda—Usually accepted at the soda fountain to mean ice cream soda.

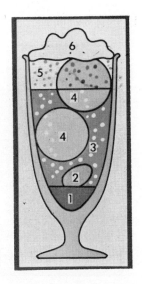

FIG. 56. THE SODA

Ingredients:

6—garnish—whipped cream
5—carbonated water—to fill (about 2 oz.)
4—ice cream—two dippers
3—carbonated water to ³/₄ full (about 6 oz.)
2—a spoonful of ice cream or ¹/₂ oz. of coffee cream
1—1¹/₂ oz. of syrup or fruit in syrup

Sundae—A portion of ice cream over which one or more dressings of syrups, fruits, nuts or other toppings are poured.

Twin Sundae—A two-in-one method of making a sundae. Two molds of ice cream alongside one another in the same dish and topped with the usual sundae materials.

FORMULAS

Ice cream can be served in many ways. Some of the common combinations and preparations include: ice cream with fruit, fruit sundaes, sodas, milk shakes, the banana split and the parfait. The procedure for making these items is as follows:

The Dish of Ice Cream with Fruit

(1) Place two dippers in dish (glass or paper).
(2) Surround with 1 oz. fresh sliced fruit of preference.

The Sundae

(1) Place ¹/₂ oz. of crushed, sliced or whole fruit into a dish.
(2) Add two dippers of ice cream.
(3) Surround ice cream with crushed, sliced or whole fruit.
(4) Add nuts.
(5) Top with whipped cream and a single item of fruit.

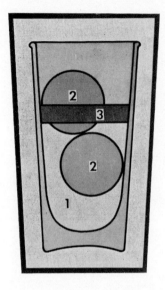

FIG. 57. THE MILK SHAKE

Ingredients:

3—1¹/₂ oz. syrup
2—ice cream—two dippers
1—6 oz. of cold pasteurized milk

The Soda

(1) Place 1¹/₂ oz. of syrup into 14-oz. glass.
(2) Stir spoon of ice cream or 1¹/₂ oz. of coffee cream into syrup.
(3) Fill glass ³/₄ full with carbonated water.
(4) Float into mix two dippers of ice cream.
(5) Mix gently.
(6) Top with whipped cream.

The Milk Shake

(1) Place two dippers of ice cream into chilled cup.
(2) Add 1¹/₂ oz. of syrup.
(3) Add 6 oz. of milk.
(4) Mix thoroughly and rapidly.
(5) Pour into serving glass.

The Banana Split

(1) Split banana in half, lengthwise, with peel on. Place one half on each side of dish, flat side down, then remove peel.
(2) Place three dippers of ice cream on banana halves. Vanilla in center and other flavors on each side.
(3) Cover each dipper of ice cream with different topping.
(4) Garnish the top and between dippers with whipped cream.
(5) Add single piece of fruit.
(6) Place slices of banana or fruit around center of item.

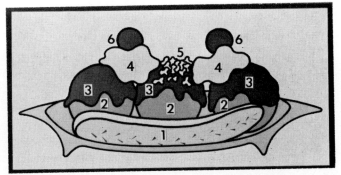

FIG. 58. THE BANANA SPLIT

Ingredients:
    6—cherry
    5—nuts
    4—whipped cream
    3—¹/₂ oz. each of three toppings
    2—ice cream—three dippers—assorted flavors
    1—medium ripe banana

The Parfait
(1) Place one spoon of crushed fruit in parfait glass.
(2) Add one dipper of ice cream.
(3) Cover with one spoon crushed fruit.
(4) Add one dipper ice cream.
(5) Cover with one spoon crushed fruit.
(6) Add one dipper ice cream.
(7) Cover with one spoon crushed fruit.
(8) Top with whipped cream.
(9) Decorate with single piece of fruit or nut.

SUNDAES AND SPECIALS

American Beauty
(flat or footed round dish)

1 #10 dipper vanilla ice cream
1 oz. chocolate fudge
5 stem whole maraschino
  cherries

Sprinkle chopped nuts over fudge. Garnish with a straight line of whipped cream through center and sprinkle chocolate decorettes over all.

Balloon
(tulip glass)

¹/₂ oz. chocolate sauce
2 #20 dippers vanilla ice
  cream
1 oz. chocolate sauce

Top with whipped cream and a cherry.

Note: Use the "give-away balloon" idea with this sundae.

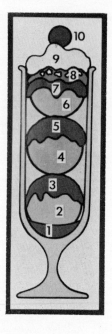

FIG. 59.   THE PARFAIT

Ingredients:

10—*cherry*
9—*whipped cream*
8—*1 spoon nuts in syrup*
7—*1 spoon crushed fruit*
6—*ice cream—one dipper*
5—*1 spoon crushed fruit*
4—*ice cream—one dipper*
3—*1 spoon crushed fruit*
2—*ice cream—one dipper*
1—*1 spoon crushed fruit*

Banana Whip
(stem sundae dish)
2 #20 dippers chocolate ice cream
Sliced banana—to cover
Top with a generous portion of whipped cream and a cherry.

Bee-Hive
(tulip glass)
$^1/_2$ oz. pure honey
2 #20 dippers vanilla ice cream
1 oz. pure honey
Over the top sprinkle a portion of fresh crunchy roasted salted almonds.   Garnish with whipped cream and a red cherry.

Birthdae
(tulip glass) (for February 12)
$^1/_2$ oz. Log Cabin or maple syrup
2 #20 dippers chocolate ice cream
1 oz. Log Cabin syrup
Two pretzel sticks on each side of dish to form a sundae.   Top with cherry.

Black Cherry Sundae
(tulip glass)
$^1/_2$ oz. Burgundy cherries
2 #20 dippers vanilla ice cream
1 oz. Burgundy cherries (over ice cream)
Decorate with whipped cream.

Blueberry Banana
(tulip glass)
$^1/_2$ oz. fresh blueberries
2 #20 dippers vanilla ice cream
1 oz. fresh blueberries
Decorate with whipped cream and sliced banana around edge of glass. Top with a whole blueberry.

Brandi-Peach
(stem glass or paper service)
1 #12 dipper vanilla ice cream
1 oz. brandi-peach
Border of whipped cream around edge of dish. Place a date on each side and English walnut halves between each date. Place a whole cherry in center.

Budget Chocolate
(paper cup)
1 #16 dipper vanilla ice cream
1 oz. chocolate syrup
Garnish with whole or half Maraschino cherry.

Butterscotch Peanut Royal
(ice cream bowl or round dish)
Slices of banana (to cover bottom of dish)
2 #20 dippers butterscotch variegated ice cream
$1^1/_2$ oz. butterscotch (between molds)
Top with blanched salted peanuts.

Caramel Crunch
(crimp or tulip glass)
$^1/_2$ oz. caramel topping
2 #20 dippers vanilla ice cream
1 oz. caramel topping
Grape Nuts or chopped nuts.
Top with a cherry.

Chocolate Brownie
(tulip glass)
1 #20 dipper chocolate ice cream
$^1/_2$ Crumbled chocolate brownie
1 #20 dipper chocolate ice cream
The other half of chocolate brownie crumbled over it
Whipped cream, red or green cherry
Serve with a whole chocolate brownie on the underlying plate.

Chocolate Peanut
(tulip glass)
$^1/_2$ oz. of marshmallow topping
1 #20 dipper chocolate ice cream
1 #20 dipper vanilla ice cream
1 oz. chocolate topping
1 spoon salted peanuts over topping

Chocolate Rice Krispies
(tulip glass)
$^1/_2$ oz. chocolate topping
2 #20 dippers vanilla ice cream
1 oz. chocolate topping and a good portion of Rice Krispies
Garnish with whipped cream and a cherry.

Christmas Fountain Special
(tulip glass)
2 #20 dippers chocolate ice cream
Small portion of special Christmas whipped cream dressing
Garnish with whipped cream and red and green cherries or red and green pineapple cubes.

Co-ed Special
(tulip glass)
$1/_2$ oz. chocolate topping
2 #20 dippers vanilla ice cream
$1/_2$ oz. chocolate topping
$1/_2$ oz. marshmallow topping
4 slices of banana around the outside
Whipped cream and cherry.

Coffee and Cream
(tulip glass)
$1/_2$ oz. coffee syrup
2 #20 dippers coffee or vanilla ice cream
1 oz. coffee syrup
Garnish with whipped cream and a cherry.

Cold Fudge Baby Ruth
(stem glass or paper service)
1 #12 dipper vanilla ice cream
1 oz. cold fudge
1 small Baby Ruth bar
Garnish with whipped cream and a slice of the bar.

Double Feature Strawberry
(banana split dish)
2 #20 dippers Strawberry or vanilla ice cream (side by side)
$1^1/_2$ oz. fresh frozen or preserved strawberries over both molds
Whipped cream between the 2 molds. Whole strawberry on whipped cream.

Double Raspberry
(crimp glass)
$1/_2$ oz. fresh red raspberry topping
2 #20 dippers raspberry ice cream
1 oz. fresh red raspberry topping
Garnish with whipped cream and a red cherry.

Egg Nog No. 1
(tulip glass)
$1/_2$ oz. crushed pineapple
2 #20 dippers egg nog ice cream
1 oz. crushed pineapple
Garnish with whipped cream and a cherry.

Frosted Frutti
(tulip glass)
$1/_2$ oz. fresh fruit salad
1 #20 dipper vanilla ice cream
1 #20 dipper strawberry sherbet or fruit ice
1 oz. fresh fruit salad
Top with a soda spoon of strawberry sherbet or fruit ice and imbed a red cherry in the center.

Fruited Strawberry
(tulip glass)

$^1/_2$ oz. crushed strawberries
2 #20 dippers vanilla ice
  cream
1 oz. crushed strawberries
Top with a whipped cream ring
and one whole strawberry.

Georgia Peach
(crimp glass)

$^1/_2$ oz. crushed peaches
2 #20 dippers vanilla ice
  cream
1 oz. crushed peaches
Garnish with whipped cream and
a peach slice.

Peanut Brittle Sundae
(crimped dish)

$^1/_2$ oz. crumbled peanut brittle
2 #20 dippers vanilla ice
  cream
Cover with 1 oz. crumbled peanut
brittle.

Touch Down
(crimp glass)

1 chocolate covered Brazil nut
1 No. 16 dipper butter pecan
  ice cream
1 oz. heavy coffee syrup
Garnish with whipped cream.
Top with a red cherry.
Note: The chocolate covered
Brazil nut is intended to represent
the football; and, when the patron
eating the sundae reaches the bottom of the glass, he has "made a
touchdown."

Valentine
(tulip glass)

$^1/_2$ oz. crushed strawberries
2 #20 dippers vanilla ice
  cream
1 oz. crushed strawberries
Top with whipped cream and
decorate with 5 or 6 heart shaped
candies or make your regular
strawberry sundae and, after adding the whipped cream, decorate
with 5 or 6 heart shaped candies.

Cherry Fudge (Hot)
(twin sundae dish)

1 #20 dipper vanilla ice cream
1 #20 dipper coffee ice cream
1 oz. hot Burgundy cherries
  over the vanilla ice cream
1 oz. hot fudge over the coffee
  ice cream
Garnish with whipped cream and
a cherry.

ICE CREAM SODAS

Apple Blossom

$1^1/_2$ oz. apple syrup
  1 soda spoon of whipped
    cream or ice cream or $1^1/_2$
    oz. coffee cream
Carbonated water $^3/_4$ full
  2 #24 dippers vanilla ice
    cream
Carbonated water to fill if
    needed
Garnish with a spoon of whipped
cream and a strip of fresh apple.

California

$^3/_4$ oz. pineapple syrup
$^3/_4$ oz. orange syrup
  1 soda spoon ice cream or
    whipped cream or $1^1/_2$ oz.
    coffee cream
Carbonated water $^3/_4$ full
  1 #24 dipper orange sherbet
  1 #24 dipper vanilla ice cream
Carbonated water to fill if
    needed
Garnish with whipped cream and
half slice of fresh orange.

Cherry Blossom

$1^1/_2$ oz. cherry syrup
  1 soda spoon of ice cream or
    whipped cream or $1^1/_2$ oz.
    coffee cream
Carbonated water $^3/_4$ full
  2 #24 dippers vanilla or
    cherry ice cream
Small amount of crushed
    cherries to side of glass
Carbonated water to fill
Garnish with whipped cream.

Frosted Root Beer or Black Cow

$1^1/_2$ oz. root beer syrup
  1 soda spoon ice cream or
    whipped cream or $1^1/_2$ oz.
    coffee cream
Carbonated water $^3/_4$ full
  2 #24 dippers vanilla ice
    cream
Carbonated water to fill if
    needed
Garnish with whipped cream.

Mocha

$^3/_4$ oz. coffee syrup
$^3/_4$ oz. chocolate syrup
  1 soda spoon whipped
    cream or ice cream or $1^1/_2$
    oz. coffee cream
Carbonated water $^3/_4$ full
  2 #24 dippers chocolate or
    coffee ice cream
Carbonated water to fill
Garnish with whipped cream

Chocolate Malted

$1^1/_2$ oz. chocolate syrup
$^1/_2$ soda spoon malted milk
    powder
  1 spoon whipped cream or
    ice cream or $1^1/_2$ oz. coffee
    cream
Carbonated water $^3/_4$ full
  2 #24 dippers of either
    vanilla or chocolate ice
    cream
Carbonated water to fill
Garnish with whipped cream.

Orange-Pineapple

$1^1/_2$ oz. of orange syrup
  1 soda spoon ice cream or
    whipped cream or $1^1/_2$ oz.
    coffee cream
Carbonated water $^3/_4$ full
Pineapple or orange-pineapple
  ice cream
Carbonated water to fill if
  needed
Garnish with whipped cream.

Strawberry Frosted

$1^1/_2$ oz. strawberry syrup (or
  crushed strawberries)
  1 soda spoon ice cream or
    whipped cream or $1^1/_2$ oz.
    coffee cream
Carbonated water $^3/_4$ full
  1 #24 dipper strawberry fruit
  ice or sherbet
  1 #24 dipper strawberry ice
  cream (or vanilla ice
  cream)
Carbonated water to fill if
  needed
Garnish with whipped cream.

MILK DRINKS

Black Cow or Root Beer

  6 oz. cold pasteurized milk
  2 #24 dippers vanilla ice
    cream
$1^1/_2$ oz. root beer syrup
Blend thoroughly on mixer
Serve in tall thin glass, with
cookies at side.

Cherry

  6 oz. cold pasteurized milk
  2 #24 dippers vanilla ice
    cream
$1^1/_2$ oz. cherry syrup
Blend well on mixer
Serve in a thin shell glass, with
mixing cup on side for overpour.

Chocolate Milk Shake

  2 tsp. cocoa or chocolate syrup
$^3/_4$ cup milk
Scant tsp. strong coffee
Mix, beat well and chill
Serve in glass and top with
whipped cream and a dash of nutmeg or cinnamon. Must be ice
cold.

Lemo-Lac

This very refreshing and nutritious drink is made by adding
sugar and lemon juice to buttermilk or cultured buttermilk.
Slightly more sugar and lemon
juice are necessary than in making
ordinary lemonade and the mixture should be well iced. It is a
fine drink for hungry, thirsty folk
on a hot day. Try it with your
lunch.

Milk Julep

1 egg
1 tbsp. sugar
Salt (pinch)
1 cup milk
$1/_2$ tsp. vanilla
1 small scoop ice cream

Beat the egg until light. Add the sugar; beat the mixture, and add milk, flavoring and salt. Mix or shake well, and chill. When ready to serve, beat or shake until foamy and add small scoop desired flavor ice cream.

Many variations in flavor may be made by adding chocolate syrup, sprays of mint, cinnamon or a teaspoon of caramel syrup in place of the vanilla.

Milk Scotch High Ball

6 oz. cold pasteurized milk
2 #24 dippers vanilla ice cream
$1^1/_2$ oz. butterscotch syrup

Place on mixer and mix thoroughly. Add just enough fine stream carbonated water to partially carbonate the entire drink. Serve in thin glass with two scotch wafers.

Strawberry

$1^1/_2$ oz. strawberry syrup
2 #24 dippers of strawberry or vanilla ice cream
6 oz. of cold pasteurized milk

Blend thoroughly and rapidly and pour into serving glasses.

Mocha Milk Shake Float

3 oz. freshly made double strength coffee
3 oz. freshly made cocoa (made with milk)
2 scoops cracked ice
2 #24 dippers coffee or chocolate ice cream

Blend on mixer. Pour into a thin shell glass and top with 1 #24 dipper of chocolate ice cream.

Pineapple Buttermilk

6 oz. cold cultured buttermilk
2 #24 dippers vanilla ice cream
2 oz. pineapple juice (canned)

Place on mixer until well blended. Serve in tall glass, with mixing cup at side.

Spiced Milk

2 cups sweet milk
2 tsp. sugar
$1/_8$ tsp. nutmeg
$1/_8$ tsp. cloves
$1/_8$ tsp. cinnamon
Few grains salt

Heat milk in double boiler. Blend sugar, spices and salt. Add to the hot milk. Beat until spices blend and then chill and serve. Add small scoop of vanilla ice cream to each serving.

Grape

$1^1/_2$ oz. grape syrup
2 #24 dippers of vanilla ice cream
6 oz. of cold pasteurized milk

Blend thoroughly and rapidly and pour into serving glasses.

TOPPINGS

Whipped cream may serve as topping. Fruit toppings may include strawberry, peach, pineapple blueberry, raspberry and cherry. Four parts of sliced or crushed fruit plus one part of sugar is the usual fruit topping preparation. Other topping recipes are included below.

Bittersweet Chocolate Topping

3 lbs. glucose

1 lb. cocoa

1 gal. condensed milk

Cook to good boil and when off fire add 5 lbs. marshmallow or nougat cream.

Ritzy Rich Chocolate Topping

$1^1/_4$ lbs. mild bittersweet cocoa

5 pints milk

6 lbs. sugar

$^1/_4$ tsp. salt

Mix cocoa and sugar together dry. Put salt in milk and bring to boiling point. Gradually work in the cocoa-sugar mixture. Bring to boiling point, stirring constantly and boil about two minutes. Turn off heat, strain, put in covered container and cool rapidly.

Swiss Chocolate Topping

2 lbs. XXXX confectioner's sugar (powdered sugar)

6 oz. Van Houten or Rona cocoa

1 pint coffee cream

Roll the powdered sugar and cocoa on a flat surface, preferably a cutting board covered with wax paper, until all the lumps in the sugar have disappeared. Add to this 1 pint regular coffee cream. Whip with egg whipper until perfectly smooth. Add $^1/_2$ teaspoon vanilla extract and whip again.

Orange-Pineapple Topping

Blend equal portions orange marmalade and simple syrup. Add 1 part prepared orange marmalade to 2 parts crushed pineapple topping or canned crushed pineapple.

Fudge Mallow

Fudge mallow is made by blending together two portions of chocolate fudge topping to one portion marshmallow creme. Place in the fudge warmer and serve hot.

Maple Mallow

To 1 qt. of marshmallow creme, add $^1/_4$ oz. good quality maple extract; whip the flavor thoroughly into the marshmallow.

Raspberry Mallow

1 pt. crushed black raspberries

1 qt. marshmallow creme

Beat until well blended, stir well before use.

SYRUPS

Simple Syrup (30° Baumé)

5.8 lbs. sugar
75 oz. (4.7 lbs.) water
Heat to dissolve. Do not boil.
Makes 1 gal. syrup.

Simple Syrup—Practical Recipe for 10 Gallons

65 lbs. sugar
35 lbs. water
Dilute with water to Baumé degree desired.

Recipe for 32° Baumé Syrup

6.25 lbs. sugar
4.3 lbs. water

Almond Syrup

Into a gallon of simple syrup put 2 ounces of almond extract.

Bittersweet Chocolate Syrup

1¼ lbs. cocoa
2 qts. water
5 lbs. sugar
½ tsp. salt
Mix cocoa and sugar together dry. Put salt in water and bring to boiling point. Add cocoa-sugar mixture and again bring to boiling point. Turn off heat, whip smooth, strain, pour into covered container and chill rapidly.

Chocolate Syrup (heavy)

2 lbs. high quality cocoa
12 lbs. sugar
½ gal. milk
½ gal. water
1 level teaspoon salt

Mix cocoa and sugar together dry. Put salt in water, add the milk, and bring to boiling point. Gradually work in the cocoa-sugar mixture and bring back to boiling point, stirring constantly. Turn off the heat, whip smooth, add 1 ounce vanilla extract, strain, put in covered container and cool rapidly.

Coffee Syrup

5 qts. water
1½ lbs. coffee
Pinch of salt
10 lbs. sugar (white and brown, half and half)
Have coffee ground fine. Place coffee in a drip funnel. Bring water to a boil—pour over coffee and let seep through. Add sugar and salt while coffee extract is warm. Will finish about 7 qts.

Lemon Syrup

1 oz. lemon extract
2½ oz. citric acid solution (50%)
¼ oz. yellow color, liquid
1 gal. simple syrup 32°

Orange Syrup

1 oz. orange extract
2 oz. citric acid solution (50%)
¼ oz. orange color, liquid
1 gal. simple syrup 32°

Pineapple Syrup

3 oz. pineapple extract
2 oz. citric acid solution
   (50%)
$1/4$ oz. yellow color, liquid
1 gal. simple syrup 32°

Raspberry Syrup

3 oz. raspberry extract
2 oz. citric acid solution
   (50%)
$1/2$ oz. red color, liquid
1 gal. simple syrup 32°

Root Beer Syrup (Creamy)

4 oz. No. 9 or No. 11 root beer
   flavor
$1/4$ oz. citric acid solution
   (50%)
1 gal. simple syrup 32°

CHAPTER 24

Reference Material

WEIGHTS, MEASURES AND OTHER TABLES, LEGAL STANDARDS AND PLANT INSPECTION FORM

TABLE 61

HOW TO MAKE SUGAR SOLUTIONS AND DETERMINE THEIR CONCENTRATION BY USE OF THE BAUMÉ AND BRIX HYDROMETERS[1]

Degrees Baumé[2] M-145 68°F.	Degrees Brix 68°F.	Weight per gallon in air 68°F.	Sugar per gallon	Water per gallon
		lbs.	lbs.	lbs.
30.0	55.2	10.50	5.80	4.70
30.5	56.2	10.54	5.92	4.62
31.0	57.1	10.59	6.05	4.54
31.5	58.1	10.64	6.18	4.46
32.0	59.1	10.68	6.31	4.37
32.5	60.0	10.73	6.44	4.29
33.0	61.0	10.78	6.58	4.20
33.5	62.0	10.83	6.71	4.12
34.0	63.0	10.88	6.85	4.03
34.5	63.9	10.92	6.98	3.94
35.0	64.9	10.97	7.12	3.85
35.5	65.9	11.02	7.26	3.76
36.0	66.9	11.07	7.41	3.66
36.5	67.9	11.13	7.56	3.57
37.0	68.9	11.18	7.70	3.48
37.5	69.9	11.23	7.85	3.38
38.0	70.9	11.28	8.00	3.28
38.5	71.9	11.33	8.15	3.18
39.0	72.9	11.39	8.30	3.09
39.5	73.9	11.44	8.45	2.99
40.0	74.9	11.49	8.61	2.88

[1] This table is based on information given in U.S. Bureau of Standards Circular No. 375, Table I.
[2] Baumé degree equals 145 minus 145 over Sp. Gr. Specific Gravity equals 145 over 145 minus Baumé reading.

TABLE 62

FOUNTAIN SYRUP MANUFACTURE—BASED ON SIZE OF BATCH WANTED

Baumé	1 Gallon Batch			10 Gallon Batch			
	Sugar		Water	Sugar		Water	
deg.	lbs.	oz.	oz.	lbs.	oz.	gals.	oz.
30	5	13	72	58	..	5	80
31	6	..	69	60	8	5	48
32	6	5	67	63	8	5	32
33	6	9$^1/_2$	64	66	..	5	..
34	6	14	69	69	..	4	96

How to Use Table 61

EXAMPLE I. Required to make 50 gallons of 30° Baumé sugar syrup.

Formula: Read directly from the table the Baumé degree and the pounds of sugar and pounds of water needed to make 1 gallon of that degree syrup. Note also the weight per gallon of syrup. Multiply each of these amounts by the number of gallons to be made.

Solution (for 30° Baumé):

5.80 × 50 = 290 lbs. sugar needed
4.70 × 50 = 235 lbs. water needed
10.50 × 50 = 525 total weight in pounds of 50 gallons 30° Baumé syrup.

EXAMPLE II. To find the pounds of water required to dilute 1 gallon of 34° Baumé syrup to 30° Baumé syrup.

Formula:

$$\frac{(\text{lbs. water per gal. dil. syrup}) \times (\text{lbs. sugar per gal. original syrup})}{\text{lbs. sugar per gal. dil. syrup}}$$
$$- (\text{lbs. water per gal. original syrup}) = \text{lbs. water required.}$$

Solution: From the table substitute figures in the formula thus:

$$\frac{4.70 \times 6.85}{5.80} - 4.03 = 1.52 \text{ lbs. water required to dilute 1 gallon 34°}$$
Baumé syrup to 30° Baumé.

For any larger quantity multiply 1.52 by the number of gallons to be diluted.

EXAMPLE III. To find the amount of sugar required to thicken 1 gallon of 30° Baumé syrup to 34° Baumé.

Formula:

$$\frac{(\text{lbs. sugar per gal. thickened syrup}) \times (\text{lbs. water per gal. original syrup})}{\text{lbs. water per gal. thickened syrup}}$$
$$- (\text{lbs. sugar per gal. original syrup}) = \text{lbs. sugar to be added}$$

Solution: From table substitute figures in the formula thus:

$$\frac{6.85 \times 4.70}{4.03} - 5.80 = 2.19 \text{ lbs. sugar to be added to 1 gal. 30° Baumé}$$
syrup to thicken it to 34° Baumé.

For any larger quantity multiply 2.19 lbs. by the number of gal. to be thickened.

EXAMPLE IV. Find Baumé of syrup wanted in extreme left-hand column. Read across to column beneath Baumé of syrup to be diluted. The

TABLE 63

FOUNTAIN SYRUP MANUFACTURE—BASED ON THE USE OF 100 POUNDS OF SUGAR AT 77°F.

Baumé Wanted	Amount Water to Add		Amount Syrup Made	
deg.	gals.	oz.	gals.	oz.
34	6	119	14	61
33	7	68	15	8
32	8	23	15	84
31	8	111	16	47
30	9	74	17	10

figure given is the amount of water, in fluid ounces, to be added to one gallon of syrup. Example IV refers to Table 64.

WEIGHT, MEASURE AND FOOD SOLIDS IN VARIOUS ICE CREAMS

All foods contain water, and everything not water is called a "solid."

In producing ice cream having certain characteristics, as for example, weighing so much per gallon or quart, or having certain volume per unit of weight, or certain food solids per gallon, and having at all times 12% fat, the relationships in Tables 65 and 66 will be helpful.

A mix of 31 to 48% total solids, having the weights per gallon as shown, then made to take on 100% overrun, or to have 1.6 lbs. of food solids per gallon, or to weigh 4.25 lbs. per finished gallon, will give the figures shown in Table 66.

VISCOGEN—PREPARATION AND USE

The method of preparing Viscogen as given in Bulletin 54 of the Wisconsin Experiment Station[1] is as follows:

Two and one-half parts by weight of a good quality cane sugar (granulated) are dissolved in five parts of water. One part of quick lime is gradually slacked in three parts of water. This milk of lime should be poured through a wire strainer to remove coarse, undissolved particles, and then this solution is added to the sugar solution.

The mixture should be agitated at frequent intervals for two or three hours, then should be allowed to settle until the clear supernatant fluid (Viscogen) can be siphoned off.

METHOD OF USING VISCOGEN

Both raw and pasteurized cream contain small amounts of lactic acid. In using viscogen great care must be exercised not to add too much because even a slight excess of it will give the cream a bitter and soapy

[1] Babcock and Russell (1896).

TABLE 64

FOUNTAIN SYRUP DILUTION—BASED ON THE USE OF ONE GALLON OF SYRUP

Baumé of Syrup Wanted	Baumé, degrees, of Syrup to Be Diluted				
	30	31	32	33	34
deg.					
30	..	6	$11^1/_2$	$17^1/_2$	$23^1/_2$
31	..	..	6	$11^1/_2$	17
32	..	..	..	$5^1/_2$	11
33	..	..	..	..	$5^1/_2$

TABLE 65

WEIGHT PER GALLON OF FINISHED ICE CREAM, WITH VARIOUS WEIGHTS PER GALLON OF MIX, AND VARIOUS PERCENTAGES OF OVERRUN

Mix per Gallon	Percentage of Overrun								
	50	60	70	75	80	85	90	95	100
lbs.	lbs.	lbs.	lbs.	lbs.	lbs.	lbs.	lbs.	lbs.	lbs.
8.75	5.80	5.47	5.15	5.00	4.86	4.73	4.60	4.48	4.38
9.00	6.00	5.63	5.29	5.14	5.00	4.86	4.74	4.63	4.50
9.25	6.17	5.78	5.44	5.29	5.14	5.00	4.85	4.74	4.62
9.50	6.33	5.94	5.59	5.43	5.28	5.14	5.00	4.97	4.75
9.75	6.50	6.09	5.74	5.57	5.42	5.27	5.13	5.00	4.87

Mix per Gallon	Percentage of Overrun							
	105	110	115	120	125	130	135	140
lbs.	lbs.	lbs.	lbs.	lbs.	lbs.	lbs.	lbs.	lbs.
8.75	4.27	4.17	4.07	3.98	3.88	3.80	3.72	3.65
9.00	4.39	4.29	4.19	4.09	4.00	3.91	3.38	3.75
9.25	4.51	4.40	4.30	4.20	4.11	4.02	3.93	3.85
9.50	4.63	4.52	4.41	4.32	4.22	4.13	4.04	3.96
9.75	4.76	4.64	4.53	4.43	4.33	4.24	4.15	4.06

TABLE 66

RELATIONS OF MIX FACTORS

The Mix			When Yield Is 100%		When Food Solids per Gal. Is 1.6 Lbs.		When Weight per Gal. Is 4.25 Lbs.	
Total Solids	Wt. per Gallon	Total Solids per Gallon	Wt. Frozen	Food Solids	Yield	Wt. Frozen	Yield	Food Solids per Gallon
per cent	lbs.	lbs.	lbs.	lbs.	per cent	lbs.	per cent	lbs.
21	8.92	2.77	4.49	1.39	73.1	5.20	109.8	1.32
31	8.95	2.95	4.49	1.62	84.4	4.85	110.5	1.40
36	8.98	3.23	4.49	1.71	102.0	4.45	110.0	1.53
38	9.00	3.42	4.50	1.85	114.0	4.21	111.8	1.62
40	9.03	3.61	4.52	1.88	126.0	4.01	112.6	1.70
42	9.07	3.81	4.53	1.90	138.1	3.81	113.4	1.79
46	9.14	4.20	4.57	2.10	162.5	3.48	115.0	1.96
48	9.16	4.40	4.58	2.20	175.0	3.33	115.4	2.04

TABLE 67

COMPOSITION, RELATIONS AND DENSITIES OF MILKS AND CREAMS

Fat	Solids-not fat	Total Solids	Ratio Fat to Solids-not-fat	Fat, Per Cent of Solids	Specific Gravity at 68°F.	Lbs. per Gallon	Lbs. per Quart
per cent	per cent	per cent					
3.0	8.33	11.33	1:2.77	25.20	1.034	8.61	2.15
3.1	8.40	11.50	1:2.71	26.95			
3.2	8.46	11.66	1:2.64	27.47			
3.3	8.52	11.82	1:2.58	27.93			
3.4	8.55	11.95	1:2.52	28.41			
3.5	8.60	12.10	1:2.46	28.90	1.033	8.60	2.15
3.6	8.65	12.25	1:2.40	29.40			
3.7	8.69	12.39	1:2.35	29.85			
3.8	8.72	12.52	1:2.30	30.30			
3.9	8.76	12.66	1:2.25	30.77			
4.0	8.79	12.79	1:2.20	31.25	1.032	8.59	2.15
4.1	8.82	12.92	1:2.15	31.74			
4.2	8.86	13.06	1:2.11	32.15			
4.3	8.89	13.19	1:2.07	32.57			
4.4	8.92	13.32	1:2.03	33.00			
4.5	8.95	13.45	1:1.99	33.44	1.032	8.58	2.14
4.6	8.98	13.58	1:1.95	33.90			
4.7	9.01	13.71	1:1.92	34.25			
4.8	9.04	13.84	1:1.88	34.72			
4.9	9.07	13.97	1:1.85	35.09			
5.0	9.10	14.10	1:1.82	35.46	1.031	8.58	2.14
18.0	7.31	25.31	1:0.41	71.11	1.015	8.48	2.12
20.0	7.13	27.13	1:0.36	73.71	1.013	8.43	2.11
22.0	6.95	28.95	1:0.31	75.30	1.011	8.42	2.11
25.0	6.68	31.68	1:0.27	78.91	1.008	8.37	2.10
30.0	6.24	36.24	1:0.21	82.78	1.004	8.36	2.09
35.0	5.79	40.79	1:0.16	85.81	1.000	8.32	2.08
40.0	5.35	45.35	1:0.13	88.20	0.995	8.28	2.07
45.0	4.90	49.90	1:0.09	90.11	0.985	8.22	2.05

TABLE 68

RELATION OF BAUMÉ TO TOTAL SOLIDS IN SWEETENED CONDENSED SKIM MILK
(Assuming a sucrose-in-water ratio of approximately 62%)

Baumé at 120°F.	Sucrose	Milk Solids not-fat	Total Solids
	per cent	per cent	per cent
37.4	45.63	27	72.63
37.6	45.00	28	73.00
37.8	44.38	29	73.38
38.0	43.75	30	73.75
38.2	43.13	31	74.13
38.4	42.50	32	74.50

Note: While the Baumé reading for total solids is approximately right, too much value should not be given this test for there may be considerable variation due to varying proportions of serum solids and sucrose of different types, and the amount of fat content, etc.

flavor. The safest method of procedure is to determine the amount of viscogen necessary to neutralize the acid in a definite amount of cream and from this determine the amount necessary for the whole batch to be treated. The cream must not be completely neutralized, so one-half to two-thirds of the amount of viscogen necessary for complete neutralization will be sufficient to restore the viscosity to the cream.

Babcock and Russell suggest the following method for determining the amount of viscogen to add: By means of a graduated pipette or burette find the number of cubic centimeters of viscogen needed to neutralize the acid in a pound of cream. Multiply the number of cubic centimeters of viscogen used for one pound of cream by the weight of the cream to be treated. Then find two-thirds of that figure. This will be the number of cubic centimeters of viscogen to add.

Example: If it requires 4 ml. of viscogen to neutralize 1 pound of cream, and there are 100 pounds of cream to be treated, then 100×4 ml. = 400 ml. of viscogen to neutralize 100 pounds of cream. But the cream should not be completely neutralized; consequently, the amount of viscogen to add to 100 pounds of cream to restore the viscosity will be two-thirds of 400 ml. or 267 ml.

Larsen and White suggest the use of a smaller quantity of cream for titration and make the necessary calculations by the following method.

TABLE 69

SODIUM CHLORIDE (SALT) SOLUTION

Degrees Baumé at 60°F.	Specific Gravity at 39°F.	Degrees Salometer at 60°F.	Salt per Gallon of Solution	Salt per Cubic Foot	Salt by Weight	Freezing Point	Specific Heat[1]	Weight per Gallon at 39°F.
			lbs.	lbs.	per cent	°F.		lbs.
1	1.007	4	0.084	0.628	1	31.8	0.992	8.40
2	1.015	8	0.169	1.264	2	29.3	0.984	8.46
3	1.023	12	0.256	1.914	3	27.8	0.976	8.53
4	1.030	16	0.344	3.573	4	26.6	0.968	8.59
5	1.037	20	0.433	3.238	5	25.2	0.960	8.65
6	1.045	24	0.523	3.912	6	23.9	0.946	8.72
7	1.053	28	0.617	4.615	7	22.5	0.932	8.78
8	1.061	32	0.708	5.295	8	21.2	0.919	8.85
9	1.068	36	0.802	5.998	9	19.9	0.905	8.91
10	1.076	40	0.897	6.709	10	18.7	0.892	8.97
12	1.091	48	1.092	8.168	12	16.0	0.874	9.10
15	1.115	60	1.389	10.389	15	12.2	0.855	9.26
20	1.155	80	1.928	14.421	20	6.1	0.829	9.64
24	1.187	96	2.376	17.772	24	1.2	0.795	9.90
25	1.196	100	2.488	18.610	25	+0.5	0.783	9.97
26	1.204	104	2.610	19.522	26	−1.1	0.771	10.04

[1] Specific Heat: The ratio between the amount of heat required to raise a given weight of substance to a given temperature and the amount of heat required to raise the same amount of water to the same temperature.

Assuming that it requires 0.6 ml. of viscogen to neutralize 25 ml. of cream, the amount of viscogen needed for say 800 pounds of cream would be 35:0.6::800:x or 13.7 pounds of viscogen. Half this amount is sufficient to restore the viscosity of the cream; therefore,

$$\frac{0.6 \times 800}{35 \times 2} = 6.8 \text{ lbs. of viscogen}$$

Caution. In many states the laws prohibit the addition of any substance to milk or cream, either for the purpose of neutralizing the acidity or for restoring the viscosity, unless the product is so labeled.

TABLE 70

THE FREEZING POINT RELATIONSHIPS OF CALCIUM CHLORIDE BRINE

Calcium Chloride Anhydrous	Calcium Chloride Hydrous $CaCl-6H_2O$	Specific Gravity 18/4 C	Weight per Gallon	Degrees Baumé	Degrees Salometer	Freezing Point
per cent	per cent		lbs.			°F.
1	1.98	1.0070	8.41	1.0	4	31.6
2	3.96	1.0154	8.45	2.2	8	31.3
3	5.94	1.0239	8.54	3.4	12	30.6
4	7.92	1.0319	8.61	4.5	16	29.8
5	9.90	1.0409	8.67	5.7	22	28.9
6	11.88	1.0495	8.75	6.8	26	27.9
7	13.86	1.0582	8.82	8.0	32	26.8
8	15.84	1.0660	8.89	9.0	36	25.5
9	17.82	1.0757	8.96	10.2	40	24.3
10	19.80	1.0847	9.04	11.3	44	22.8
11	21.78	1.0937	9.12	12.4	48	21.6
12	23.76	1.1029	9.19	13.5	52	20.1
13	25.74	1.1121	9.28	14.6	58	18.3
14	27.72	1.1214	9.35	15.7	62	16.7
15	29.70	1.1307	9.42	16.8	68	14.7
16	31.68	1.1402	9.50	17.8	72	12.9
17	33.66	1.1497	9.58	18.9	76	10.8
18	35.64	1.1594	9.67	19.9	80	8.4
19	37.62	1.1692	9.75	21.0	84	5.5
20	39.60	1.1791	9.83	22.0	88	2.7
21	41.58	1.1890	9.91	23.1	92	−0.6
22	43.56	1.1990	10.00	24.1	96	−4.4
23	45.54	1.2090	10.08	25.1	100	−8.3
24	47.52	1.2192	10.16	26.0	104	−13.2
25	49.50	1.2294	10.24	27.1	108	−18.8
26	51.48	1.2398	10.34	28.1	112	−25.1
27	53.46	1.2503	10.42	29.0	116	−32.8
28	55.44	1.2610	10.51	30.0	120	−42.2
29	57.42	1.2718	10.60	31.0	124	−54.4
29.8	58.80	1.2804	10.67	31.8	128	−67.0

TABLE 71

APPROXIMATE MILK EQUIVALENTS OF DAIRY PRODUCTS[1]

Product	Milk Required, Lbs., to Make 1 Lb. of Product
Butter	22.8
Cheese	10.0
Condensed Milk—Whole	2.3
Evaporated Milk—Whole	2.4
Powdered Milk	7.6
Powdered Cream	19.0
Ice Cream—per gal.[2]	15.0
Ice Cream—per gal.[3] (eliminating fat from butter and concentrated milk)	12.0
Cottage Cheese	6.25 (skim milk)
Non-Fat Dry Milk Solids	11.0 (skim milk)

[1] From Dept. Agr. and Milk Industry Foundation (1960).
[2] The milk equivalent of ice cream per gallon is 15 lbs.
[3] Plant reports indicate that 81.24 per cent of the butterfat in ice cream is from milk and cream. Thus the milk equivalent of the milk and cream in ice cream is about 12 lbs.

FEDERAL STANDARDS FOR FROZEN DESSERTS

"Frozen Desserts," Definitions and Standards of Identity under the Federal Food, Drug, and Cosmetic Act, Part 20, Title 21, Code of Federal Regulations, as issued by U.S. Department of Health, Education, and Welfare, Food and Drug Administration, and Reprinted from Federal Register of July 27, 1960 (volume 25, number 145).

The reader's attention is also called to Parts I and II (25 pages) which are omitted in this printing.

This publication is an unofficial reprint of the definitions and standards of identity for frozen desserts promulgated under the Federal Food, Drug, and Cosmetic Act. This publication is being issued in loose-leaf form, and those who wish to receive amendments to these standards should request that their name be added to a special mailing list (FDT-7) for future reprints. Such request should be directed to the Editorial Branch, Division of Public Information, Food and Drug Administration, Washington 25, D.C.

The Act requires the Secretary of Health, Education, and Welfare to promulgate reasonable definitions and standards for food to promote honesty and fair dealing in the interest of consumers. After a standard goes into effect, it constitutes the official specification for that food for the purposes of enforcement of the Act. To bear the name of the standardized food, a product may contain only those ingredients and components listed in the standard, in the amount specified. When optional ingredients are permitted, the standard designates those that must be named on the label. The common or usual name of standardized foods must appear on the label, but the Act does not compel label declaration of required ingredients. In the case of unstandardized foods, the labels must name the ingredients.

Section 10.0(c) of the general regulations relating to definitions and standards for food states: "No provision of any regulation prescribing a definition and standard of identity or standard of quality or fill of container under section 401 of the Act shall be construed as affecting the application of any provision of the

Act or regulations thereunder." For example, all regulations under Section 401 contemplate that the food and all articles used as components or ingredients thereof shall be clean, sound and fit for food; a provision in such regulations for the use of coloring or flavoring does not authorize such use under circumstances or in a manner whereby damage or inferiority is concealed or whereby the food is made to appear better or of greater value than it is.

Ice Cream, Ice Milk, Frozen Custard, Sherbet, Water Ices, and Related Foods; Order Establishing Standards of Identity

In the matter of fixing and establishing definitions and standards of identity for ice cream, frozen custard, ice milk, sherbet, water ices, and related foods:

After due notices published in the Federal Register, public hearings were held in the above-entitled matter in 1942, 1951, and 1952. Based upon evidence received at these hearings, the Commissioner of Food and Drugs, under authority delegated to him by the Secretary of Health, Education, and Welfare, published on March 26, 1958 (23 F.R. 1991) proposed findings of fact, conclusions, and proposed identity standards for these foods. After consideration of the exceptions and written arguments received, some of which were adopted

TABLE 72

WEIGHTS AND MEASURES

Avoirdupois Weight

1 grain or minim	= smallest unit	16 ounces	= 1 pound = 7,000 grains
27.34375 grains	= 1 drachm (dram)	2,000 pounds	= 1 ton
16 drams	= 1 ounce	2,240 pounds	= 1 long ton

Apothecaries' Weight

20 grains or minims	= 1 scruple	8 drams	= 1 ounce
3 scruples	= 1 dram	12 ounces	= 1 pound = 5,760 grains

Troy Weight (Used by Jewelers)

24 grains	= 1 pennyweight	12 ounces = 1 pound
20 pwts.	= 1 ounce	

(The ounce and pound are the same as in Apothecaries' weight)

Metric (Mass) Weight

10 milligrams	= 1 centigram	10 hectograms	= 1 kilogram (1,000 gm.)
10 centigrams	= 1 decigram	10 kilograms	= 1 myriagram
10 decigrams	= 1 gram (gm.)	10 myriagrams	= 1 quintal
10 grams	= 1 decagram	10 quintals	= 1 metric ton
10 decagrams	= 1 hectogram	(1,000,000 gm. or 1 cu. meter of water or	
		1 metric ton = 2,204.6 lbs.)	

Liquid Measure (Capacity or Volume)

60 minims	= 1 dram	31^1/$_2$ gallons	= 1 barrel
8 drams	= 1 ounce	2 barrels	= 1 hogshead
16 ounces (4 gills)	= 1 pint	1 teaspoonful	= ^{1}/$_6$ oz. (1^1/$_3$ dram)
2 pints	= 1 quart	(U.S. meas. tsp.)	
4 quarts	= 1 gallon (231 cu. in.)	1 tablespoonful	= ^{1}/$_2$ oz. (3 tsp.)

1 standard measuring cup = 8 ounces or 16 tablespoonfuls

Metric Liquid Measure[1]

10 milliliters (ml.)	= 1 centiliter	10 liters	= 1 decaliter
10 centiliters	= 1 deciliter	10 decaliters	= 1 hectoliter
10 deciliters	= 1 liter (1,000 ml.)	10 hectoliters	= 1 kiloliter or stere

[1] Metric dry measure can be expressed in cubic centimeters (cc)., liters (l.), or cubic meters.

Quick Reference Table U.S. Liquid Measure

(Shows the number of smaller units of measure contained in each larger standard measure)

	Gallon	Quart	Pint	Ounce	Tbsp.	Tsp.	
Quarts	4						
Pints	8....	2					
Ounces	128....	32....	16				
Tablespoons	256....	64	32.....	2			
Teaspoons (U.S.)	768....	192....	96.....	6......	3		
Drops	61,440....15,360....7,680.....480......240.......80						

U.S. Standard Dry Measure

33.6 cubic inches = 1 pint
2 pints = 1 quart
4 quarts = 1 gallon (268.8 cu. in.)

2 gallons (8 qts.) = 1 peck
4 pecks = 1 bushel
36 bushels = 1 chaldron

U.S. Linear Measure (Length)

12 inches = 1 foot
3 feet = 1 yard

$5^1/_2$ yards = 1 rod
320 rods (5,280 ft.) = 1 mile (statute)

Metric Linear Measure

10 Angstrom units = 1 millimicron
1,000 millimicrons = 1 micron
1,000 microns = 1 millimeter
10 millimeters = 1 centimeter
10 centimeters = 1 decimeter

10 decimeters = 1 meter
10 meters = 1 decameter
10 decameters = 1 hectometer
10 hectometers = 1 kilometer (0.62137 mile)

U.S. Standard Square Measure (Area)

144 sq. in. = 1 sq. foot
9 sq. ft. = 1 sq. yard
$30^1/_4$ sq yd. = 1 sq. rod

160 sq. rd. = 1 acre
43,560 sq. ft = 1 acre
640 acres = 1 sq. mile

Weight

1 grain (Avoir.) = 0.0648 gram
1 scruple (Apoth.) = 1.296 gm.
1 ounce (Avoir.) = 28.3491 gm.
1 ounce (Troy) = 31.103 gm.
1 lb. (Avoir.) = 0.4536 kilogram
1 lb. (Troy) = 0.3729 kilogram

1 gram = 15.432 grains
1 gram = 0.772 scruple (Apoth.)
1 gram = 0.035 ounce (Avoir.)
1 gram = 0.032 ounce (Troy)
1 kilogram = 2.20462 lbs. (Avoir.)
1 kilogram = 2.679 lbs. (Troy)

Capacity

1 cu. in. = 16.4 cc.
1 U.S. minim = 0.0616 milliliter
1 U.S. dram = 3.697 ml. or cc.[2]
1 U.S. teaspoon
(1$^1/_3$ drams) = 4.9 ml. or cc.
1 U.S. fluid oz. = 29.574 ml. or cc.
1 U.S. liquid qt. = 0.946 liter
1 U.S. gallon = 3.785 liters

1 U.S. bushel = 0.3524 hectoliter
1 ml.[2] or 1 cc. = 0.061 cu. in.
1 ml. or 1 cc. = 16.228 minims
1 ml. or 1 cc. = 0.2705 dram
1 ml. or 1 cc. = 0.034 U.S. fluid oz.
1 liter = 1.05668 U.S. liquid qt.
1 liter = 0.264 U.S. gal.
1 hectoliter = 2.838 U.S. bu.

Length

1 inch = 2.5400 centimeters (cm.)
1 foot = 0.3048 meter or 30.480 cm.
1 yard = 0.9144 meter or 91.4401 cm.
1 mile = 1.609 kilometers

1 cm. = 0.3937 in.
1 cm. = 0.0328 ft.
1 meter = 1.09361 yd.
1 kilometer = 0.621 mile

Temperature

To Convert Degrees Fahrenheit to Degrees Centigrade: $°C. = (°F. - 32) \times {}^5/_9.$
To Convert Degrees Centigrade to Degrees Fahrenheit: $°F. = (°C. \times {}^9/_5) + 32.$

[2] For practical purposes 1 milliliter equals 1 cubic centimeter (cc).

TABLE 73

SEASONAL SALES EXPECTANCY TABLE

THIS TABLE WILL HELP TO DETERMINE THE EQUIPMENT NECESSARY TO SERVE PROPERLY ANY DEALER WHO WILL TELL YOU HIS TOTAL MONTHLY SALES AT ANY TIME, BASED UPON NATIONAL AVERAGES

	Per Cent of Year	Gallons Used per Month												
		200	300	400	500	600	700	800	900	1,000	1,200	1,500	2,000	3,000
January	3.42	7	10	14	17	20	24	27	30	34	40	51	68	102
February	3.80	8	12	16	20	24	27	31	36	38	48	57	76	114
March	5.33	11	16	22	27	32	37	43	48	53	64	80	107	160
April	7.17	14	21	28	35	42	50	57	63	72	84	108	143	215
May	10.90	22	33	44	55	66	76	87	99	109	132	164	218	327
June	14.50	29	44	58	73	88	102	116	132	145	176	217	290	435
July	16.58	33	50	66	83	100	116	133	150	166	200	249	332	498
August	14.27	29	43	58	72	86	100	114	129	143	172	214	285	428
September	10.04	20	30	40	50	60	70	80	90	100	120	151	201	301
October	6.17	12	18	24	30	36	43	49	54	62	72	93	123	185
November	4.19	8	12	16	20	24	29	34	36	42	48	62	84	126
December	3.63	7	11	14	18	22	26	29	33	36	44	54	73	109
Total	100.00	200	300	400	500	600	700	800	900	1,000	1,200	1,500	2,000	3,000

in whole or in part and some of which were rejected, as is shown by marginal notations on the exceptions on file in the office of the Hearing Clerk, the Commissioner, pursuant to the authority provided in the Federal Food, Drug, and Cosmetic Act (secs. 401, 701(e), 52 Stat. 1046, 1055, as amended 70 Stat. 919; 21 U.S.C. 341, 371 (e)), and delegated to him by the Secretary of Health, Education, and Welfare (25 F.R. 5611), and on the basis of reliable, probative, and substantial evidence in the whole record, orders the promulgation of the following findings of fact, conclusions, and definitions and standards of identity for the subject foods.

Conclusion. Upon consideration of the whole record and the foregoing findings of fact, it is concluded that it will promote honesty and fair dealing in the interest of consumers to fix and establish the definitions and standards of identity hereinafter set forth for the following foods: Ice cream, frozen custard, French ice cream, ice milk; fruit sherbet; and water ices.

Part III

PART 20—FROZEN DESSERTS; DEFINITIONS AND STANDARDS OF IDENTITY 1

Sec. 20.1   Ice cream; identity; label statement of optional ingredients.

Sec. 20.2   Frozen custard, French ice cream, French custard ice cream; identity; label statement of optional ingredients.

Sec. 20.3   Ice milk; identity; label statement of optional ingredients.

Sec. 20.4   Fruit sherbets; identity; label statement of optional ingredients.

Sec. 20.5   Water ices; identity; label statement of optional ingredients.

§20.1 Ice Cream; Identity; Label Statement of Optional Ingredients

(a) Ice cream is the food prepared by freezing, while stirring, a pasteurized mix composed of one or more of the optional dairy ingredients specified in paragraph (c) of this section, sweetened with one or more of the optional sweetening ingredients specified in paragraph (d) of this section. One or more of the optional characterizing ingredients specified in paragraph (b) of this section and one or more of the optional ingredients specified in paragraphs (d) (5) to (10) may be used to characterize the ice cream. One or more of the optional caseinates specified in paragraph (e) and one or more of the optional ingredients specified in paragraph (f) of this section may be used, subject to the conditions hereinafter set forth. Coloring may be added. The mix may be seasoned with salt, and may be homogenized. The kind and quantity of optional dairy ingredients used, as specified in paragraph (c) of this section, and the content of milk fat and nonfat milk solids therein, are such that the weights of milk fat and total milk solids are not less than 10 percent and 20 percent, respectively, of the weight of the finished ice cream; but in no case shall the content of milk solids not fat be less than 6 percent, except that when one or more of the bulky optional ingredients as specified in paragraph (b) (3) to (8), inclusive, of this section, are used, the weights of milk fat and total milk solids (exclusive of such fat and solids in any malted milk used) are not less than 10 per cent and 20 per cent, respectively, of the remainder obtained by subtracting the weight of such optional ingredients, modified as prescribed below, from the weight of the finished ice cream; but in no case is the weight of milk fat or total milks solids less than 8 percent and 16 percent, respectively, of the weight of the finished ice cream. The optional caseinates specified in paragraph (e) of this section are not deemed to be milk solids.

TABLE 74

FEDERAL AND STATE STANDARDS FOR THE COMPOSITION OF FROZEN DESSERTS

	Plain Ice Cream					Fruit, Nut or Chocolate Ice Cream					Frozen Custard[45]					
	Milk Fat Min., %	Total Milk Solids Min., %	Stabilizer Max., %	Weight per Gallon Min., lbs.	Food Solids per Gallon Min., lbs.	Milk Fat Min., %	Total Milk Solids Min., %	Stabilizer Max., %	Weight per Gallon Min., lbs.	Food Solids per Gallon Min., lbs.	Milk Fat Min., %	Total Milk Solids Min., %	Stabilizer Max., %	Weight per Gallon Min., lbs.	Food Solids per Gallon Min., lbs.	Egg Yolks per 90 Lbs. Min., % per dozen
Federal[44]	10.0	20.0	0.5	4.5	1.5	8.0	16.0	0.5	4.5	1.6	10.0	20.0	0.5	4.5	1.6	1.4
Alabama	10.0	18.0[01]	0.5		1.6	8.0[2]	18.0[1,2]	0.5		1.6[3,4]	10.0	18.0[1]	0.5		1.6	[6]
Alaska	10.0	18.0	0.5		1.6	8.0[2]	14.0[2]	0.6		1.6[9]	8.0		0.5		1.6	[7]
Arizona	10.0		0.6	4.5	1.6	8.0[2]	14.0[2]		4.5	1.6[8,9]	10.0	14.0		4.5		
Arkansas	10.0	18.0	0.5		1.6	8.0		0.6		1.6	10.0					
California	10.0		0.6			10.0				1.6[8,9,10]	10.0					2.5
Colorado	12.0					8.0[2]	[10]			1.6	10.0[4]	14.0[11]				5.0
Connecticut	10.0	[11]	0.5[12]	4.5	1.6	8.0[2,17]	+5.0	0.5[12]	4.5		12.0		0.5	4.25	1.6	[15,16]
Delaware	12.0	+5.0	0.5			8.0					10.0	18.0	0.5	4.5		5.0
District of Columbia	8.0					8.0[2]	14.0[2]	0.5		1.6	12.0	18.0			1.6	5.0
Florida	10.0	18.0	0.5		1.6	8.0[2,17]			4.5	1.6	8.0	18.0[13]	0.5	4.5	1.6	5.0
Georgia	10.0				1.6	10.0[2]	14.0[2]	0.5	4.5	1.6	12.0	18.0[13]	0.5	4.5	1.6	[15]
Hawaii	12.0	18.0[18]	0.5	4.5	1.6	10.0[2]	15.0[19]	0.5	4.25	1.6						
Idaho	12.0	18.0	0.5	4.5	1.6	10.0[2]	14.0[2]	0.5		1.6						
Illinois	12.0	[22]		4.25[20]		10.0[2]	14.0[2]	0.5		1.6	Classified as ice milk					
Indiana	10.0	18.0	0.5	4.25	1.6	10.0[21]	16.0[21]	0.5	4.25	1.6	10.0	18.0	0.5	4.25	1.6	
Iowa	12.0	20.0	0.6	4.5	1.6	10.0[2]	20.0[23]	0.5	4.5	1.6	12.0	20.0	0.5	4.5	1.6	5.0
Kansas	12.0	20.0[23]		4.5		10.0[23]	18.0[23]			1.6						
Kentucky	10.0	18.0	0.5			8.0[2]	16.0[2]	0.5	4.5	1.6[3,25,26]	10.0[4]	18.0[24]	0.5[24]	4.5	1.6	2.5
Louisiana	10.0		0.5	4.5	1.6	9.0[2]	[11,2]	0.5	4.5	1.6	6.0	20.0	0.5		1.6	[15]
Maine	11.0	[22]	0.5	4.5	1.6	8.0[2]	15.0[2]	0.5		1.6	12.0[27]	20.0[27]	0.512	4.5	1.6	27,15
Maryland	12.0	20.0	0.6		1.6	8.0	16.5[2]	0.5		1.6	10.0	18.5	0.5	4.5	1.6	5.0
Massachusetts	10.0	18.5				8.0[2]	[26]	0.6		1.6[4,20]	12.027	[28]	0.6	4.5	1.6	
Michigan	12.0	[28]	0.6	4.5	1.6	10.0	16.0[2]			1.6	12.0	20.0	0.5	4.5	1.6	[31]
Minnesota	10.0	20.0		4.5	1.6	8.0	[33]			1.6	8.0	16.0	0.5	4.5	1.6	[32]
Mississippi	10.0	[33]	0.5[12]	4.5	1.6	8.0[2]	16.0[2]	0.5[12]	4.5		10.0	20.0	0.512	4.25	1.6	5.0
Missouri	10.0	20.0	0.5	4.25	1.6	9.0[2]	16.0[2]	0.5	4.25	1.6	10.0	20.0	0.5	4.5	1.6	34,15
Montana	10.0	20.036	0.5	4.5	1.6	10.035	18.035	0.5	4.5		12.0	20.0	0.5	4.5		15,3 4
Nebraska	12.036			4.5		14.036	[11]	0.5	4.5			20.0	0.5	4.5		5.0
Nevada	14.0	[11]	0.5	4.5		12.02	+5.017	0.5	4.5		[37]	[11]	0.5	4.5		[38]
New Hampshire	14.0	+5.0	0.5			8.0[17]	[17]	0.5			14.0	+5.0	0.5			[15]
New Jersey	10.0	20.0	0.5			10.0[17]					10.0	18.0	0.5			5.0
New Mexico	12.0	18.0				8.0[2]	14.0[2]	0.5								[15]
New York	10.0		0.5		1.6	8.0[2]				1.6					1.6	

State							
North Carolina	10.0	³³	4.5	0.5	1.6	8.0	³³
North Dakota	12.0		4.5	0.5		10.0	14.0²
Ohio	10.0	18.0	4.25	0.5	1.6	8.0²	18.0
Oklahoma	10.0³⁰	18.0	4.5	0.5	1.6³³	8.0	18.0
Oregon	10.0	18.0³⁰	4.75	0.5	1.8	8.0¹⁷	
Pennsylvania	10.0		4.75	0.5	1.8	8.0¹⁷	
Puerto Rico	10.0	20.0	4.5		1.6	8.0²	16.0²
Rhode Island	10.0	18.0	4.25	0.5	1.6	8.0²	16.0²
South Carolina	12.0	²⁸	4.5	0.5	1.6	10.0	²⁸
South Dakota	10.0	18.0	4.5	0.5	1.6	8.0²	14.0²
Tennessee	10.0		4.5	0.5		6.0	16.0²
Texas	8.0		4.2	0.5¹²	1.6	8.0²	16.0²
Utah	12.0	20.0	4.5	0.5	1.6¹¹	8.0²	17.0²,¹¹
Vermont	10.0	20.0¹¹		0.5	1.6	8.0²	16.0²
Virginia	10.0	20.0	4.25			10.0	16.0²
Washington	10.0	20.0				10.0²³	20.0²,³,⁴¹
West Virginia	8.0	⁴¹	4.5	0.5	1.6	8.0²	⁴²
Wisconsin	13.0	⁴²	4.5	0.5	1.6	11.0	⁴³
Wyoming	10.0	⁴³	4.25	0.5	1.6	10.0	

State						
North Carolina	4.5	0.5	1.6			
North Dakota	4.5	0.5		10.0	18.0	0.5
Ohio	4.25	0.5	1.6	10.0	18.0	0.5
Oklahoma	4.5	0.5	1.6	10.0	18.0	0.5
Oregon	4.75	0.5	1.8	10.0		0.5
Pennsylvania	4.75	0.5	1.8	10.0		0.5
Puerto Rico	4.5		1.6	10.0	20.0	
Rhode Island	4.25	0.5	1.6	10.0	18.0	0.5
South Carolina	4.25	0.5	1.6	12.0	²⁸	0.5
South Dakota	4.5	0.5	1.6	8.0	14.0	0.5
Tennessee	4.5	0.5¹²	1.6	12.0	20.0	0.5¹²
Texas	4.2	0.5	1.6¹¹	10.0	20.0	0.5
Utah	4.5	0.5	1.6	10.0	20.0	0.5
Vermont	4.5	0.5		10.0	20.0	0.5
Virginia		0.5	1.6	13.0	⁴²	
Washington	4.5	0.5	1.6	10.0	³⁶	0.5
West Virginia	4.5	0.5	1.6			
Wisconsin	4.5	0.5				
Wyoming	4.25	0.5				

State				
North Carolina				
North Dakota	4.25	1.6	5.0	
Ohio	4.0	1.6	5.0	
Oklahoma		1.8	15	
Oregon	4.75		15	
Pennsylvania				
Puerto Rico	4.5	1.6	5.0	
Rhode Island	4.25	1.6	5.0	
South Carolina	4.5	1.6	2.5	
South Dakota	4.5	1.6	15,34	
Utah	4.5	1.6¹¹	15,34	
Virginia	4.5	1.6		
Wisconsin	4.5	1.6	15	
Wyoming	4.25	1.6	32	

1 Total solids minimum 33.0 per cent.
2 Must meet the standards for plain ice cream except for such reduction as is due to the added flavoring, but in no case less than the minimum shown.
3 Fruit ice cream: not less than 10.0 per cent by weight of fruit and fruit juice.
4 Nut ice cream: not less than 2.0 per cent by weight of nut meats.
5 Total solids minimum 30.0 per cent.
6 Dry egg yolk or its equivalent: not less than 1.0 per cent.
7 Egg yolks minimum 2 1/2 dozen per 46.0 pounds.
8 Fruit ice cream: not less than 3.0 per cent fruit and fruit juices.
9 Chocolate ice cream: not less than 1.0 per cent chocolate or cocoa.
10 Nut ice cream: not less than 1.0 per cent nut meats.
11 Total solids minimum 36.0 per cent.
12 Including emulsifier.
13 Total solids minimum 24.0 per cent.
14 Flavored, maximum reduction 2.0 per cent.
15 Egg yolk solids minimum 1.4 per cent.
16 When flavored, egg yolk solids minimum 1.0 per cent.
17 Chocolate ice cream must meet the standards for plain ice cream.
18 Milk solids-not-fat minimum 6.0 per cent.
19 Milk solids-not-fat minimum 5.0 per cent.
20 Not more than 100 per cent overrun.
21 Artificially flavored ice cream must meet the standards for plain ice cream.
22 Total solids minimum 35.6 per cent.
23 Before the addition of fruit, chocolate or nuts.
24 Before the addition of eggs.
25 Fruit ice cream: not less than 1.4 pounds food solids per gallon.

26 Nut ice cream: not less than 6.0 per cent by weight of nut meats.
27 When fruits, chocolate or nuts are added: milk fat minimum 8.0 per cent, total milk solids minimum 15.0 per cent, egg yolk solids minimum 1.0 per cent.
28 Total milk solids minimum 0.9 pound per gallon.
29 Fruit ice cream: not less than 5.0 per cent fruit or juice.
30 Citrus fruit flavors must contain not less than 2.0 per cent fruit juice; berry fruit flavors, not less than 6.0 per cent fruit; stone or bulky fruits, not less than 10.0 per cent fruit.
31 Egg yolk solids, minimum 1.1 per cent.
32 Not less than 5 egg yolks per gallon.
33 Total solids minimum 35.0 per cent.
34 When flavored: egg yolk solids minimum 1.12 per cent.
35 Tolerance of 0.5 per cent if not constantly below standard.
36 Fruit and nut ice cream: milk fat minimum 12.0 per cent.
37 French ice cream: milk fat minimum 14.0 per cent.
38 Egg yolk solids minimum 2.0 per cent.
39 Vanilla only: milk fat minimum 12.0 per cent, total milk solids minimum 20.0 per cent.
40 Food solids per gallon minimum 1.8 pounds.
41 Solids-not-fat minimum 10.0 per cent.
42 Solids-not-fat minimum 8.0 percent.
43 Total solids minimum 37.0 per cent.
44 Values for Federal standards derived from USDA Handbook 51, October 1959.
45 Federal Frozen Custard standards are same as for ice cream, except 1.4% min. egg yolk solids content required for plain and 1.12% for bulky flavors.

In calculating the reduction of milk fat and total milk solids from the use of bulky optional ingredients, chocolate and cocoa solids used shall be considered the bulky ingredients of paragraph (b) (3) of this section. In order to make allowance for additional sweetening ingredients needed when bulky ingredients are used, the weight of chocolate or cocoa solids may be multiplied by 1.5; the weight of fruit or nuts used may be multiplied by 1.4; and the weight of partially or wholly dried fruits or fruit juices may be multiplied by appropriate factors to obtain the original weights before drying and this weight multiplied by 1.4. The finished ice cream contains not less than 1.6 pounds of total solids to the gallon and weighs not less than 4.5 pounds to the gallon. Any artificial flavoring in any chocolate, cocoa, confectionery, or other ingredient used is an optional ingredient of the finished ice cream.

(b) The optional characterizing ingredients referred to in paragraph (a) of this section are:

(1) Ground spice, ground vanilla beans, infusion of coffee or tea, or any natural food flavoring.

(2) Any artificial food flavoring.

(3) Chocolate or cocoa, which may be added as such or as a suspension in sirup, and which may contain disodium phosphate or sodium citrate in such quantity that the finished ice cream contains not more than 0.2 percent by weight of disodium phosphate or sodium citrate. For the purposes of this section, the term "cocoa" means one or any combination of two or more of the following: Cocoa, breakfast cocoa, low-fat cocoa, and the unpulverized residual material prepared by removing part of the fat from ground cacao nibs.

(4) Mature fruit or the juice of mature fruit, either of which may be fresh, frozen, canned, concentrated, or partially or wholly dried. The fruit may be whole, shredded, or comminuted; it may be sweetened, thickened with pectin or with one or more of the ingredients named in paragraph (f) (2) of this section, subject to the restriction on the total quantity of such substances in ice cream prescribed in that paragraph, and it may be acidulated with citric or ascorbic acid. The fruit is prepared by the removal of pits, seeds, skins, and cores, where such removal is usual in preparing that kind of fruit for consumption as fresh fruit. In the case of fruit or fruit juice from which part of the water is removed, the substances contributing flavor volatilized during water removal may be condensed and reincorporated in the concentrated fruit or fruit juice. In the case of the citrus fruits the whole fruit, including the peel but excluding the seeds, may be used, and in the case of citrus juice or concentrated citrus juice, cold-pressed citrus oil may be added in an amount not exceeding that which would have been obtained if the peel from the whole fruit had been used. For the purposes of this section, the flesh of the coconut shall be considered a fruit.

(5) Nut meats, which may be roasted, cooked in an edible fat or oil, or preserved in sirup, and which may be salted.

(6) Malted milk.

(7) Confectionery. For the purposes of this section, the term "confectionery" means candy, cakes, cookies, and glacéed fruits.

(8) Properly prepared and cooked cereal.

(9) Any distilled alcoholic beverage, including liqueurs, or any wine, or mixtures of two or more of these.

(c) The optional dairy ingredients referred to in paragraph (a) of this section are: Cream, dried cream, plastic cream (sometimes known as concentrated milk fat), butter, butter oil, milk, concentrated milk, evaporated milk, sweetened condensed milk, superheated condensed milk, dried milk, skim milk, concentrated skim milk, evaporated skim milk, condensed skim milk, superheated condensed skim milk, sweetened condensed skim milk, sweetened condensed part-skim milk, nonfat dry milk, sweet cream buttermilk, condensed sweet cream buttermilk, dried sweet cream buttermilk, and skim milk that has been concentrated and from which part of the lactose has been removed by crystallization. Water may be added, or water may be evaporated from the mix. The sweet cream buttermilk and the concentrated sweet cream buttermilk or dried sweet cream buttermilk, when adjusted with water to a total solids content of 8.5 percent, has a titratable acidity of not more than 0.17 percent, calculated as lactic acid. The term "milk" as used in this section means cow's milk.

(d) The optional sweetening ingredients referred to in paragraph (a) of this section are:

(1) Sugar (sucrose) or sugar sirup.
(2) Dextrose.
(3) Invert sugar (in paste or sirup form).
(4) Corn sirup, dried corn sirup, glucose sirup, dried glucose sirup.
(5) Maple sirup, maple sugar.
(6) Honey.
(7) Brown sugar.
(8) Malt sirup, maltose sirup, malt extract.
(9) Dried malt sirup, dried maltose sirup, dried malt extract.
(10) Refiner's sirup.
(11) Molasses (other than blackstrap).
(12) Lactose.

(e) The optional caseinates referred to in paragraph (a) of this section which may be added to ice cream mix containing not less than 20 per cent total milk solids are: Casein prepared by precipitation with gums, ammonium caseinate, calcium caseinate, potassium caseinate, and sodium caseinate. Caseinates may be added in liquid or dry form, but must be free of excess alkali.

(f) Other optional ingredients referred to in paragraph (a) of this section are:

(1) liquid eggs, frozen eggs, dried eggs, egg yolks, frozen egg yolks, and dried egg yolks. Any egg ingredients used is added to the mix before it is pasteurized. The total weight of egg yolk solids in the finished ice cream from one or a combination of two or more such ingredients is less than the minimum prescribed for frozen custard by §20.2 of this chapter (1.4 percent).

(2) Agar-agar, algin (sodium alginate), calcium sulfate, gelatin, gum acacia, guar seed gum, gum karaya, locust bean gum, oat gum, gum tragacanth, Irish moss, extract of Irish moss, lecithin, psyllium seed husk, sodium carboxymethylcellulose. The total weight of the solids of any such ingredient used singly or of any combination of two or more such ingredients used (including any such ingredient and pectin added separately to the fruit ingredient) is not more than 0.5 per cent of the weight of the finished ice cream. Such ingredients may be added in admixture with dextrin.

(3) Monoglycerides or diglycerides or both from the glycerolysis of edible fats. The total weight of such ingredient is not more than 0.2 percent of the weight of the finished ice cream.

(g) (1) The name of the food is "ice cream." All statements permitted or required by this section relating to principal characterizing ingredient shall appear in written or printed words of equal size and prominence as those used for the name of the food, and shall appear on the label so as to be easily read by the consumer under customary conditions of purchase.

(2) When only natural flavoring is used as the sole principal characterizing ingredient, the label shall bear, as the characterizing ingredient statement, the common or usual name of the natural flavor; e.g., "vanilla ice cream, or vanilla-flavored ice cream."

(3) When any artificial flavoring is used as the sole principal characterizing ingredient in ice cream, the label shall bear, as the characterizing ingredient statement, "artificially flavored_____," the blank being filled in with the common or usual name of the flavor simulated; e.g., "artificially flavored vanilla."

(4) When both natural and artificial flavorings are used as the principal characterizing ingredients and the natural flavor ingredient constitutes the predominant flavor of any one of the principal flavoring ingredients, the label shall bear as the characterizing ingredient statement for that ingredient the common or usual name of the natural flavoring together with the statement "and artificial _____" or "and artificial_____flavor," the blank being filled in with the common or usual name of the flavor simulated; e.g., "vanilla and artificial vanilla flavor." Where the artificial flavoring constitutes the predominant flavor of any one of the principal flavoring ingredients, the label shall bear as the sole characterizing statement for that ingredient, "artificial_____ flavor," the blank being filled in with the common or usual name of the flavor simulated; e.g., "artificial vanilla flavor."

(5) Whenever a characterizing ingredient is used with an artificial flavor which does not simulate the principal flavor, the label shall include the statement "artificial flavor added" or "artificial_____flavor added," the blank being filled in with the common or usual name of the flavor simulated; e.g., "chocolate, artificial flavoring added," "chocolate, artificial vanilla flavor added."

§20.2 Frozen Custard, French Ice Cream, French Custard Ice Cream; Identity; Label Statement of Optional Ingredients

Frozen custard, French ice cream, French custard ice cream conforms to the definition and standard of identity, and is subject to the requirements for label statement of optional ingredients, prescribed for ice cream by §20.1, except that one or more of the optional egg ingredients permitted by §20.1(f) (1) are used in such quantity that the total weight of egg yolk solids therein is not less than 1.4 per cent of the weight of the finished frozen custard: *Provided however,* that when the ingredients named in §20.1 (b) (3) through (8), inclusive, are used the content of egg yolk solids may be reduced in proportion to the bulky ingredient or ingredients added, under the conditions prescribed by §20.1(a) for reduction in milk fat and total milk solids; but in no case is the content of egg yolk solids less than 1.12 per cent.

§20.3 Ice Milk; Identity; Label Statement of Optional Ingredients

Ice milk is the food prepared from the same ingredients and in the same manner prescribed in §20.1 for ice cream and complies with all the provisions of §20.1 (including the requirements for label statement of optional ingredients), except that:

(a) Its content of milk fat is more than 2 per cent but not more than 7 percent.

(b) Its content of total milk solids is not less than 11 per cent.

(c) Caseinates may be added when the content of total milk solids is not less than 11 percent.

(d) The provision for reduction in milk fat and total milk solids from the addition of bulky ingredients in §20.1(a) does not apply.

(e) The quantity of food solids per gallon is not less than 1.3 pounds.

(f) When any artificial coloring is used in ice milk, directly or as a component of any other ingredient, the label shall bear the statement "artificially colored," "artificial coloring added," "with added artificial color," or "_____, an artificial color added," the blank being filled in with the common or usual name of the artificial color; or in lieu thereof, in case the artificial color is a component of another ingredient, "_____artificially colored."

(g) The name of the food is "ice milk."

(h) If both artificial color and artificial flavorings are used, the label statements may be combined.

§20.4 Fruit Sherbets; Identity; Label Statement of Optional Ingredients

(a) Fruit sherbets are the foods each of which is prepared by freezing, while stirring, a mix composed of one or more of the optional characterizing fruit ingredients specified in paragraph (b) of this section and one or more of the optional dairy ingredients specified in paragraph (c) of this section, sweetened with one or more of the optional sweetening ingredients specified in paragraph (d) of this section. One or more of the optional ingredients specified in paragraph (e) of this section may be used, subject to the conditions hereinafter set forth. The mix of combined dairy ingredients, with or without other ingredients, is pasteurized. The titratable acidity of the finished fruit sherbet, calculated as lactic acid, is not less than 0.35 percent. Coloring may be added. The mix with or without added water may be seasoned with salt, and may be homogenized. The optional dairy ingredients used and the content of milk fat and nonfat milk solids therein are such that the weight of milk fat is not less than 1 percent and not more than 2 percent, and the weight of total milk solids is not less than 2 percent and not more than 5 percent of the weight of the finished fruit sherbet. The optional caseinates specified in paragraph (e) (5) of this section are not deemed to be milk solids. The finished fruit sherbet weighs not less than 6 pounds to the gallon.

(b) The optional fruit characterizing ingredients referred to in paragraph (a) of this section are any mature fruit or the juice of any mature fruit. The fruit or fruit juice used may be fresh, frozen, canned, concentrated, or partially or wholly dried. The fruit may be thickened with pectin or other of the optional ingredients named in paragraph (e) (2) of this section, subject to the restriction on the total quantity of such substances in fruit sherbets prescribed in that paragraph. The fruit is prepared by the removal of pits, seeds, skins, and cores, where such removal is usual in preparing that kind of fruit for consumption as fresh fruit. The fruit may be screened, crushed, or otherwise comminuted. It may be acidulated with citric or ascorbic acid. In the case of concentrated fruit or fruit juices, from which part of the water is removed, substances contributing flavor volatilized during water removal may be condensed and reincorporated in the concentrated fruit or fruit juice. In the case of citrus fruits, the whole fruit, including the peel but excluding the seeds, may be used, and in the case of citrus juice or concentrated citrus juices, cold-pressed citrus oil may be added thereto in an amount not exceeding that which would have been obtained if the whole fruit had been used. The quantity of fruit ingredients used is such that, in relation to the weight of the finished sherbet, the weight of fruit or fruit juice, as the case may be (including water necessary to reconstitute partially or wholly dried fruits or fruit juices to their original moisture content), is not less than 2 per cent in the case of citrus sherbets, 6 per cent in the case of berry sherbets, and 10 per cent in the case of sherbets prepared with other fruits. For the purposes of this section, tomatoes and rhubarb are considered as kinds of fruit.

(c) The optional dairy ingredients referred to in paragraph (a) of this section are: Cream, dried cream, plastic cream (sometimes known as concentrated milk fat), butter, butter oil, milk, concentrated milk, evaporated milk, superheated condensed milk, sweetened condensed milk, dried milk, skim milk, concentrated skim milk, evaporated skim milk, condensed skim milk, superheated condensed skim milk, sweetened condensed skim milk, sweetened condensed part-skim milk, nonfat dry milk, sweet cream buttermilk, condensed sweet cream buttermilk, dried sweet cream buttermilk, skim milk that has been concentrated and from which part of the lactose has been removed after crystallization, cheese whey, concentrated cheese whey, dried cheese whey. Water may be added. The sweet cream buttermilk, concentrated sweet cream buttermilk, or dried sweet cream buttermilk, adjusted with water to a total solids content of 8.5 per cent in each case, has a titratable acidity of not more than 0.17 per cent, calculated as lactic acid. The term "milk" as used in this section means cow's milk.

(d) The optional sweetening ingredients referred to in paragraph (a) of this section are: Sugar (sucrose), dextrose, invert sugar (paste or sirup), glucose sirup, dried glucose sirup, corn sirup, dried corn sirup, malt sirup, malt extract, dried malt sirup, dried malt extract, maltose sirup, dried maltose sirup.

(e) Other optional ingredients referred to in paragraph (a) of this section are:

(1) Liquid eggs, frozen eggs, dried eggs, egg yolks, frozen yolks, dried yolks; but the weight of egg yolk solids therein is less than $1/2$ of 1 per cent of the weight of the finished fruit sherbet.

(2) Agar-agar, algin (sodium alginate), calcium sulfate, egg white, gelatin, gum acacia, guar seed gum, gum karaya, locust bean gum, oat gum, gum tragacanth, Irish moss, extract of Irish moss, lecithin, pectin, psyllium seed husk, sodium carboxymethylcellulose. The total weight of the solids of any such ingredient used singly or of any combination of two or more such ingredients used (including any such ingredient added separately to the fruit ingredient) is not more than 0.5 per cent of the weight of the finished fruit sherbet. Such ingredients may be added in admixture with dextrin.

(3) Monoglycerides or diglycerides or both from the glycerolysis of edible fats. The total weight of such ingredient is not more than 0.2 per cent of the weight of the finished fruit sherbet.

(4) Citric acid, tartaric acid, malic acid, lactic acid, ascorbic acid, or any combination of two or more of these in such quantity as seasons the finished food.

(5) Casein prepared by precipitation with gums, ammonium caseinate, calcium caseinate, potassium caseinate, sodium caseinate.

(6) Any natural food flavoring.

(7) Any artificial flavoring.

(f) The name of each such fruit sherbet is "_____sherbet," the blank being filled in with the common name of the fruit or fruits from which the fruit ingredients used are obtained. When the names of two or more fruits are included, such names shall be arranged in order of predominance, if any, by weight of the respective fruit ingredients used.

(g) (1) When the optional ingredients, artificial coloring, artificial flavoring, or natural flavoring are used in fruit sherbet they shall be named on the labels as follows:

(i) The label shall designate artificial coloring by the statement "artificially colored," "artificial coloring added," "with added artificial coloring," or "_____, an artificial color added," the blank being filled in with the name of the artificial coloring used.

(ii) The label shall designate artificial flavoring by the statement "artificially colored," "artificial coloring added," "with added artificial coloring," or "_____ ____, an artificial flavor added," the blank being filled in with name of the artificial flavoring used.

(iii) The label shall designate natural flavoring by the statement "flavoring added," "with added flavoring," or "_____flavoring added," the blank being filled in with the name of the flavoring used.

(iv) Whenever artificial flavoring is not added as such but as a component of some other ingredient, the label shall include the statement "_____ artificially flavored," the blank being filled in with the name of such other ingredient.

Label statements may be combined, as for example, "with added flavoring and artificial coloring."

(2) When cheese whey, concentrated cheese whey, or dried cheese whey is used in fruit sherbet the label shall bear the statement "_____added," or "with added_____," the blank being filled in with the appropriate name "whey," "concentrated whey," or "dried whey."

(h) Where one or more of the optional ingredients, artificial coloring, artificial flavoring, or natural flavoring are used and there appears on the label any representation as to the fruit or fruits in the sherbet, such representation shall be immediately and conspicuously accompanied by appropriate label statements as prescribed in paragraph (g) (1) of this section, showing the optional ingredients used.

(i) Wherever the name of the food appears on the label so conspicuously as to be easily seen under customary conditions of purchase the statements specified in this section, showing the optional ingredients used, shall immediately and conspiciously precede or follow such name without intervening written, printed, or graphic matter.

§ 20.5 Water Ices; Identity; Label Statement of Optional Ingredients

(a) Water ices are the foods, each of which is prepared by freezing, while stirring, a mix composed of one or more of the optional characterizing fruit ingredients specified in paragraph (b) of this section, sweetened with one or more of the optional sweetening ingredients specified in paragraph (c) of this section. One or more of the optional ingredients specified in paragraph (d) of this section may be used, subject to the conditions hereinafter set forth. The titratable acidity of the finished water ice, calculated as lactic acid, is not less than 0.35 percent. Coloring may be added. The mix, with or without added water, may be seasoned with salt, and may be homogenized. The finished water ice weighs not less than 6 pounds to the gallon.

(b) The optional fruit ingredients referred to in paragraph (a) of this section are any mature fruit or the juice of any mature fruit. The fruit or fruit juice used may be fresh, frozen, canned, concentrated, or partially or wholly dried. The fruit may be thickened with pectin or other of the optional ingredients named in paragraph (d) (1) of this section subject to the restriction on the total quantity of such substances in water ices prescribed in that paragraph. The fruit is prepared by the removal of pits, seeds, skins, and cores where such removal is usual in preparing that kind of fruit for consumption as fresh fruit. The fruit may be screened, crushed, or otherwise comminuted. It may be acidulated with citric or ascorbic acid. In the case of fruit or fruit juices from which part of the water is removed, substances contributing flavor volatilized during water removal may be condensed and reincorporated in the concentrated fruit or fruit juice. In the case of citrus fruits, the whole fruit, including the peel but excluding the seeds, may be used, and in the case of citrus juice or concentrated citrus juices, cold-pressed citrus oil may be added thereto in an amount not exceeding that which would have been obtained if the whole fruit had been used. The quantity of fruit ingredients used is such that in relation to the weight of the finished water ice, the weight of fruit or fruit juice as the case may be (including water necessary to reconstitute partially or wholly dried fruits or fruit juices to their original moisture content) is not less than 2 per cent in the case of citrus ices, 6 per cent in the case of berry ices, and 10 per cent in the case of ices prepared with other fruits.

(c) The optional sweetening ingredients referred to in paragraph (a) of this section are: Sugar (sucrose), dextrose, invert sugar (paste or sirup), glucose sirup, dried glucose sirup, corn sirup, dried corn sirup, malt sirup, malt extract, dried malt sirup, dried malt extract, maltose sirup, dried maltrose sirup.

(d) Other optional ingredients referred to in paragraph (a) of this section are:

(1) Agar-agar, algin (sodium alginate), egg white, gelatin, gum acacia, guar seed gum, gum karaya, locust bean gum, oat gum, gum tragacanth, Irish moss, extract of Irish moss, pectin, psyllium seed husk, sodium carboxymethylcellulose. The total weight of the solids of any such ingredient used singly, or of any combination of two or more such ingredients used (including any such ingredient added separately to the fruit ingredient), is not more than 0.5 per cent of the weight of the finished water ice. Such ingredients may be added in admixture with dextrin.

(2) Citric acid, tartaric acid, malic acid, lactic acid, ascorbic acid, or any combination of two or more of these in such quantity as seasons the finished food.

(3) Any natural flavoring.

(4) Any artificial flavoring.

(e) The name of each such water ice is "_____ice," the blank being filled in with the common name of the fruit or fruits from which the fruit ingredient used is obtained. When the names of two or more fruits are included, such names shall appear in the order of predominance, if any, by weight of the respective fruit ingredients used.

(f) When the optional ingredients, artificial coloring, artificial flavoring, or natural flavoring are used in water ices they shall be named on the labels as follows:

(1) The label shall designate artificial coloring by the statement "artificially colored," "artificial coloring added," "with added artificial coloring," or "_____, an artificial color added," the blank being filled in with the name of the artificial coloring used.

(2) The label shall designate artificial flavoring by the statement "artificially flavored," "artificial flavoring added," "with added artificial flavoring," or "_____, an artificial flavor added," the blank being filled in with the name of the artificial flavoring used.

(3) The label shall designate natural flavoring by the statement "flavoring added," "with added flavoring," or "_____flavoring added," the blank being filled in with the name of the flavoring used.

Label statements may be combined, as for example, "flavoring and artificial coloring added."

(g) Where one or more of the optional ingredients, artificial coloring, artificial flavoring, or natural flavoring are used and there appears on the labeling any representation as to the fruit or fruits in the ice, such representation shall be immediately and conspicuously accompanied by appropriate label statements as prescribed in paragraph (f) of this section, showing the optional ingredients used.

(h) Wherever the name of the food appears on the label so conspicuously as to be easily seen under customary conditions of purchase, the statements set out in this section, showing the optional ingredients used, shall immediately and conspicuously precede or follow such name, without intervening written, printed, or graphic matter.

FROZEN DESSERTS ORDINANCE PLANT INSPECTION FORM

The Federal Security Agency of the U.S. Public Health Service has recommended a "Frozen Desserts Ordinance and Code" which embodies the best information at present available on frozen-desserts-control legislation. It includes the following items of sanitation to be considered when inspecting a frozen desserts factory.

Provisions of the Ordinance

A brief outline of the provisions of the ordinance may be of value in this discussion.

Section 1 deals exclusively with definitions. Frozen desserts include partially frozen combinations of the usual ingredients, so as to enable the

TABLE 75

CITY, COUNTY, OR DISTRICT FROZEN DESSERT PLANT INSPECTION FORM

Name.. Location..............
Sir: An inspection of your plant has this day been made, and you are notified of the defects marked below with a cross (x). Violation of the same item on two successive inspections calls for immediate degrading or suspension of permit.

(1) *Floors.*—Smooth finish, no pools ( ), wall joints and floor surface impervious ( ), trapped drains (cold storage rooms and counter freezer plants excepted), no sewage back-flow ( ), clean and free of litter ( )...........................( )

(2) *Walls and ceilings.*—Smooth, washable, light-colored finish (hardening and storage rooms excepted), good repair ( ), clean ( ).........................( )

(3) *Doors and windows.*—In fly season outer openings with effective screens and self-closing doors, or fly-repellent fans or flaps.......................( )

(4a) *Lighting.*—10 foot-candles 30 in. above floor (for natural light in new plants see Code)...( )

(4b) *Ventilation.*—No undue condensation and odors (cold storage rooms excepted)...( )

(5) *Miscellaneous protection from contamination.*—Tanks and vats covered, ports protected ( ), no woven-wire strainers, no straining pasteurized mix except through perforated metal ( ), no drip from mezzanine or overhead pipes ( ), flies under control ( ), processes partitioned (or approved enclosures in counter freezer plants) ( ), processes partitioned (or approved enclosures in counter freezer plants) ( ), rooms of sufficient size ( ), ingredients not unloaded directly into processing rooms ( ), pasteurized product not in contact with equipment used for raw or lower grade products unless sterilized ( ), no plant operations in living quarters ( )........( )

(6) *Toilet facilities.*—Comply with plumbing code ( ), good repair ( ), clean ( ), outside ventilation ( ), no direct opening ( ), self-closing doors ( ), free of flies ( ), washing sign ( ), privies, if used, comply State standards ( )..............( )

(7) *Water supply.*—Sufficient outlets ( ), adequate ( ), safe, complies State standards ( )...( )

(8) *Hand-washing facilities.*—Adequate, convenient ( ), hot and cold water, soap, sanitary towels ( ), hands washed after toilet ( )........................( )

(9) *Sanitary piping.*—Easily cleanable size, shape, and length ( ), smooth uncorroded surfaces ( ), sanitary fittings, interior surfaces accessible for inspection ( ) ....( )

(10) *Construction and repair of containers and equipment.*—Easily cleanable, smooth non-corrodible surfaces ( ), no open seams, good repair ( ), self-draining ( ), pressure-tight seats on submerged thermometers ( ).........................( )

(11) *Disposal of wastes.*—In public sewer or as approved by State board of Health ( ), no connection or back-siphonage into water supplies ( ), trash and garbage kept in covered containers ( ).......................................( )

(12a) *Cleaning of containers and equipment.*—Multi-use containers thoroughly cleaned after each usage ( ), equipment each day ( )................................( )

(12b) *Bactericidal treatment of containers and equipment.*—Containers treated after each cleaning in steam cabinet 170°F. for 15 min., or 200°F. for 5 min., or hot-air cabinet 180°F. for 20 min., or steam jet 1 min., or immersed in standard chlorine or 170°F. water for 2 min., or automatic washers (residual count not over 1 per cc of capacity, test 11), assembled equipment treated daily immediately before run, with flow of 200°F. steam or 170°F. water at outlets for 5 min. or standard chlorine flow for 2 min. (test 12); supplementary treatment for surfaces not thus reached ( )............( )

(13) *Storage of containers.*—In clean crates or racks above floor, protected from flies, splash, dust, inverted when practicable. ....( )

(14) *Handling of containers and equipment.*—No handling of surfaces to which ingredients or products are exposed ....( )

(15) *Storage and handling of single-service containers and utensils.*—Purchased in sanitary tubes or cartons ( ), kept therein in cabinet or other clean dry place ( ), sanitary handling ( )...( )

(16a) *Specifications for pasteurization thermometers.*—All Code specifications met by all new indicating and recording thermometers, by all replacements, and by recording thermometers under repair which require renewal of tube system ( ); existing thermometers meet at least accuracy and lag specifications (tests 1, 2, 3) ( ).........( )

(16b) *Maintenance of pasteurization time and temperature.*—Entire mix, excluding fruits, etc., pasteurized, no raw products bypass around pasteurizers ( ). Requirements for manual-discharge heated holders (for others see Code):

Temperature control.—Adequate agitation throughout holding period, agitator sufficiently submerged ( ); indicating and recording thermometers on each vat throughout pasteurization ( ); recorder reads no higher than indicator (test 4) ( ); thermometer bulbs submerged ( ). ....( )

Time control.—Charts show 155°F. for 30 minutes, plus emptying time if cooling begun after outlet valve opened (also plus filling time when required) (test 6) ( ); no milk added after holding begun ( )..( )

Charts.—Used only 1 day, preserved 3 months ( ); must show date, location, daily check against indicating thermometer, amount and product represented, unusual occurrences, and operator's signature ( )...( )

(16c) *Inlet and outlet valves and connections.*—Any inlet and outlet valves used on single-vat installations must be leak-protector type, otherwise piping disconnected ( ), all multiple-vat installations have leak-protector inlets, also leak-protector outlets except where Code permits disconnecting outlet piping instead ( ), 30-minute tubular holders have leak-protector outlet or outlet piping disconnected until 30 minutes after filling begun ( ); leak-protector valves of approved design, effective in all closed positions, and installed in proper position (test 8) ( ); inlets and outlets below mix level have close-coupled valves ( ); plug-type valves have approved stops ( ); top inlets have air relief if submerged ( ). Valves kept fully closed except inlet while filling and outlet while emptying ( ); outlet valves sterilized automatically before opening if not leak protected or if mix accumulates in channel (test 9) ( ) ..... ( )

(16d) *Air heating.*—Air in vats and pockets heated to at least 5°F. above mix temperature during heating and kept at 160°F. or higher during holding, with approved device ( ), approved trap on steam line ( ), approved air thermometer (test 7), bulb at least 1 inch above mix ( )...( )

(16e) *Vat and pocket covers and cover ports.*—No drainage from top of cover into vat, open or closed ( ), ports surrounded by raised edges ( ), pipes, thermometers, etc., through cover have aprons unless joint watertight ( ); covers kept closed ( )..( )

(16f) *Preheating holders.*—Holders not used as heaters are preheated to pasteurization temperature just before run, also when empty after shutdown exceeding holding period, unless outlet has flow-diversion valve..( )

(17a) *Cooling.*—All fluid milk products cooled to 50°F. on receipt unless to be pasteurized within 2 hours ( ), pasteurizing mix cooled to 50°F. and held thereat until frozen ( ); header gap on surface coolers not less than $^1/_4$ inch or thickness of header at gap ( ), condensation and leakage from cooler supports and headers, unless completely enclosed in covers, directed away from tubes and milk trough ( ), recirculated water and refrigerant of required sanitary quality ( ), cooler covered or in separate room ( ), cooler shields tight fitting ( ), in regenerators, pasteurized-mix (or heat-transfer-medium) side automatically under greater pressure than raw mix at all times (see Code) ( )..( )

(17b) *Handling of mix.*—If not frozen where pasteurized, mix transported in sealed containers ( ), protected against contamination, no dipping, kept covered ( )..... ( )

(18) *Packaging.*—If not approved automatic equipment: no contact surfaces handled, packages adequately covered immediately after filling ( ); hands washed and disinfected before beginning moulding, wrapping, or packaging and after each interruption ( ), brick and fancy moulds handled in sanitary manner by trained persons ( )..( )

(19) *Overflow or spillage.*—Discarded...( )

(20) *Returns.*—No opened containers of mix or frozen desserts returned except for inspection...( )

(21) *Personnel, health.*—Required examinations and tests ( ), rejected persons not employed ( ), no person with infected wound or lesion ( )................................( )

(22) *Personnel, cleanliness.*—Clean outer garment, washable for inside employees ( ), hands clean ( ) ....( )

(23) *Miscellaneous.*—Vehicles: Clean ( ), covered ( ), no contaminating substances transported ( ), distributor's name shown ( ). *Surroundings:* Kept neat and clean ( )..( )

(24) *Bacterial plate count of pasteurized mix or frozen desserts.*—Log average not over 50,000 ( ), 100,000 for grade B ( ) ....( )

(25) *Ingredients.*—Clean, fresh wholesome flavor, odor, and appearance ( ), stored above floor, kept covered, properly handled and refrigerated ( ); milk products meet bacterial standards ( ), also production standards, where locally required ( ); ingredients added after mix pasteurized are of approved quality ( ) ....( )

health officer to control also similar products which are not completely frozen. Composition standards for the various types of frozen desserts have been omitted, but when such standards are issued by the Food and Drug Administration they will be included as suggested standards in later editions of the ordinance. All mix must be pasteurized by heating every particle to 155°F. and holding for at least 30 minutes in approved equipment, or by any other equally efficient process approved by the state health authority. A number of other terms are defined.

Section 2 prohibits the sale of adulterated or misbranded mix or frozen desserts. Section 3 deals with the issuing, suspension and revocation of permits, and is broad enough to include retailers who do not manufacture or freeze if the health officer wishes so to interpret it. Section 4 prescribes the labeling of containers and prohibits the use of unapproved grade placards.

Section 5 requires the inspection of all plants at least once every 6 months. A plant found violating any item of sanitation must be notified in writing and must be given a reasonable time to correct the defect. If the same violation is again found on the next inspection the plant is subject to degrading or suspension of permit.

Section 6 provides for the examination of at least 4 samples of the finished product from each plant every 6 months. The decision as to whether at least 4 samples of each flavor of each product should be taken or random sampling should be relied upon to represent all products of the plant is left to the individual health officer's judgment and will depend on the laboratory facilities available. Ingredients may be sampled as often as the health officer may deem necessary in order to determine compliance with the bacterial requirements. If the logarithmic average of the last 4 bacterial counts exceeds the specified standard, the plant must be notified and an additional sample taken before punitive action is in order.

Section 7, the longest and most important of the sections, lists the sanitation standards for Grade A frozen dessert plants, which are identical with the minimum requirements where the non-grading form is adopted. These cover construction and cleanliness of floors, walls and ceilings, doors and windows, lighting and ventilation, protection from contamination, toilet, water supply, handwashing facilities, sanitary piping, disposal of wastes, the construction, cleaning, bactericidal treatment, storage, and handling of containers and equipment, pasteurization of mix, cooling, handling, packaging spillage, returns, health and cleanliness of personnel, vehicles, plant surroundings, bacterial count of frozen desserts and standards for ingredients. These items of sanitation are conveniently summarized in the frozen desserts plant inspection form prepared for use with this ordinance. Except for the few items specifically applying to frozen desserts, the sanitation requirements are similar to those for pasteurization plants in the recommended milk ordinance, and need not be discussed here.

The bacterial standard for pasteurized mix and frozen desserts is a logarithmic average plate count not exceeding 50,000 per gram. With pasteurization set at 155°F. for 30 minutes, this standard is not considered too stringent for the top grade.

Sanitary Control of Ingredients

For the present, only platform control is made mandatory in the ordinance. Item 25p, which deals with ingredients, contains a general requirement as to cleanliness, quality, and handling of ingredients, and establishes bacterial standards for ingredients derived from milk. Those used in the raw state are limited to a logarithmic average plate count not exceeding 200,000; those used in the pasteurized, condensed, evaporated or dried state are limited to an average of 50,000. These limits are doubled in the case of cream. In the Code, tentative microbiological standards are recommended for ingredients not derived from milk, including a plate count of under 200,000 for egg products, and for other flavoring or coloring materials a plate count not exceeding 10,000 and mold and yeast counts not exceeding 100. These standards are particularly recommended for all ingredients added after the mix has been pasteurized.

IMPORTANT PUBLICATIONS

Ice Cream Trade Journal
466 Lexington Avenue
New York 17, N.Y.

Ice Cream Review
1445 N. 5th St. at W. Cherry
Milwaukee 12, Wisconsin

Ice Cream Field
23 W. 47th St.
New York 36, N.Y.

Ice Cream World
99 Hudson Street
New York 13, N.Y.

Canadian Dairy and Ice Cream Journal
122 Richmond St., West,
Toronto, Ontario, Canada

Journal of Dairy Science
Official Organ of the American Dairy Science Association
H. F. Judkins, Secretary-Treasurer
32 Ridgeway Circle
White Plains, N.Y.

DAIRY ASSOCIATIONS WHICH PROMOTE THE ICE CREAM INDUSTRY

American Dairy Science Association
Columbus 10, Ohio

International Association of Ice Cream Manufacturers
Robert H. North, Executive Secretary
1105 Barr Building, Washington 6, D.C.

The National Association of Retail Ice Cream Manufacturers, Inc.
E. M. Warder, Executive Secretary
Executive Headquarters, Commerce Building, Toledo 4, Ohio

National Ice Cream Mix Association, Inc.
234 Bowen Building, Washington 5, D.C.

National Dairy Council
111 North Canal Street, Chicago 6, Illinois

Dairy Industries Supply Association, Inc.
Joseph S. Cunningham, Executive Vice-President
1108 Sixteenth Street N.W., Washington 6, D.C.

American Dairy Association
M. J. Framberger, General Manager
20 N. Wacker Drive Building, Chicago 6, Illinois

Bibliography

AMERICAN DAIRY SCIENCE ASSOCIATION. 1959. Dairy Industry Plant Training Manual.

ANDERSON, GEORGE A. M. 1958. Fast hardening systems for ice cream. The Ice Cream Trade J. *54*, No. 5, 26, 27, 30, 122, 123, 124.

ARBUCKLE, W. S. 1940. A microscopical and statistical analysis of texture and structure of ice cream as affected by composition, physical properties and processing methods. Missouri Bull. *320*, 25–32.

ARBUCKLE, W. S. 1948. Will egg products improve ice cream? Ice Cream Field *52*, No. 6, 24–25.

ARBUCKLE, W. S. 1950. Emulsifiers in ice cream. Ice Cream Trade J. *46*, No. 10, 106, 114.

ARBUCKLE, W. S. 1950. Stabilized berries for strawberry ice cream. Ice Cream Field *56*, No. 4, 80, 81, 82.

ARBUCKLE, W. S., and NISONGER, J. W. 1951. The effects on mix of high temperature short time pasteurization. Ice Cream Field *58*, No. 6, 60, 61, 68.

ARBUCKLE, W. S. 1952. Stabilized fruits for ice cream. Ice Cream Trade J. *48*, No. 5, 32, 33, 36, 86.

ARBUCKLE, W. S., and CREMERS, LOUIS F. M. 1953. Special products research. Ice Cream Field *63*, No. 4, 86–88.

ARBUCKLE, W. S. 1955. High temperature processing and its effect on product properties. The Roswell Heater Report of Proceedings of 51st Annual Convention International Assn. of Ice Cream Manufacturers, Production and Laboratory Council 2.

BABCOCK, S. H., and RUSSEL, H. L. 1896. The Restoration of Consistency of Pasteurized Cream. Wis. Agr. Expt. Sta. Bull. 54.

BIERMAN, H. R. 1926. Effect of temperature on dipping. Ice Cream Review *10*, No. 8, 126.

BIERMAN, H. R. 1926. How the composition of ice cream affects dipping. Ice Cream Trade J. *23*, No. 2, 45.

BIERMAN, H. R. 1927. The effect of overrun, temperature and composition on the dipping losses in ice cream. Maryland Agr. Expt. Sta. Bull. *293*, 23–24.

FRANDSEN, J. H., and MARKHAM, E. A. 1915. The Manufacture of Ice Cream and Ices. Orange Judd Publishing Co., New York.

HAMMER, B. W. 1912. Bacteria in Ice Cream. Iowa State Bull. No. 134

HEINZ NUTRITIONAL RESEARCH DIVISION. 1958. Nutritional data, Third Edition—Second Revised Printing. H. J. Heinz Company, Pittsburgh, Pa.

HENNERICH, GEORGE W. 1947. Let's Sell Ice Cream. The Ice Cream Merchandising Institute, Inc., Affiliate of The International Assn. of Ice Cream Manufacturers, 84–159, 275–303.

HERRINGTON, B. L. 1948. Milk and Milk Processing. McGraw-Hill Book Co., Inc., New York.

INTERNATIONAL ASSOCIATION OF ICE CREAM MFRS. 1951. The History of Ice Cream. Washington, D.C.

JENNESS, ROBERT, and PATTON, S. 1959. Principles of Dairy Chemistry. John Wiley and Sons, Inc., New York.

MACK, M. J. 1934. Controlling physical properties of high solids mixes. J. Dairy Science *17*, No. 12, 781.

MERORY, J.   1960.   Food Flavorings, Composition, Manufacture, and Use. Avi Publ. Co., Westport, Conn.

MILK INDUSTRY FOUNDATION.   1960.   Milk Facts 29, Washington, D.C.

MORTENSEN, M.   1911.   Classification of Ice Cream and Related Frozen Products, Iowa State Bull. No. 123.

NATIONAL RESEARCH COUNCIL.   1950.   The Composition of Milks.   Bull. No. 119, Food and Nutrition Board.   Washington, D.C.

PRITLE, T. R.   1926.   History of Dairying.   Mojonnier Bros. Co., Chicago,

SHERMAN, H. C.   1946.   Chemistry of Food and Nutrition.   7th Edition.   The Macmillan Publishing Co., New York.

SOMMER, H. H.   1946.   Theory and Practice of Ice Cream Making.   5th Edition.   16, Chapter 2.   Published by the Author, Madison, Wis.

TRACY, P. H., and EDMAN, GEORGE.   1950.   Ice Cream for Diabetics Using Sorbitol.   Ice Cream Trade J. 46, No. 7, 50.

TRACY, P. H., TURNBOW, G. D., and RAFETTO, L. A.   1947.   The Ice Cream Industry.   2nd Edition, Chapter 5.   John Wiley & Sons, Inc., New York.

TRACY, P. H., and MCGARRAHAN.   1957.   How to Plan and Operate a Soft-Frozen Dairy Products Store.   Garrard Press, Champaign, Ill.

U.S. Dept of Agr.   1950.   Composition of Foods—Raw, Processed, Prepared. Agriculture Handbook No. 8, U.S.D.A.   Washington, D.C.

U.S. Dept. of Agr.   1959.   Food—The Yearbook of Agriculture, U.S.D.A.

U.S. Dept. of Agr.   Agricultural Handbook No. 51.   Revised October 1959. Agricultural Marketing Service.   Washington, D.C.

WASHBURN, R. W.   1910.   Principles and Practices of Ice Cream Making. Vermont State Bull. No. 155.

Index

Lactose, composition of, 42
  content of milk, 42
  crystalline lactose, 42
  crystallization of, 55, 191, 256
  forms of, 42
  maximum concentration, 55
  relation to sandiness, 55
  source of, 38, 41, 55
Latent heat of fusion, 156, 286
  of vaporization, 286
lb., 88
Lecithin, 41
Lemo-Lac milk drink, 321
Lemon syrup, 324
Liquid sugar (No. 1 syrup), 53
  relation to Baumé to concentration of 54
Low flavor (defect), 247
Low lactose milk, 48
"Low pressure side," 279
Low-temperature sanitizing, 269

M

Making forget-me nots, rose-buds, sweet peas and pinks, (illus.) 216
Malt syrup, 51
Malted milk, 49
Maltose, 51, 58
Manton Gaulin homogenizer, (illus.) 147
Maple ice cream, 230
Maple mallow topping, 323
Maple pecan ice cream, 231
Maple sugar, 49
Maple syrup in ice cream, 53
Maple walnut ice cream, 231
Market grades for ice cream, 263
  classification of, 263
Measure in ice creams, 330
Measures, see *Weights and Measures*
Mechanical refrigeration, 276
  see *Refrigeration*
Mellofreeze, 21
Mellorine type products, 20–21
  definition of, 20
  mello-freeze, 21
  minimum standards of, 21
  olarine, 21
  production data of, 21
  see *Table 1*, 6–7
Meltdown defects, 209
  in sherbets and ices, 209
Melting quality defects, 257–258
Metallic flavor, 249
Metric weights and measures, 332
Micron, 38
Micro-organisms, 266, 267
  bacteria, yeast, mold, 266
  factors affecting growth, 267
Microscopic appearance of fat globules, (illus.) 40
Milk, acidity test for, 296
  Babcock test for fat in, 288, 289

apparatus and reagents, 288
  procedure, 289
  taking sample, 288
constituents, 39–43
  lactose, 41; mineral salts, 42
  milk fat, 39; other substances, 43
  protein components, 41
  water, 39; whey protein, 41
food value, compared with ice cream, 10–14
  sediment test, 265
  standardizing, 133–134
  utilization of, in U. S., 9
  vitamins in, 13–14, 43
Milk ash (mineral salts), 42
  importance of, 42
Milk drinks, 321
Milk fat, 27, 28, 33, 38, 40
Milk julep, 322
Milk products used in ice cream
  approximate composition, 38
  butterfat, 43; butter oil, 45
  constituents, of, 38
  evaporated milk, 48
  factors affecting, 37
  fresh skim milk, 45
  frozen cream, 44
  low-lactose milk, 48
  malted milk, 49
  milk salts, 43
  milk solids-not-fat, 43
  milk sugar, 43
  non-fat dry milk, 46
  plain condensed skim, 46
  plain condensed whole, 46
  plastic cream, 44
  powdered whey solids, 49
  powdered whole milk, 46
  proteins, 43
  solids-not-fat content 37–38
  sweet cream buttermilk, 46
  superheated condensed skim, 46
  sweetened condensed skim, 47
  sweetened condensed whole, 47
  total solids content of, 37–38
  whole milk, 43
  weights, relation and composition of (Table 67), 330
Milk proteins, 11, 41
  casein, 41
  components of, 41
  whey protein, 41
Milk Scotch high ball, 322
Milk shake, (illus.) 314
  formula for base, 196
Milk solids, 205
  amount, 205; source of, 205
  use in sherbet, 205
Milk solids-not-fat,
  advantage of, 33
  effect on texture, 253

Nut ice cream, definitions of, 18
formulas (recipes) 232
Nutrient content of vanilla ice cream, 14
Nutrimix (non-fat milk solids product),
48
Nuts
meats and extracts, 82
preparation for ice cream mix, 83
sanitizing of, 83

O

Oat flour, 65
use in ice cream, 65
Official and tentative methods of Analysis,
299
Olarine, 21
Old ingredient flavor, 249
Orange ice cream, 231
Orange-pineapple ice cream, 231
Orange-pineapple ice cream soda, 321
Orange-pineapple topping, 323
Orange syrup, 324
Ordinance and Code, Frozen Dessert,
provisions of, 347
Overrun,
calculating per cent, 135
control in ices, importance of methods
used, 204
definition of, 176
factors determining amount of, 177
how overrun affects dipping losses and
weight per gallon, 307
how to obtain, factors affecting, 177
in sherberts and ices, 203, 208
percentages overrun for different products, 178
testers for, 177
uniform control, 177
importance of, 178
"Oxidized" flavors, 65, 248, 249

P

Packages (containers), 179
bulk package, 180
carry-out ((take-home), 180
dipped, 307
multi-service package, 179
single-service package, 179
advantages and disadvantages of
single service, 179
take-home, 301
Packaging machines (fillers), 180
advantages and disadvantages, 181
Packers for shipping ice cream, see *Shipping methods*
"Pancakes" (defect), causes of, 259
Paper, containers, single service
lining for metal cans, 179
serviceware for soda fountain, 303
Parfait, The, (illus.) 315
Parfait ice cream, 233
definition of, 19

Particle size, 39
milk constituents, 39
Ice cream constituents, 39
Pasteurization of ice cream mix,
Batch system, 145
effect of, 143, 144
high temperature mix system, 145
benefits, of
H.T.S.T. method, 8, 144
influence on body and texture of ice
cream, 255–256
legal aspects of, 144
methods, 144–145
purpose of, 145
ultra high temperature, 144
vacreation, 144
Pasteurizers, continuous regeneration principle of, 146
Pasteurizing machines, introduction of, 2
Peach ice cream, 231
sundae, 317
Peanut Brittle ice cream, 232
sundae, 319
Pearson square method, 87, 132
Pectin, sources of, 64
use in ice cream, ices and sherbets, 64,
203
Pennsylvania test, 291
equipment; method used, 291
precaution, 291
preparation, 291
procedure, 292
reagents, 291
Peppermint stick ice cream, 232
Per cent overrun, see *Overrun*
Personnel, health examination of, 274
characteristics of, 274
dispenser, training, 304
health habits, 273
hygienic relation of, to
quality of product, 274
selection and training, 303
training for fountain service, 304
Phosphatase test, 299
Phospholipids, 41
lecithin and cephalin, 41
Phosphorus
content of ice cream, 10
content of milk, 10
in ice cream, see 14
Pies, ice cream, 213
Pineapple, flavoring solution, 231
syrup, 325
Pineapple buttermilk, 322
Pineapple ice cream, 231
Pistachio ice cream, 232
Plain ice cream, 22
Plant sanitation, 265
Plastic cream, 45
Plate cooler, modern, 152
Plate hardener, 187
rotary type, 187